STUDENT RESOURCE MANUAL

NEIL WIGLEY
University of Windsor

ALBERT HERR
Drexel University

to accompany

Calculus

....

A NEW HORIZON

SIXTH EDITION

VOLUME ONE

HOWARD ANTON
Drexel University

With Sample Tests
Prepared By

HENRY SMITH
Southeastern Louisiana University

JOHN WILEY & SONS, INC.
New York Chichester Weinheim Brisbane Singapore Toronto

COVER PHOTO   © Dann Coffey/The Image Bank

ISBN 0-471-24616-6

Printed in the United States of America

10 9 8 7 6 5 4 3

Printed and bound by Victor Graphics, Inc.

CONTENTS

SOLUTIONS

SAMPLE TESTS

CALCULUS:

A New Horizon from Ancient Roots

EXERCISE SET FOR INTRODUCTION

1. **(a)** $x = 0.123123123\ldots$; $1000x = 123.123123123\ldots = 123 + x$; $999x = 123$; $x = \dfrac{123}{999} = \dfrac{41}{333}$

(b) $x = 12.7777\ldots$; $10x = 127.7777\ldots$, so $9x = 10x - x = 115$; $x = \dfrac{115}{9}$

(c) $x = 38.07818181\ldots$; $100x = 3807.818181\ldots$; $99x = 3769.74$;

$x = \dfrac{3769.74}{99} = \dfrac{376974}{9900} = \dfrac{41886}{1100} = \dfrac{20943}{550}$

(d) $0.4296000\ldots = 0.4296 = \dfrac{4296}{10000} = \dfrac{537}{1250}$

3. **(a)** $\dfrac{223}{71} < \dfrac{333}{106} < \dfrac{63}{25}\left(\dfrac{17 + 15\sqrt{5}}{7 + 15\sqrt{5}}\right) < \dfrac{355}{113} < \dfrac{22}{7}$ **(b)** $\dfrac{63}{25}\left(\dfrac{17 + 15\sqrt{5}}{7 + 15\sqrt{5}}\right)$

(c) $\dfrac{333}{106}$ **(d)** $\dfrac{63}{25}\left(\dfrac{17 + 15\sqrt{5}}{7 + 15\sqrt{5}}\right)$

5. The first series, taken to ten terms, adds to 3.0418; the second, as printed, adds to 3.1416.

(c) $\dfrac{14}{45} = 0.311111\ldots = \dfrac{3}{10} + \dfrac{1}{100} + \dfrac{1}{1000} + \dfrac{1}{10000} + \dfrac{1}{100000} + \dfrac{1}{1000000} + \cdots$

7. **(a)** $\dfrac{7}{11} = 0.636363\ldots = \dfrac{6}{10} + \dfrac{3}{100} + \dfrac{6}{1000} + \dfrac{3}{10000} + \dfrac{6}{100000} + \dfrac{3}{1000000} + \cdots$

(b) $\dfrac{8}{33} = 0.242424\ldots = \dfrac{2}{10} + \dfrac{4}{100} + \dfrac{2}{1000} + \dfrac{4}{10000} + \dfrac{2}{100000} + \dfrac{4}{1000000} + \cdots$

(c) $\dfrac{5}{12} = 0.416666\ldots = \dfrac{4}{10} + \dfrac{1}{100} + \dfrac{6}{1000} + \dfrac{6}{10000} + \dfrac{6}{100000} + \dfrac{6}{1000000} + \cdots$

9. **(a)** 1, 4, 2.875, 2.6549, 2.6458

(b) 1, 25.5, 13.7, 8.69, 7.22, 7.0726, 7.0711

CHAPTER 1

Functions

EXERCISE SET 1.1

1. **(a)** around 1943
   (b) 1960; 4200
   (c) no; you need the year's population
   (d) war; marketing techniques
   (e) news of health risk; social pressure, antismoking campaigns, increased taxation

3. **(a)** $-2.9, -2.0, 2.35, 2.9$ **(b)** none   **(c)** $y = 0$
   (d) $-1.75 \le x \le 2.15$ **(e)** $y_{\max} = 2.8$ at $x = -2.6$; $y_{\min} = -2.2$ at $x = 1.2$

5. **(a)** $x = 2, 4$ **(b)** none   **(c)** $x \le 2$; $4 \le x$ **(d)** $y_{\min} = -1$; no maximum value

7. **(a)** Breaks could be caused by war, pestilence, flood, earthquakes, for example.
   (b) C decreases for eight hours, takes a jump upwards, and then repeats.

9. **(a)** If the side adjacent to the building has length x then $L = x + 2y$. Since $A = xy = 1000$, $L = x + 2000/x$.

   (b) $x > 0$ and x must be smaller than the width of the building, which was not given.

   (c)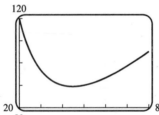
   (d) $L_{min} \approx 89.44$

11. **(a)** $V = 500 = \pi r^2 h$ so $h = \dfrac{500}{\pi r^2}$. Then
    $$C = (0.02)(2)\pi r^2 + (0.01)2\pi rh = 0.04\pi r^2 + 0.02\pi r\frac{500}{\pi r^2}$$
    $$= 0.04\pi r^2 + \frac{10}{r}; \quad C_{\min} \approx 4.39 \text{ at } r \approx 3.4, \ h \approx 13.8.$$

    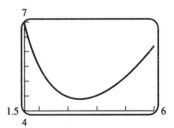

    (b) $C = (0.02)(2)(2r)^2 + (0.01)2\pi rh = 0.16r^2 + \dfrac{10}{r}$. Since $0.04\pi < 0.16$, the top and bottom now get more weight. Since they cost more, we diminish their sizes in the solution, and the cans become taller.

    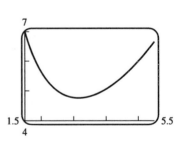

    (c) $r \approx 3.1, \ h \approx 16.0, \ C \approx 4.76$

EXERCISE SET 1.2

1. **(a)** $f(0) = 3(0)^2 - 2 = -2; f(2) = 3(2)^2 - 2 = 10; f(-2) = 3(-2)^2 - 2 = 10; f(3) = 3(3)^2 - 2 = 25;$
   $f(\sqrt{2}) = 3(\sqrt{2})^2 - 2 = 4; f(3t) = 3(3t)^2 - 2 = 27t^2 - 2$

   (b) $f(0) = 2(0) = 0; f(2) = 2(2) = 4; f(-2) = 2(-2) = -4; f(3) = 2(3) = 6; f(\sqrt{2}) = 2\sqrt{2};$
   $f(3t) = 1/3t$ for $t > 1$ and $f(3t) = 6t$ for $t \leq 1$.

3. **(a)** $x \neq 3$ **(b)** $x \leq -\sqrt{3}$ or $x \geq \sqrt{3}$

   (c) $x^2 - 2x + 5 = 0$ has no real solutions so $x^2 - 2x + 5$ is always positive or always negative. If $x = 0$, then $x^2 - 2x + 5 = 5 > 0$; domain: $(-\infty, +\infty)$.

   (d) $x \neq 0$ **(e)** $\sin x \neq 1$, so $x \neq (2n + \frac{1}{2})\pi$,
   $n = 0, \pm1, \pm2, \ldots$

5. **(a)** $x \leq 3$ **(b)** $-2 \leq x \leq 2$ **(c)** $x \geq 0$ **(d)** all x **(e)** all x

7. **(a)** yes   **(b)** yes
   (c) no (vertical line test fails)   **(d)** no (vertical line test fails)

9. The cosine of θ is $(L - h)/L$ (side adjacent over hypotenuse), so $h = L(1 - \cos\theta)$.

11.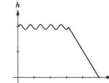

13. **(a)** If $x < 0$, then $|x| = -x$ so $f(x) = -x + 3x + 1 = 2x + 1$. If $x \geq 0$, then $|x| = x$ so $f(x) = x + 3x + 1 = 4x + 1$;

   $$f(x) = \begin{cases} 2x + 1, & x < 0 \\ 4x + 1, & x \geq 0 \end{cases}$$

   (b) If $x < 0$, then $|x| = -x$ and $|x - 1| = 1 - x$ so $g(x) = -x + 1 - x = 1 - 2x$. If $0 \leq x < 1$, then $|x| = x$ and $|x - 1| = 1 - x$ so $g(x) = x + 1 - x = 1$. If $x \geq 1$, then $|x| = x$ and $|x - 1| = x - 1$ so $g(x) = x + x - 1 = 2x - 1$;

   $$g(x) = \begin{cases} 1 - 2x, & x < 0 \\ 1, & 0 \leq x < 1 \\ 2x - 1, & x \geq 1 \end{cases}$$

15. **(a)** $V = (8 - 2x)(15 - 2x)x$ **(b)** $-\infty < x < +\infty, -\infty < V < +\infty$ **(c)** $0 < x < 4$
   (d) minimum value at $x = 0$ or at $x = 4$; maximum value somewhere in between (can be approximated by zooming with graphing calculator)

17. **(i)** $x = 1, -2$ causes division by zero   **(ii)** $g(x) = x + 1$, all x

19. **(a)** $25°F$ **(b)** $2°F$ **(c)** $-15°F$

21. If $v = 8$ then $-10 = WCI = 91.4 + (91.4 - T)(0.0203(8) - 0.304\sqrt{8} - 0.474)$; thus
   $T = 91.4 + (10 + 91.4)/(0.0203(8) - 0.304\sqrt{8} - 0.474)$ and $T = 5°F$

23. Let t denote time in minutes after 9:23 AM. Then $D(t) = 1000 - 20t$ ft.

EXERCISE SET 1.3

1. (e) seems best, though only (a) is bad.

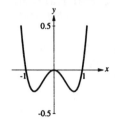

3. (b) and (c) are good; (a) is very bad.

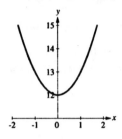

5. $[-3, 3] \times [0, 5]$

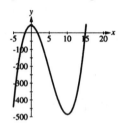

7. (a) window too narrow, too short

(b) window wide enough, but too short

(c) good window, good spacing

(d) window too narrow, too short

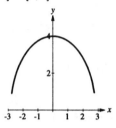

(e) window too narrow, too short

9. $[-5, 14] \times [-60, 40]$

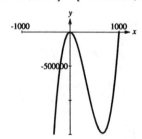

11. $[-0.1, 0.1] \times [-3, 3]$

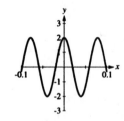

13. $[-250, 1050] \times [-1500000, 600000]$

15. $[-2, 2] \times [-20, 20]$

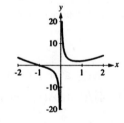

17. depends on graphing utility

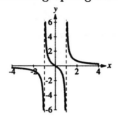

19. **(a)** $f(x) = \sqrt{16 - x^2}$ **(b)** $f(x) = -\sqrt{16 - x^2}$

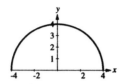
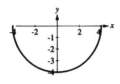

(c) 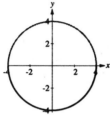   **(d)**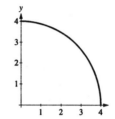

(e) No; the vertical line test fails.

21. **(a)** 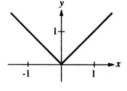   **(b)** 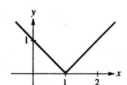   **(c)**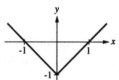

(d) 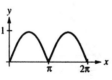   **(e)** 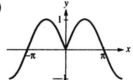   **(f)**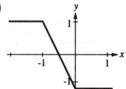

23. The portions of the graph of $y = f(x)$ which lie below the x-axis are reflected over the x-axis to give the graph of $y = |f(x)|$.

25. **(a)** for example, let $a = 1.1$

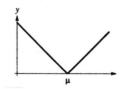

(b)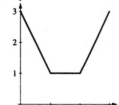

27.

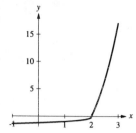

29. (a)

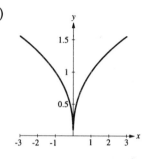

(b)

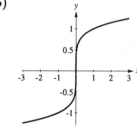

(c)

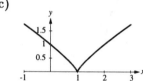

(d)

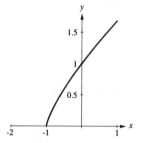

31. (a) stretches or shrinks the graph in the y-direction; flips it if c changes sign

(b) As c increases, the parabola moves down and to the left. If c increases, up and right.

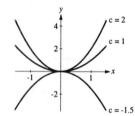

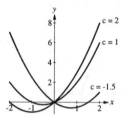

(c) The graph rises or falls in the y-direction with changes in c.

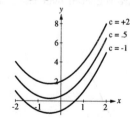

33. The curve oscillates between the lines $y = x$ and $y = -x$ with increasing rapidity as $|x|$ increases.

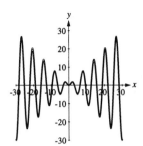

35. Plot $f(x)$ on $[-10, 10]$; then on $[-1, 0]$, $[-0.7, -0.6]$, $[-0.65, -0.64]$, $[-0.646, -0.645]$; for the other root use $[4, 5]$, $[4.6, 4.7]$, $[4.64, 4.65]$, $[4.645, 4.646]$; roots -0.6455, 4.6455.

EXERCISE SET 1.4

1. (a)

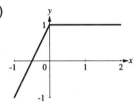

(b)

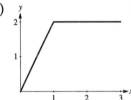

(c)

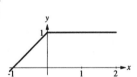

(d)

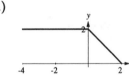

3. (a)

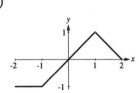

(b)

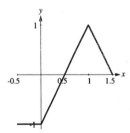

(c)

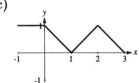

(d)

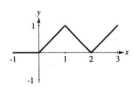

5. Translate right 2 units, and up one unit.

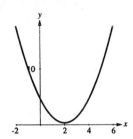

7. Translate left 1 unit, stretch vertically by a factor of 2, reflect over x-axis, translate down 3 units.

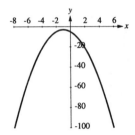

9. $y = (x + 3)^2 - 9$; translate left 3 units and down 9 units.

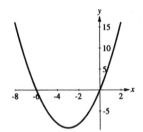

11. $y = -(x - 1)^2 + 2$; translate right 1 unit, reflect over x-axis, translate up 2 units.

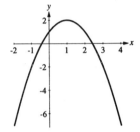

13. Translate left 1 unit, reflect over x-axis, translate up 3 units.

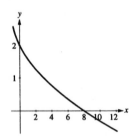

15. Compress vertically by a factor of $\frac{1}{2}$, translate up 1 unit.

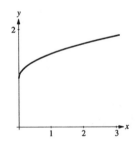

17. Translate right 3 units.

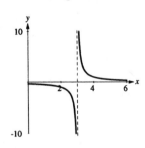

19. Translate left 1 unit, reflect over x-axis, translate up 2 units.

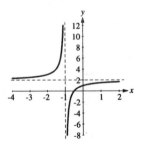

21. Translate left 2 units and down 2 units.

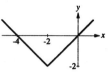

23. Stretch vertically by a factor of 2, translate right 1 unit and up 1 unit.

25. Stretch vertically by a factor of 2, reflect over x-axis, translate up 2 units.

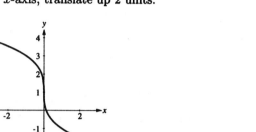

27. Translate left 1 unit and up 2 units.

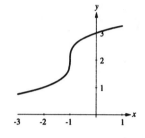

29. **(a)**

(b) $y = \begin{cases} 0 \text{ if } x \le 0 \\ 2x \text{ if } 0 < x \end{cases}$

31. $x^2 + 2x + 1$, all x; $2x - x^2 - 1$, all x; $2x^3 + 2x$, all x; $2x/(x^2 + 1)$, all x

33. $3\sqrt{x - 1}$, $x \ge 1$; $\sqrt{x - 1}$, $x \ge 1$; $2x - 2$, $x \ge 1$; 2, $x > 1$

35. **(a)** 3   **(b)** 9   **(c)** 2   **(d)** 2

37. **(a)** $t^4 + 1$ **(b)** $t^2 + 4t + 5$ **(c)** $x^2 + 4x + 5$ **(d)** $\dfrac{1}{x^2} + 1$

     (e) $x^2 + 2xh + h^2 + 1$ **(f)** $x^2 + 1$ **(g)** $x + 1$ **(h)** $9x^2 + 1$

39. $2x^2 - 2x + 1$, all x; $4x^2 + 2x$, all x **41.** $1 - x$, $x \le 1$; $\sqrt{1 - x^2}$, $|x| \le 1$

43. $\dfrac{1}{1 - 2x}$, $x \ne \dfrac{1}{2}, 1$; $-\dfrac{1}{2x} - \dfrac{1}{2}$, $x \ne 0, 1$ **45.** $x^{-6} + 1$

47. **(a)** $g(x) = \sqrt{x}$, $h(x) = x + 2$ **(b)** $g(x) = |x|$, $h(x) = x^2 - 3x + 5$

49. **(a)** $g(x) = x^2$, $h(x) = \sin x$ **(b)** $g(x) = 3/x$, $h(x) = 5 + \cos x$

51. **(a)** $f(x) = x^3$, $g(x) = 1 + \sin x$, $h(x) = x^2$ **(b)** $f(x) = \sqrt{x}$, $g(x) = 1 - x$, $h(x) = \sqrt[3]{x}$

53.

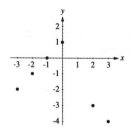

55. Note that $f(g(-x)) = f(-g(x)) = f(g(x))$, so $f(g(x))$ is even.

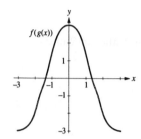

57. $f(g(x)) = 0$ when $g(x) = \pm 2$, so $x = \pm 1.4$; $g(f(x)) = 0$ when $f(x) = 0$, so $x = \pm 2$.

59. $\dfrac{3(x+h)^2 - 5 - (3x^2 - 5)}{h} = \dfrac{6xh + 3h^2}{h} = 6x + 3h$

61. $\dfrac{1/(x+h) - 1/x}{h} = \dfrac{x - (x+h)}{xh(x+h)} = \dfrac{-1}{x(x+h)}$

63. **(a)** the origin   **(b)** the x-axis   **(c)** the y-axis   **(d)** none

65. **(a)**

x	-3	-2	-1	0	1	2	3
$f(x)$	1	-5	-1	0	-1	-5	1

(b)

x	-3	-2	-1	0	1	2	3
$f(x)$	1	5	-1	0	1	-5	-1

67. **(a)** even   **(b)** odd   **(c)** odd   **(d)** neither

69. **(a)** $f(-x) = (-x)^2 = x^2 = f(x)$, even   **(b)** $f(-x) = (-x)^3 = -x^3 = -f(x)$, odd

     (c) $f(-x) = |-x| = |x| = f(x)$, even   **(d)** $f(-x) = -x + 1$, neither

     (e) $f(-x) = \dfrac{(-x)^3 - (-x)}{1 + (-x)^2} = -\dfrac{x^3 + x}{1 + x^2} = -f(x)$, odd

     (f) $f(-x) = 2 = f(x)$, even

71. **(a)** y-axis, because $(-x)^4 = 2y^3 + y$ gives $x^4 = 2y^3 + y$

     (b) origin, because $(-y) = \dfrac{(-x)}{3 + (-x)^2}$ gives $y = \dfrac{x}{3 + x^2}$

     (c) x-axis, y-axis, and origin because $(-y)^2 = |x| - 5$, $y^2 = |-x| - 5$, and $(-y)^2 = |-x| - 5$ all give $y^2 = |x| - 5$

73.

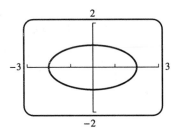

75.

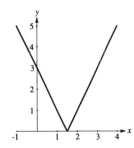

77. **(a)**

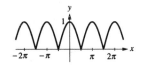

(b)

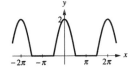

79. Yes, e.g. $f(x) = x^k$ and $g(x) = x^n$ where k and n are integers.

EXERCISE SET 1.5

1. **(a)** $\dfrac{3-0}{0-2} = -\dfrac{3}{2}, \dfrac{3-(8/3)}{0-6} = -\dfrac{1}{18}, \dfrac{0-(8/3)}{2-6} = \dfrac{2}{3}$

(b) Yes; the first and third slopes above are negative reciprocals of each other.

3. III < II < IV < I

5. **(a)** $\dfrac{1-(-5)}{1-(-2)} = 2, \dfrac{-5-(-1)}{-2-0} = 2, \dfrac{1-(-1)}{1-0} = 2$. Since the slopes connecting all pairs of points are equal, they lie on a line.

(b) $\dfrac{4-2}{-2-0} = -1, \dfrac{2-5}{0-1} = 3, \dfrac{4-5}{-2-1} = \dfrac{1}{3}$. Since the slopes connecting the pairs of points are not equal, the points do not lie on a line.

7. The slope, $m = 3$, is equal to $\dfrac{y-2}{x-1}$, and thus $y - 2 = 3(x-1)$.

(a) If $x = 5$ then $y = 14$. **(b)** If $y = -2$ then $x = -1/3$.

9. **(a)** The first slope is $\dfrac{2-0}{1-x}$ and the second is $\dfrac{5-0}{4-x}$. Since they are negatives of each other we get $2(4-x) = -5(1-x)$ or $7x = 13$, $x = 13/7$.

11. **(a)** 153° **(b)** 45° **(c)** 117° **(d)** 89°

13. **(a)** $m = \tan\phi = \sqrt{3}$, so $\phi = 60°$ **(b)** $m = \tan\phi = -2$, so $\phi = 117°$

15. $y = -2x + 4$

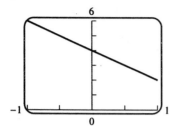

17. Parallel means the lines have equal slopes, so $y = 4x + 7$.

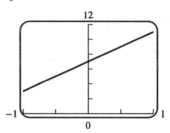

19. The negative reciprocal of 5 is $-1/5$, so $y = -\dfrac{1}{5}x + 6$.

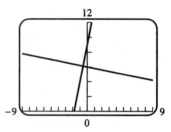

21. $\dfrac{y - (-7)}{x - 1} = \dfrac{4 - (-7)}{2 - 1}$, or $y = 11x - 18$

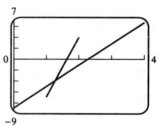

23. **(a)** $m_1 = m_2 = 4$, parallel   **(b)** $m_1 = 2 = -1/m_2$, perpendicular

     (c) $m_1 = m_2 = 5/3$, parallel

     (d) If $A \neq 0$ and $B \neq 0$ then $m_1 = -A/B = -1/m_2$, perpendicular; if $A = 0$ or $B = 0$ (not both) then one line is horizontal, the other vertical, so perpendicular.

     (e) neither

25. **(a)** $m = (0 - (-3))/(2 - 0)) = 3/2$ so $y = 3x/2 - 3$

     (b) $m = (-3 - 0)/(4 - 0) = -3/4$ so $y = -3x/4$

27. **(a)** The velocity is the slope, which is $\dfrac{5 - (-4)}{10 - 0} = 9/10$ ft/s.

     (b) $x = -4$

     (c) The line has slope 9/10 and passes through $(0, -4)$, so has equation $x = 9t/10 - 4$; at $t = 2$, $x = -2.2$.

     (d) $t = 80/9$

29. **(a)** The acceleration is the slope of the velocity, so $a = \dfrac{3 - (-1)}{1 - 4} = -\dfrac{4}{3}$ ft/s^2.

     (b) $v - 3 = -\dfrac{4}{3}(t - 1)$, or $v = -\dfrac{4}{3}t + \dfrac{13}{3}$ **(c)** $v = \dfrac{13}{3}$ ft/s

31. **(a)** It moves (to the left) 6 units with velocity $v = -3$ cm/s, then remains motionless for 5 s, then moves 3 units to the left with velocity $v = -1$ cm/s.

(b) $v_{\text{ave}} = \dfrac{0-9}{10-0} = -\dfrac{9}{10}$ cm/s

(c) Since the motion is in one direction only, the speed is the negative of the velocity, so
$s_{\text{ave}} = \dfrac{9}{10}$ cm/s.

33. **(a)** If x_1 denotes the final position and x_0 the initial position, then $v = (x_1 - x_0)/(t_1 - t_0) = 0$ mi/h, since $x_1 = x_0$.

(b) If the distance traveled in one direction is d, then the outward journey took $t = d/40$ h. Thus
$$s_{\text{ave}} = \frac{\text{total dist}}{\text{total time}} = \frac{2d}{t + (2/3)t} = \frac{80t}{t + (2/3)t} = 48 \text{ mi/h.}$$

(c) $t + (2/3)t = 5$, so $t = 3$ and $2d = 80t = 240$ mi round trip

35. **(a)**

v

100
80
60
40
20

20 40 60 80 100 120 t

(b) $v = \begin{cases} 10t & \text{if} \quad 0 \le t \le 10 \\ 100 & \text{if} \quad 10 \le t \le 100 \\ 600 - 5t & \text{if} \quad 100 \le t \le 120 \end{cases}$

37. **(a)** $y = 20 - 15 = 5$ when $x = 45$, so $5 = 45k$, $k = 1/9$, $y = x/9$

(b)

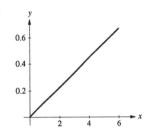

y

0.6
0.4
0.2

2   4   6 x

(c) $l = 15 + y = 15 + 100(1/9) = 26.11$ in.

(d) If $y_{\text{max}} = 15$ then solve $15 = kx = x/9$ for $x = 135$ lb.

39. Each increment of 1 in the value of x yields the increment of 1.2 for y, so the relationship is linear. If $y = mx + b$ then $m = 1.2$; from $x = 0$, $y = 2$, follows $b = 2$, so $y = 1.2x + 2$

41. **(a)** With T_F as independent variable, we have $\dfrac{T_C - 100}{T_F - 212} = \dfrac{0 - 100}{32 - 212}$, so $T_C = \dfrac{5}{9}(T_F - 32)$.

(b) $5/9$ **(c)** Set $T_F = T_C = \dfrac{5}{9}(T_F - 32)$ and solve for T_F: $T_F = T_C = -40°$ (F or C).

(d) $37°$ C

43. **(a)** $\dfrac{p-1}{h-0} = \dfrac{5.9-1}{50-0}$, or $p = 0.098h + 1$ **(b)** when $p = 2$, or $h = 1/0.098 \approx 10.20$ m

45. **(a)** $\dfrac{r - 0.80}{t - 0} = \dfrac{0.75 - 0.80}{4 - 0}$, so $r = -0.0125t + 0.8$

(b) 64 days

47. **(a)** For x trips we have $C_1 = 2x$ and $C_2 = 25 + x/4$

(b) $2x = 25 + x/4$, or $x = 100/7$, so the commuter pass becomes worthwhile at $x = 15$.

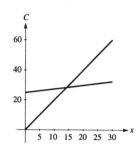

49. **(a)** $H \approx 20000/110 \approx 181$

(b) One light year is 9.408×10^{12} km and $t = \dfrac{d}{v} = \dfrac{1}{H} = \dfrac{1}{20\text{km/s/Mly}} = \dfrac{9.408 \times 10^{18}\text{km}}{20\text{km/s}}$
$= 4.704 \times 10^{17}$ s $= 1.492 \times 10^{10}$ years.

(c) The Universe would be even older.

EXERCISE SET 1.6

1. **(a)** $y = 3x + b$

(b) $y = 3x + 6$

(c)

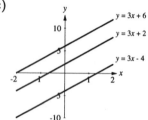

3. **(a)** $y = mx + 2$

(b) $m = \tan\phi = \tan 135° = -1$, so $y = -x + 2$

(c)

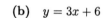

5. **(a)** The slope is -1.

(b) The y-intercept is $y = -1$.

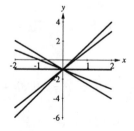

(c) They pass through the point $(-4, 2)$. **(d)** The x-intercept is $x = 1$.

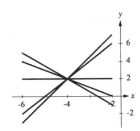

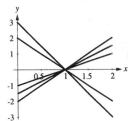

7. Let the line be tangent to the circle at the point (x_0, y_0) where $x_0^2 + y_0^2 = 9$. The slope of the tangent line is the negative reciprocal of y_0/x_0 (why?), so $m = -x_0/y_0$ and $y = -(x_0/y_0)x + b$. Substituting the point (x_0, y_0) as well as $y_0 = \pm\sqrt{9 - x_0^2}$ we get $y = \pm\dfrac{9 - x_0 x}{\sqrt{9 - x_0^2}}$.

9. The x-intercept is $x = 10$ so that with depreciation at 10% per year the final value is always zero, and hence $y = m(x - 10)$. The y-intercept is the original value.

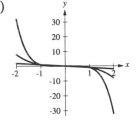

11. **(a)** VI **(b)** IV **(c)** III **(d)** V **(e)** I **(f)** II

13. **(a)**

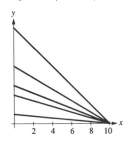

(b)

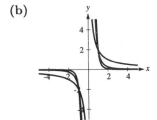

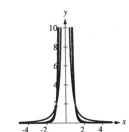

(c)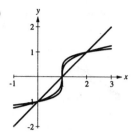

15. (a) 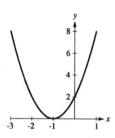 **(b)** 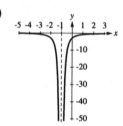 **(c)**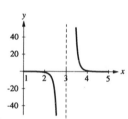

17. (a) 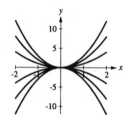 **(b)**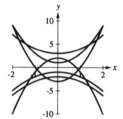

(c) 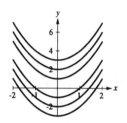 **(d)**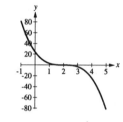

19. (a) 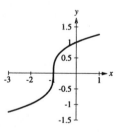 **(b)**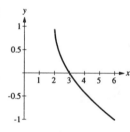

(c) 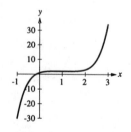 **(d)**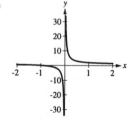

21.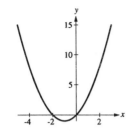

23. $t = 0.445\sqrt{d}$

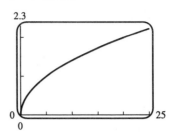

25. **(a)** N·m

(b) 20 N·m

(c)

V (L)	0.25	0.5	1.0	1.5	2.0
P (N/m^2)	80×10^3	40×10^3	20×10^3	13.3×10^3	10×10^3

27. **(a)** $F = k/x^2$ so $0.0005 = k/(0.3)^2$ and $k = 0.000045$ N·m^2.

(b) 0.000005 N

(c)

(d) When they approach one another, the force becomes infinite; when they get far apart it tends to zero.

29. **(a)** II; $y = 1$, $x = -1, 2$

(b) I; $y = 0$, $x = -2, 3$

(c) IV; $y = 2$

(d) III; $y = 0$, $x = -2$

31. Order the six trigonometric functions as sin, cos, tan, cot, sec, csc:

(a) pos, pos, pos, pos, pos, pos

(b) neg, zero, undef, zero, undef, neg

(c) pos, neg, neg, neg, neg, pos

(d) neg, pos, neg, neg, pos, neg

(e) neg, neg, pos, pos, neg, neg

(f) neg, pos, neg, neg, pos, neg

33. **(a)** $\sin(\pi - x) = \sin x$; 0.588

(b) $\cos(-x) = \cos x$; 0.924

(c) $\sin(2\pi + x) = \sin x$; 0.588

(d) $\cos(\pi - x) = -\cos x$; −0.924

(e) $\sin 2x = \pm 2\sin x\sqrt{1 - \sin^2 x}$; use the + sign for x small and positive; 0.951

(f) $\cos^2 x = 1 - \sin^2 x$; 0.654

35. **(a)** $-a$

(b) b

(c) $-c$

(d) $\pm\sqrt{1 - a^2}$

(e) $-b$

(f) $-a$

(g) $\pm 2b\sqrt{1 - b^2}$

(h) $2b^2 - 1$

(i) $1/b$

(j) $-1/a$

(k) $1/c$

(l) $(1 - b)/2$

37. If the arc length is 1, then solve the ratio $\dfrac{x}{1} = \dfrac{2\pi r}{29.5}$ to get $x \approx 80{,}936$ km.

39. The second quarter revolves twice (720°) about its own center.

41. **(a)** $y = 3\sin(x/2)$

(b) $y = 4\cos 2x$

(c) $y = -5\sin 4x$

43. **(a)** $y = \sin(x + \pi/2)$

(b) $y = 3 + 3\sin(2x/9)$

(c) $y = 1 + 2\sin(2(x - \pi/4))$

45. **(a)** $3, \pi/2, 0$ **(b)** $2, 2, 0$ **(c)** $1, 4\pi, 0$

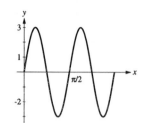 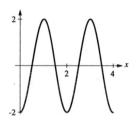 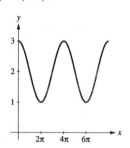

47. **(a)** $A\sin(\omega t + \theta) = A\sin(\omega t)\cos\theta + A\cos(\omega t)\sin\theta = A_1\sin(\omega t) + A_2\cos(\omega t)$

(b) $A_1 = A\cos\theta, A_2 = A\sin\theta$, so $A = \sqrt{A_1^2 + A_2^2}$ and $\theta = \tan^{-1}(A_2/A_1)$.

(c) $A = 5\sqrt{13}/2, \theta = \tan^{-1}\dfrac{1}{2\sqrt{3}};$

$$x = \frac{5\sqrt{13}}{2}\sin\left(2\pi t + \tan^{-1}\frac{1}{2\sqrt{3}}\right)$$

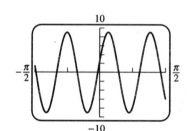

EXERCISE SET 1.7

1. **(a)** $x + 1 = t = y - 1, y = x + 2$

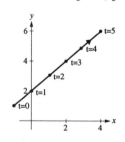

(c)

t	0	1	2	3	4	5
x	-1	0	1	2	3	4
y	1	2	3	4	5	6

3. $t = (x + 4)/3; y = 2x + 10$

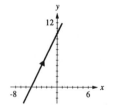

5. $\cos t = x/2, \ \sin t = y/5; x^2/4 + y^2/25 = 1$

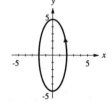

7. $\cos t = (x-3)/2, \sin t = (y-2)/4;$
$(x-3)^2/4 + (y-2)^2/16 = 1$

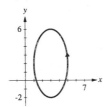

9. $\cos 2t = 1 - 2\sin^2 t; x = 1 - 2y^2, -1 \le y \le 1$

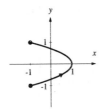

11. $x/2 + y/3 = 1, 0 \le x \le 2, 0 \le y \le 3$

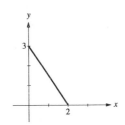

13. $x = 5\cos t, y = -5\sin t, 0 \le t \le 2\pi$

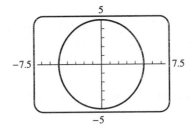

15. $x = 2, y = t$

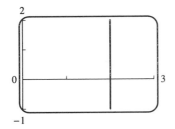

17. $x = t^2, y = t, -1 \le t \le 1$

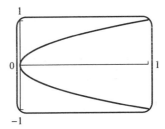

19. **(a)** IV, because x always increases whereas y oscillates.

(b) II, because $(x/2)^2 + (y/3)^2 = 1$, an ellipse.

(c) V, because $x^2 + y^2 = t^2$ increases in magnitude while x and y keep changing sign.

(d) VI; examine the cases $t < -1$ and $t > -1$ and you see the curve lies in the first, second and fourth quadrants only.

(e) III because $y > 0$.

(f) I; since x and y are bounded, the answer must be I or II; but as t runs, say, from 0 to π, x goes directly from 2 to -2, but y goes from 0 to 1 to 0 to -1 and back to 0, which describes I but not II.

21. **(a)**

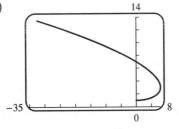

(b)

t	0	1	2	3	4	5
x	0	5.5	8	4.5	−8	−32.5
y	1	1.5	3	5.5	9	13.5

(c) $x = 0$ when $t = 0, 2\sqrt{3}$.

(d) for $0 < t < 2\sqrt{2}$

(e) at $t = 2$

23. **(a)**

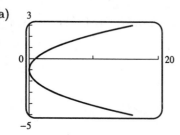

(b)

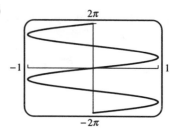

25. **(a)** $\dfrac{x - x_0}{x_1 - x_0} = \dfrac{y - y_0}{y_1 - y_0}$ **(b)** Set $t = 0$ to get (x_0, y_0); $t = 1$ for (x_1, y_1).

      (c) $x = 1 + t$, $y = -2 + 6t$ **(d)** $x = 2 - t$, $y = 4 - 6t$

27. **(a)** $|R - P|^2 = (x - x_0)^2 + (y - y_0)^2 = t^2[(x_1 - x_0)^2 + (y_1 - y_0)^2]$ and $|Q - P|^2 = (x_1 - x_0)^2 + (y_1 - y_0)^2$,

        so $r = |R - P| = |Q - P|t = qt$.

      (b) $t = 1/2$ **(c)** $t = 3/4$

29. The two branches corresponding to $-1 \le t \le 0$ and $0 \le t \le 1$ coincide.

31. **(a)** $\dfrac{x - b}{a} = \dfrac{y - d}{c}$ **(b)**

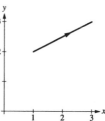

33.

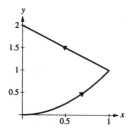

35. **(a)** $x = 4\cos t$, $y = 3\sin t$ **(b)** $x = -1 + 4\cos t$, $y = 2 + 3\sin t$

      (c)

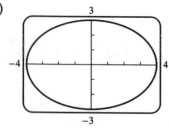 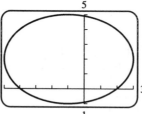

37. **(a)** From Exercise 36, $x = 400\sqrt{2}t$, $y = 400\sqrt{2}t - 4.9t^2$.   **(b)** 16,326.53 m   **(c)** 65,306.12 m

39. Assume that $a \ne 0$ and $b \ne 0$; eliminate the parameter to get $(x - h)^2/a^2 + (y - k)^2/b^2 = 1$. If $|a| = |b|$ the curve is a circle with center (h, k) and radius $|a|$; if $|a| \ne |b|$ the curve is an ellipse with center (h, k) and major axis parallel to the x-axis when $|a| > |b|$, or major axis parallel to the y-axis when $|a| < |b|$.

      (a) ellipses with a fixed center and varying axes of symmetry

(b) (assume $a \neq 0$ and $b \neq 0$) ellipses with varying center and fixed axes of symmetry

(c) circles of radius 1 with centers on the line $y = x - 1$

41. (a)

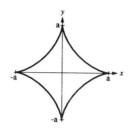

(b) Use $b = a/4$ in the equations of Exercise 40 to get
$$x = \frac{3}{4}a\cos\phi + \frac{1}{4}a\cos 3\phi, \; y = \frac{3}{4}a\sin\phi - \frac{1}{4}a\sin 3\phi;$$
but trigonometric identities yield $\cos 3\phi = 4\cos^3\phi - 3\cos\phi$, $\sin 3\phi = 3\sin\phi - 4\sin^3\phi$,

so $x = a\cos^3\phi$, $y = a\sin^3\phi$.

(c) $x^{2/3} + y^{2/3} = a^{2/3}(\cos^2\phi + \sin^2\phi) = a^{2/3}$

CHAPTER 1 SUPPLEMENTARY EXERCISES

1. 1940-45; the greatest five-year slope

3.

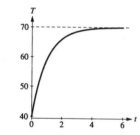

5. If the side has length x and height h, then $V = 8 = x^2h$, so $h = 8/x^2$. Then the cost $C = 5x^2 + 2(4)(xh) = 5x^2 + 64/x$.

7.

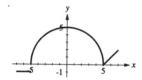

9. (a) The base has sides $(10 - 2x)/2$ and $6 - 2x$, and the height is x, so $V = (6 - 2x)(5 - x)x$ ft^3.

(b) From the picture we see that $x < 5$ and $2x < 6$, so $0 < x < 3$.

(c) 3.57 ft $\times 3.79$ ft $\times 1.21$ ft

11. impossible; we would have to solve $2(3x - 2) - 5 = 3(2x - 5) - 2$, or $-9 = -17$

13. $1/(2 - x^2)$

15.

x	-4	-3	-2	-1	0	1	2	3	4
$f(x)$	0	-1	2	1	3	-2	-3	4	-4
$g(x)$	3	2	1	-3	-1	-4	4	-2	0
$(f \circ g)(x)$	4	-3	-2	-1	1	0	-4	2	3
$(g \circ f)(x)$	-1	-3	4	-4	-2	1	2	0	3

17. **(a)** even × odd = odd   **(b)** a square is even

      (c) even + odd is neither   **(d)** odd × odd = even

19. **(a)** If x denotes the distance from A to the base of the tower, and y the distance from B to the base, then $x^2 + d^2 = y^2$. Moreover $h = x \tan \alpha = y \tan \beta$, so $d^2 = y^2 - x^2 = h^2(\cot^2 \beta - \cot^2 \alpha)$,

$$h^2 = \frac{d^2}{\cot^2 \beta - \cot^2 \alpha} = \frac{d^2 \sin^2 \alpha \sin^2 \beta}{\sin^2 \alpha \cos^2 \beta - \cos^2 \alpha \sin^2 \beta}.$$ The trigonometric identity

$$\sin(\alpha + \beta)\sin(\alpha - \beta) = \sin^2 \alpha \cos^2 \beta - \cos^2 \alpha \sin^2 \beta \text{ yields } h = \frac{d \sin \alpha \sin \beta}{\sqrt{\sin(\alpha + \beta)\sin(\alpha - \beta)}}.$$

     (b) 295.72 ft.

21. C is the highest nearby point on the graph; zoom to find that the coordinates of C are $(2.0944, 1.9132)$. Similarly, D is the lowest nearby point, and its coordinates are $(4.1888, 1.2284)$. Since $f(x) = \frac{1}{2}x - \sin x$ is an odd function, the coordinates of B are $(-2.0944, -1.9132)$ and those of A are $(-4.1888, -1.2284)$.

23. **(a)** The circle of radius 1 centered at (a, a^2); therefore, the family of all circles of radius 1 with centers on the parabola $y = x^2$.

     (b) All parabolas which open up, have latus rectum equal to 1 and vertex on the line $y = x/2$.

25.

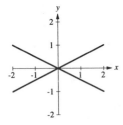

27.

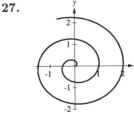

29. $d = \sqrt{(x-1)^2 + (\sqrt{x} - 2)^2}$;
$d = 9.1$ at $x = 1.358094$

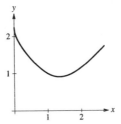

31. $w = 63.9V$, $w = 63.9\pi h^2(5/2 - h/3)$; $h = 0.48$ ft when $w = 108$ lb

33. **(a)**

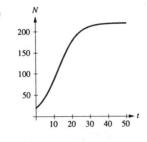

     (b) $N = 80$ when $t = 9.35$ yrs

     (c) 220 sheep

35. (a)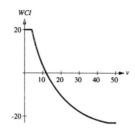

(b) $T = 3°F, -11°F, -18°F, -22°F$

(c) $v = 35, 19, 12, 7$ mi/h

37. The domain is the set $-0.7245 \le x \le 1.2207$, the range is $-1.0551 \le y \le 1.4902$.

39. (a)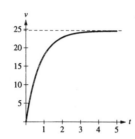

(b) As $t \to \infty$, $(0.273)^t \to 0$, and thus $v \to 24.61$ ft/s.

(c) For large t the velocity approaches c.

(d) no; but it comes very close (arbitrarily close).

(e) 3.013 s

CHAPTER 1 HORIZON MODULE

1. (a) $0.25, 6.25 \times 10^{-2}, 3.91 \times 10^{-3}, 1.53 \times 10^{-5}, 2.32 \times 10^{-10}, 5.42 \times 10^{-20}, 2.94 \times 10^{-39}, 8.64 \times 10^{-78},$
$7.46 \times 10^{-155}, 5.56 \times 10^{-309};$
$1, 1, 1, 1, 1, 1, 1, 1, 1, 1;$
$4, 16, 256, 65536, 4.29 \times 10^9, 1.84 \times 10^{19}, 3.40 \times 10^{38}, 1.16 \times 10^{77}, 1.34 \times 10^{154}, 1.80 \times 10^{308}$

3. (a) $\dfrac{1}{2}, \dfrac{1}{4}, \dfrac{1}{8}, \dfrac{1}{16}, \dfrac{1}{32}, \dfrac{1}{64}$

(b) $y_n = \dfrac{1}{2^n}$

5. (a) $x^{1/2}, x^{1/4}, x^{1/8}, x^{1/16}, x^{1/32}$

(b) They tend to the horizontal line $y = 1$, with a hole at $x = 0$.

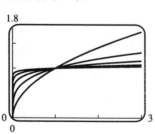

7. (a) $y_1 = cr, y_2 = cy_1 = cr^2, y_3 = cr^3, y_4 = cr^4$

(b) $y_n = cr^n$

(c) If $r = 1$ then $y_n = c$ for all n; if $r < 1$ then y_n tends to zero; if $r > 1$, then y_n gets ever larger (tends to $+\infty$).

9. (a) $0.261, 0.559, 0.715, 0.591, 0.701$

(b) It appears to approach a point somewhere near 0.65.

CHAPTER 2
Limits and Continuity

EXERCISE SET 2.1

1. (a) −1   (b) 3   (c) does not exist
    (d) 1   (e) −1   (f) 3

3. (a) 1   (b) 1   (c) 1   (d) 1   (e) $-\infty$ (f) $+\infty$

5. (a) 0   (b) 0   (c) 0   (d) 3   (e) $+\infty$ (f) $+\infty$

7. (a) $-\infty$ (b) $+\infty$ (c) does not exist
    (d) undef   (e) 2   (f) 0

9. (a) $-\infty$ (b) $-\infty$ (c) $-\infty$ (d) 1   (e) 1   (f) 2

11. (a) 0   (b) 0   (c) 0
    (d) 0   (e) does not exist   (f) does not exist

13. for all $x_0 \neq -4$

15. (a) At $x = 3$ the one-sided limits fail to exist.

    (b) At $x = -2$ the two-sided limit exists but is not equal to $F(-2)$.

    (c) At $x = 3$ the limit fails to exist.

17. (a)

2	1.5	1.1	1.01	1.001	0	0.5	0.9	0.99	0.999
0.1429	0.2105	0.3021	0.3300	0.3330	1.0000	0.5714	0.3690	0.3367	0.3337

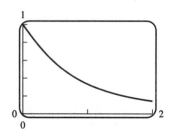

The limit is 1/3.

    (b)

2	1.5	1.1	1.01	1.001	1.0001
0.4286	1.0526	6.344	66.33	666.3	6666.3

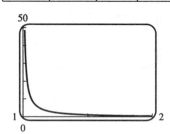

The limit is $+\infty$.

(c)

0	0.5	0.9	0.99	0.999	0.9999
−1	−1.7143	−7.0111	−67.001	−667.0	−6667.0

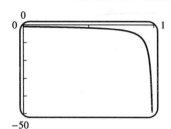

The limit is $-\infty$.

19. **(a)**

−0.25	−0.1	−0.001	−0.0001	0.0001	0.001	0.1	0.25
2.7266	2.9552	3.0000	3.0000	3.0000	3.0000	2.9552	2.7266

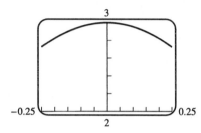

The limit is 3.

(b)

0	−0.5	−0.9	−0.99	−0.999	−1.5	−1.1	−1.01	−1.001
1	1.7552	6.2161	54.87	541.1	−0.1415	−4.536	−53.19	−539.5

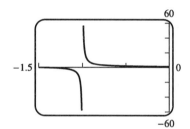

The limit does not exist.

21. **(a)**

−100,000,000	−100,000	−1000	−100	−10	10	100	1000
2.0000	2.0001	2.0050	2.0521	2.8333	1.6429	1.9519	1.9950

100,000	100,000,000
2.0000	2.0000

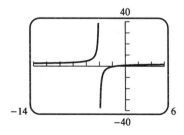

asymptote $y = 2$ as $x \to \pm\infty$

(b)

−100,000,000	−100,000	−1000	−100	−10	10	100	1000
20.0855	20.0864	20.1763	21.0294	35.4013	13.7858	19.2186	19.9955

100,000	100,000,000
20.0846	20.0855

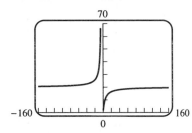

asymptote $y = 20.086$.

(c)

−100,000,000	−100,000	−1000	−100	−10	10	100	1000	100,000	100,000,000
−100,000,001	−100,000	−1001	−101.0	−11.2	9.2	99.0	999.0	99,999	99,999,999

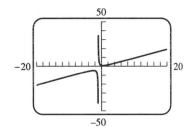

no horizontal asymptote

23. (a) $\lim\limits_{x \to 0^+} \dfrac{\sin x}{x}$ (b) $\lim\limits_{x \to 0^+} \dfrac{x-1}{x+1}$ (c) $\lim\limits_{x \to 0^-} (1+2x)^{1/x}$

25. (a) 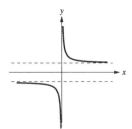   (b) yes; for example $f(x) = (\sin x)/x$

29. (a) The plot over the interval $[-a, a]$ becomes subject to catastrophic subtraction if a is small enough (the size depending on the machine).

   (c) It does not.

EXERCISE SET 2.2

1. (a) -6 (b) 13   (c) -8 (d) 16   (e) 2   (f) $-1/2$

   (g) The limit doesn't exist because the denominator tends to zero but the numerator doesn't.

   (h) The limit doesn't exist because the denominator tends to zero but the numerator doesn't.

3. (a) 7   (b) -3 (c) π (d) -6 (e) 36   (f) $-\infty$

5. 0   **7.** 8   **9.** 4   **11.** $-4/5$ **13.** $3/2$

15. 0   **17.** 0   **19.** $-\sqrt{5}$ **21.** $1/\sqrt{6}$ **23.** $\sqrt{3}$

25. $+\infty$ **27.** does not exist   **29.** $-\infty$ **31.** $+\infty$ **33.** does not exist

35. $+\infty$ **37.** $-\infty$ **39.** $-1/7$ **41.** 6   **43.** $+\infty$

45. $+\infty$ **47.** $-\infty$

49. (a) 2   (b) 2   (c) 2

51. (a) 3   (b)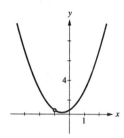

53. (a) Theorem 2.2.2(a) doesn't apply; moreover one cannot add/subtract infinities.

(b) $\lim\limits_{x \to 0^+} \left(\dfrac{1}{x} - \dfrac{1}{x^2} \right) = \lim\limits_{x \to 0^+} \left(\dfrac{x-1}{x^2} \right) = -\infty$

55. $\lim\limits_{x \to 0} \dfrac{x}{x \left(\sqrt{x+4} + 2 \right)} = \dfrac{1}{4}$

57. $\lim\limits_{x \to +\infty} (\sqrt{x^2+3} - x) \dfrac{\sqrt{x^2+3}+x}{\sqrt{x^2+3}+x} = \lim\limits_{x \to +\infty} \dfrac{3}{\sqrt{x^2+3}+x} = 0$

59. $\lim\limits_{x \to +\infty} \left(\sqrt{x^2+ax} - x \right) \dfrac{\sqrt{x^2+ax}+x}{\sqrt{x^2+ax}+x} = \lim\limits_{x \to +\infty} \dfrac{ax}{\sqrt{x^2+ax}+x} = a/2$

61. $\lim\limits_{x \to +\infty} p(x) = (-1)^n \infty$ and $\lim\limits_{x \to -\infty} p(x) = +\infty$

63. If $m > n$ the limits are both zero. If $m = n$ the limits are both equal to a_m, the leading coefficient of p. If $n > m$ the limits are $\pm\infty$ where the sign depends on the sign of a_m and whether n is even or odd.

65. The left and/or right limits could be plus or minus infinity; or the limit could exist, or equal any preassigned real number. For example, let $q(x) = x - x_0$ and let $p(x) = a(x - x_0)^n$ where n takes on the values $0, 1, 2$.

EXERCISE SET 2.3

1. (a) $|f(x) - f(0)| = |x + 2 - 2| = |x| < 0.1$ if and only if $|x| < 0.1$

(b) $|f(x) - f(3)| = |(4x - 5) - 7| = 4|x - 3| < 0.1$ if and only if $|x - 3| < (0.1)/4 = 0.0025$

(c) $|f(x) - f(4)| = |x^2 - 16| < \epsilon$ if $|x - 4| < \delta$. We get $f(x) = 16 + \epsilon = 16.001$ at $x = 4.000124998$, which corresponds to $\delta = 0.000124998$; and $f(x) = 16 - \epsilon = 15.999$ at $x = 3.999874998$, for which $\delta = 0.000125002$. Use the smaller δ: thus $|f(x) - 16| < \epsilon$ provided $|x - 4| < 0.000125$ (to six decimals).

3. **(a)** $x_1 = (1.95)^2 = 3.8025, x_2 = (2.05)^2 = 4.2025$

    (b) $\delta = \min\left(\,|4 - 3.8025|, |4 - 4.2025|\,\right) = 0.1975$

5. $|2x - 8| = 2|x - 4| < 0.1$ if $|x - 4| < 0.05$, $\delta = 0.05$

7. $|7x + 5 - (-2)| = 7|x - (-1)| < 0.01$ if $|x + 1| < \dfrac{1}{700}$, $\delta = \dfrac{1}{700}$

9. $\left|\dfrac{x^2 - 4}{x - 2} - 4\right| = \left|\dfrac{x^2 - 4 - 4x + 8}{x - 2}\right| = |x - 2| < 0.05$ if $|x - 2| < 0.05$, $\delta = 0.05$

11. if $\delta < 1$ then $|x^2 - 16| = |x - 4||x + 4| < 9|x - 4| < 0.001$ if $|x - 4| < \dfrac{1}{9000}$, $\delta = \dfrac{1}{9000}$

13. if $\delta \le 1$ then $\left|\dfrac{1}{x} - \dfrac{1}{5}\right| = \dfrac{|x - 5|}{5|x|} \le \dfrac{|x - 5|}{20} < 0.05$ if $|x - 5| < 1$, $\delta = 1$

15. $|3x - 15| = 3|x - 5| < \epsilon$ if $|x - 5| < \frac{1}{3}\epsilon$, $\delta = \frac{1}{3}\epsilon$

17. $|2x - 7 - (-3)| = 2|x - 2| < \epsilon$ if $|x - 2| < \frac{1}{2}\epsilon$, $\delta = \frac{1}{2}\epsilon$

19. $\left|\dfrac{x^2 + x}{x} - 1\right| = |x| < \epsilon$ if $|x| < \epsilon$, $\delta = \epsilon$

21. if $\delta < 1$ then $|2x^2 - 2| = 2|x - 1||x + 1| < 6|x - 1| < \epsilon$ if $|x - 1| < \frac{1}{6}\epsilon$, $\delta = \min(1, \frac{1}{6}\epsilon)$

23. if $\delta < \dfrac{1}{6}$ then $\left|\dfrac{1}{x} - 3\right| = \dfrac{3|x - \frac{1}{3}|}{|x|} < 18|x - \dfrac{1}{3}| < \epsilon$ if $|x - \dfrac{1}{3}| < \dfrac{1}{18}\epsilon$, $\delta = \min(\dfrac{1}{6}, \dfrac{1}{18}\epsilon)$

25. $|\sqrt{x} - 2| = \left|(\sqrt{x} - 2)\dfrac{\sqrt{x} + 2}{\sqrt{x} + 2}\right| = \left|\dfrac{x - 4}{\sqrt{x} + 2}\right| < \dfrac{1}{2}|x - 4| < \epsilon$ if $|x - 4| < 2\epsilon$, $\delta = 2\epsilon$

27. $|f(x) - 3| = |x + 2 - 3| = |x - 1| < \epsilon$ if $0 < |x - 1| < \epsilon$, $\delta = \epsilon$

29. **(a)** $|f(x) - L| = \dfrac{1}{x^2} < 0.1$ if $x > \sqrt{10}$, $N = \sqrt{10}$

    (b) $|f(x) - L| = |\dfrac{x}{x + 1} - 1| = |\dfrac{1}{x + 1}| < 0.01$ if $x + 1 > 100$, $N = 99$

    (c) $|f(x) - L| = \left|\dfrac{1}{x^3}\right| < \dfrac{1}{1000}$ if $|x| > 10$, $x < -10$, $N = -10$

    (d) $|f(x) - L| = \left|\dfrac{x}{x + 1} - 1\right| = \left|\dfrac{1}{x + 1}\right| < 0.01$ if $|x + 1| > 100$, $-x - 1 > 100$, $x < -101$, $N = -101$

31. **(a)** $\dfrac{x_1^2}{1 + x_1^2} = 1 - \epsilon$, $x_1 = -\sqrt{\dfrac{1 - \epsilon}{\epsilon}}$; $\dfrac{x_2^2}{1 + x_2^2} = 1 - \epsilon$, $x_2 = \sqrt{\dfrac{1 - \epsilon}{\epsilon}}$

    (b) $N = \sqrt{\dfrac{1 - \epsilon}{\epsilon}}$ **(c)** $N = -\sqrt{\dfrac{1 - \epsilon}{\epsilon}}$

33. $\dfrac{1}{x^2} < 0.01$ if $|x| > 10$, $N = 10$

35. $\left|\dfrac{x}{x + 1} - 1\right| = \left|\dfrac{1}{x + 1}\right| < 0.001$ if $|x + 1| > 1000$, $x > 999$, $N = 999$

37. $\left|\dfrac{1}{x+2} - 0\right| < 0.005$ if $|x+2| > 200$, $-x-2 > 200$, $x < -202$, $N = -202$

39. $\left|\dfrac{4x-1}{2x+5} - 2\right| = \left|\dfrac{11}{2x+5}\right| < 0.1$ if $|2x+5| > 110$, $-2x-5 > 110$, $2x < -115$, $x < -57.5$, $N = -57.5$

41. $\left|\dfrac{1}{x^2}\right| < \epsilon$ if $|x| > \dfrac{1}{\sqrt{\epsilon}}$, $N = \dfrac{1}{\sqrt{\epsilon}}$

43. $\left|\dfrac{1}{x+2}\right| < \epsilon$ if $|x+2| > \dfrac{1}{\epsilon}$, $-x-2 < \dfrac{1}{\epsilon}$, $x > -2 - \dfrac{1}{\epsilon}$, $N = -2 - \dfrac{1}{\epsilon}$

45. $\left|\dfrac{x}{x+1} - 1\right| = \left|\dfrac{1}{x+1}\right| < \epsilon$ if $|x+1| > \dfrac{1}{\epsilon}$, $x > \dfrac{1}{\epsilon} - 1$, $N = \dfrac{1}{\epsilon} - 1$

47. $\left|\dfrac{4x-1}{2x+5} - 2\right| = \left|\dfrac{11}{2x+5}\right| < \epsilon$ if $|2x+5| > \dfrac{11}{\epsilon}$, $-2x-5 > \dfrac{11}{\epsilon}$, $2x < -\dfrac{11}{\epsilon} - 5$, $x < -\dfrac{11}{2\epsilon} - \dfrac{5}{2}$, $N = -\dfrac{5}{2} - \dfrac{11}{2\epsilon}$

49. (a) $\dfrac{1}{x^2} > 100$ if $|x| < \dfrac{1}{10}$ (b) $\dfrac{1}{|x-1|} > 1000$ if $|x-1| < \dfrac{1}{1000}$

       (c) $\dfrac{-1}{(x-3)^2} < -1000$ if $|x-3| < \dfrac{1}{10\sqrt{10}}$ (d) $-\dfrac{1}{x^4} < -10000$ if $x^4 < \dfrac{1}{10000}$, $|x| < \dfrac{1}{10}$

51. if $M > 0$ then $\dfrac{1}{(x-3)^2} > M$, $0 < (x-3)^2 < \dfrac{1}{M}$, $0 < |x-3| < \dfrac{1}{\sqrt{M}}$, $\delta = \dfrac{1}{\sqrt{M}}$

53. if $M > 0$ then $\dfrac{1}{|x|} > M$, $0 < |x| < \dfrac{1}{M}$, $\delta = \dfrac{1}{M}$

55. if $M < 0$ then $-\dfrac{1}{x^4} < M$, $0 < x^4 < -\dfrac{1}{M}$, $|x| < \dfrac{1}{(-M)^{1/4}}$, $\delta = \dfrac{1}{(-M)^{1/4}}$

57. if $x > 2$ then $|x+1-3| = |x-2| = x-2 < \epsilon$ if $2 < x < 2 + \epsilon$, $\delta = \epsilon$

59. if $x > 4$ then $\sqrt{x-4} < \epsilon$ if $x-4 < \epsilon^2$, $4 < x < 4 + \epsilon^2$, $\delta = \epsilon^2$

61. if $x > 2$ then $|f(x) - 2| = |x-2| = x-2 < \epsilon$ if $2 < x < 2 + \epsilon$, $\delta = \epsilon$

63. (a) if $M < 0$ and $x > 1$ then $\dfrac{1}{1-x} < M$, $x - 1 < -\dfrac{1}{M}$, $1 < x < 1 - \dfrac{1}{M}$, $\delta = -\dfrac{1}{M}$

       (b) if $M > 0$ and $x < 1$ then $\dfrac{1}{1-x} > M$, $1 - x < \dfrac{1}{M}$, $1 - \dfrac{1}{M} < x < 1$, $\delta = \dfrac{1}{M}$

65. (a) Given any $M > 0$ there corresponds $N > 0$ such that if $x > N$ then $f(x) > M$, $x + 1 > M$, $x > M - 1$, $N = M - 1$.

       (b) Given any $M < 0$ there corresponds $N < 0$ such that if $x < N$ then $f(x) < M$, $x + 1 < M$, $x < M - 1$, $N = M - 1$.

67. if $\delta \leq 2$ then $|x-3| < 2$, $-2 < x-3 < 2$, $1 < x < 5$, and $|x^2 - 9| = |x+3||x-3| < 8|x-3| < \epsilon$ if $|x-3| < \dfrac{1}{8}\epsilon$, $\delta = \min\left(2, \dfrac{1}{8}\epsilon\right)$

69. $|(x^3 - 4x + 5) - 2| < 0.05$, $-0.05 < (x^3 - 4x + 5) - 2 < 0.05$, $1.95 < x^3 - 4x + 5 < 2.05$; $x^3 - 4x + 5 = 1.95$
at $x = 1.0616$, $x^3 - 4x + 5 = 2.05$ at $x = 0.9558$; $\delta = \min(1.0616 - 1, 1 - 0.9558) = 0.0442$

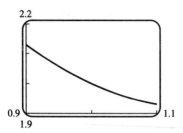

EXERCISE SET 2.4

1. **(a)** no, $x = 2$ **(b)** no, $x = 2$ **(c)** no, $x = 2$ **(d)** yes
    (e) yes   **(f)** yes

3. **(a)** no, $x = 1, 3$ **(b)** yes   **(c)** no, $x = 1$ **(d)** yes
    (e) no, $x = 3$ **(f)** yes

5. **(a)** 3   **(b)** 3

7. **(a)**

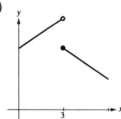

(b)

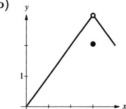

(c)

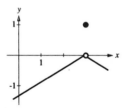

(d)

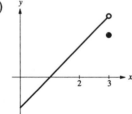

9. **(a)**

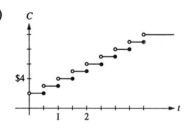

(b) One second could cost you one dollar.

11. none   **13.** none

15. f is not defined at $x = \pm 4$ **17.** f is not defined at $x = \pm 3$

19.   none

21.   none; $f(x) = 2x + 3$ is continuous on $x < 4$ and $f(x) = 7 + \dfrac{16}{x}$ is continuous on $4 < x$;
$\lim\limits_{x \to 4^-} f(x) = \lim\limits_{x \to 4^+} f(x) = f(4) = 11$ so f is continuous at $x = 4$

23.   **(a)** f is continuous for $x < 1$, and for $x > 1$; $\lim\limits_{x \to 1^-} f(x) = 5$, $\lim\limits_{x \to 1^+} f(x) = k$, so if $k = 5$ then f is continuous for all x

      (b) f is continuous for $x < 2$, and for $x > 2$; $\lim\limits_{x \to 2^-} f(x) = 4k$, $\lim\limits_{x \to 2^+} f(x) = 4 + k$, so if $4k = 4 + k$, $k = 4/3$ then f is continuous for all x

25.   **(a)** 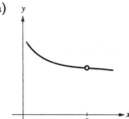   **(b)**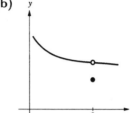

27.   **(a)** $x = 0$, $\lim\limits_{x \to 0^-} f(x) = -1 \ne +1 = \lim\limits_{x \to 0^+} f(x)$ so the discontinuity is not removable

      (b) $x = -3$; define $f(-3) = -3 = \lim\limits_{x \to -3} f(x)$, then the discontinuity is removable

      (c) f is undefined at $x = \pm 2$; at $x = 2$, $\lim\limits_{x \to 2} f(x) = 1$, so define $f(2) = 1$ and f becomes continuous there; at $x = -2$, $\lim\limits_{x \to -2}$ does not exist, so the discontinuity is not removable

29.   **(a)**   discontinuity at $x = 1/2$, not removable; at   **(b)** $2x^2 + 5x - 3 = (2x - 1)(x + 3)$
$x = -3$, removable

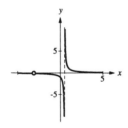

31.   For $x > 0$, $f(x) = x^{3/5} = (x^3)^{1/5}$ is the composition (Theorem 2.4.6) of the two continuous functions $g(x) = x^3$ and $h(x) = x^{1/5}$ and is thus continuous. For $x < 0$, $f(x) = f(-x)$ which is the composition of the continuous functions $f(x)$ (for positive x) and the continuous function $y = -x$. Hence $f(-x)$ is continuous for all $x > 0$. At $x = 0$, $f(0) = \lim\limits_{x \to 0} f(x) = 0$.

33.   **(a)**   Let $f(x) = k$ for $x \ne c$ and $f(c) = 0$; $g(x) = l$ for $x \ne c$ and $g(c) = 0$. If $k = -l$ then $f + g$ is continuous; otherwise it's not.

      (b) $f(x) = k$ for $x \ne c$, $f(c) = 1$; $g(x) = l \ne 0$ for $x \ne c$, $g(c) = 1$. If $kl = 1$, then fg is continuous; otherwise it is not.

35.   Since f and g are continuous at $x = c$ we know that $\lim\limits_{x \to c} f(x) = f(c)$ and $\lim\limits_{x \to c} g(x) = g(c)$. In the following we use Theorem 2.2.2.

      (a) $f(c) + g(c) = \lim\limits_{x \to c} f(x) + \lim\limits_{x \to c} g(x) = \lim\limits_{x \to c} (f(x) + g(x))$ so $f + g$ is continuous at $x = c$.

      (b)   same as (a) except the $+$ sign becomes a $-$ sign

(c) $\dfrac{f(c)}{g(c)} = \dfrac{\lim\limits_{x\to c} f(x)}{\lim\limits_{x\to c} g(x)} = \lim\limits_{x\to c}\dfrac{f(x)}{g(x)}$ so $\dfrac{f}{g}$ is continuous at $x = c$

37. Of course such a function must be discontinuous. Let $f(x) = 1$ on $0 \le x < 1$, and $f(x) = -1$ on $1 \le x \le 2$.

39. The cone has volume $\pi r^2 h/3$. The function $V(r) = \pi r^2 h$ (for variable r and fixed h) gives the volume of a right circular cylinder of height h and radius r, and satisfies $V(0) < \pi r^2 h/3 < V(r)$. By the Intermediate Value Theorem there is a value c between 0 and r such that $V(c) = \pi r^2 h/3$, so the cylinder of radius c (and height h) has volume equal to that of the cone.

41. If $f(x) = x^3 + x^2 - 2x$ then $f(-1) = 2$, $f(1) = 0$. Use the Intermediate Value Theorem.

43. For the negative root, use intervals on the x-axis as follows: $[-2, -1]$; since $f(-1.3) < 0$ and $f(-1.2) > 0$, the midpoint $x = -1.25$ of $[-1.3, -1.2]$ is the required approximation of the root. For the positive root use the interval $[0, 1]$; since $f(0.7) < 0$ and $f(0.8) > 0$, the midpoint $x = 0.75$ of $[0.7, 0.8]$ is the required approximation.

45. For the negative root, use intervals on the x-axis as follows: $[-2, -1]$; since $f(-1.7) < 0$ and $f(-1.6) > 0$, use the interval $[-1.7, -1.6]$. Since $f(-1.61) < 0$ and $f(-1.60) > 0$ the midpoint $x = -1.605$ of $[-1.61, -1.60]$ is the required approximation of the root. For the positive root use the interval $[1, 2]$; since $f(1.3) > 0$ and $f(1.4) < 0$, use the interval $[1.3, 1.4]$. Since $f(1.37) > 0$ and $f(1.38) < 0$, the midpoint $x = 1.375$ of $[1.37, 1.38]$ is the required approximation.

47. $x = 2.24$.

49. The uncoated sphere has volume $4\pi(x-1)^3/3$ and the coated sphere has volume $4\pi x^3/3$. If the volume of the uncoated sphere and of the coating itself are the same, then the coated sphere has twice the volume of the uncoated sphere. Thus $2(4\pi(x-1)^3/3) = 4\pi x^3/3$, or $x^3 - 6x^2 + 6x - 2 = 0$, with the solution $x = 4.847$ cm.

51. We must show $\lim\limits_{x\to c} f(x) = f(c)$. Let $\epsilon > 0$; then there exists $\delta > 0$ such that if $|x - c| < \delta$ then $|f(x) - f(c)| < \epsilon$. But this certainly satisfies Definition 2.3.3.

EXERCISE SET 2.5

1. none

3. $x = n\pi$, $n = 0, \pm1, \pm2, \ldots$

5. $x = n\pi$, $n = 0, \pm1, \pm2, \ldots$

7. none

9. $2n\pi + \pi/6, 2n\pi + 5\pi/6$, $n = 0, \pm1, \pm2, \ldots$

11. (a) $\sin x, x^3 + 7x + 1$ (b) $|x|, \sin x$ (c) $x^3, \cos x, x + 1$

(d) $\sqrt{x}, 3 + x, \sin x, 2x$ (e) $\sin x, \sin x$ (f) $x^5 - 2x^3 + 1, \cos x$

13. $\cos\left(\lim\limits_{x\to+\infty}\dfrac{1}{x}\right) = \cos 0 = 1$

15. $\sin\left(\lim\limits_{x\to+\infty}\dfrac{\pi x}{2 - 3x}\right) = \sin\left(-\dfrac{\pi}{3}\right) = -\dfrac{\sqrt{3}}{2}$

17. $3\lim\limits_{\theta\to0}\dfrac{\sin 3\theta}{3\theta} = 3$

19. $-\lim\limits_{x\to0^-}\dfrac{\sin x}{x} = -1$

21. $\dfrac{1}{5}\lim\limits_{x\to0^+}\sqrt{x}\lim\limits_{x\to0^+}\dfrac{\sin x}{x} = 0$

23. $\dfrac{\tan 7x}{\sin 3x} = \dfrac{7}{3\cos 7x}\dfrac{\sin 7x}{7x}\dfrac{3x}{\sin 3x}$ so $\lim\limits_{x\to0}\dfrac{\tan 7x}{\sin 3x} = \dfrac{7}{3(1)}(1)(1) = \dfrac{7}{3}$

25. $\left(\lim_{h\to 0}\cos h\right)\lim_{h\to 0}\dfrac{h}{\sin h}=1$

27. $\dfrac{\theta^2}{1-\cos\theta}\dfrac{1+\cos\theta}{1+\cos\theta}=\dfrac{\theta^2(1+\cos\theta)}{1-\cos^2\theta}=\left(\dfrac{\theta}{\sin\theta}\right)^2(1+\cos\theta)$ so $\lim_{\theta\to 0}\dfrac{\theta^2}{1-\cos\theta}=(1)^2 2=2$

29. 0

31. $\dfrac{1-\cos 5h}{\cos 7h-1}=\dfrac{(1-\cos 5h)(1+\cos 5h)(1+\cos 7h)}{(\cos 7h-1)(1+\cos 5h)(1+\cos 7h)}=-\dfrac{25}{49}\left(\dfrac{\sin 5h}{5h}\right)^2\left(\dfrac{7h}{\sin 7h}\right)^2\dfrac{1+\cos 7h}{1+\cos 5h}$ so

$\lim_{h\to 0}\dfrac{1-\cos 5h}{\cos 7h-1}=-\dfrac{25}{49}$

33. $\lim_{x\to 0^+}\cos\left(\dfrac{1}{x}\right)=\lim_{t\to+\infty}\cos t;$ **35.** $2+\lim_{x\to 0}\dfrac{\sin x}{x}=3$
limit does not exist

37. $\lim_{x\to 0^-}f(x)=k\lim_{x\to 0}\dfrac{\sin kx}{kx\cos kx}=k,\ \lim_{x\to 0^+}f(x)=2k^2$, so $k=2k^2$, $k=\dfrac{1}{2}$

39. **(a)** $\lim_{t\to 0^+}\dfrac{\sin t}{t}=1$ **(b)** $\lim_{t\to 0^-}\dfrac{1-\cos t}{t}=0$ (Theorem 2.5.3)

    (c) $\sin(\pi-t)=\sin t$, so $\lim_{x\to\pi}\dfrac{\pi-x}{\sin x}=\lim_{t\to 0}\dfrac{t}{\sin t}=1$

41. $t=x-1;\ \sin(\pi x)=\sin(\pi t+\pi)=-\sin\pi t;$ and $\lim_{x\to 1}\dfrac{\sin(\pi x)}{x-1}=-\lim_{t\to 0}\dfrac{\sin\pi t}{t}=-\pi$

43. $-x\le x\cos\left(\dfrac{50\pi}{x}\right)\le x$ **45.** $\lim_{x\to 0}f(x)=1$ by the Squeezing Theorem

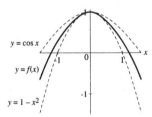

47. Let $g(x)=-\dfrac{1}{x}$ and $h(x)=\dfrac{1}{x}$; thus $\lim_{x\to+\infty}\dfrac{\sin x}{x}=0$ by the Squeezing Theorem.

49. **(a)** $\sin x=\sin t$ where x is measured in degrees, t is measured in radians and $t=\dfrac{\pi x}{180}$. Thus
$\lim_{x\to 0}\dfrac{\sin x}{x}=\lim_{t\to 0}\dfrac{\sin t}{(180t/\pi)}=\dfrac{\pi}{180}.$

51. **(a)** $\sin 10°=0.17365$ **(b)** $\sin 10°=\sin\dfrac{\pi}{18}\approx\dfrac{\pi}{18}=0.17453$

53. **(a)** 0.08749 **(b)** $\tan 5°\approx\dfrac{\pi}{36}=0.08727$

55. **(a)** Let $f(x)=x-\cos x;\ f(0)=-1,\ f(\pi/2)=\pi/2$. By the IVT there must be a solution of $f(x)=0$.

(b)   y

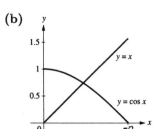

(c)   0.739

57. **(a)**   There is symmetry about the equatorial plane.

  (b)   Let $g(\phi)$ be the given function. Then $g(38) < 9.8$ and $g(39) > 9.8$, so by the Intermediate Value Theorem there is a value c between 38 and 39 for which $g(c) = 9.8$ exactly.

CHAPTER 2 SUPPLEMENTARY EXERCISES

1. **(a)** 1   **(b)** no limit   **(c)** no limit   **(d)** 1   **(e)** 3

  (f) 0   **(g)** 0   **(h)** 2   **(i)** 1/2

5. **(a)** $0.222\ldots, 0.24390, 0.24938, 0.24994, 0.24999, 0.25000$; for $x \neq 2$, $f(x) = \dfrac{1}{x+2}$, so the limit is $1/4$; the limit is 4.

  (b) $1.15782, 4.22793, 4.00213, 4.00002, 4.00000, 4.00000$; to prove, use $\dfrac{\tan 4x}{x} = \dfrac{\sin 4x}{x\cos 4x} = \dfrac{4}{\cos 4x}\dfrac{\sin 4x}{4x}$.

7. **(a)**

x	1	0.1	0.01	0.001	0.0001	0.00001	0.000001
f(x)	1.000	0.443	0.409	0.406	0.406	0.405	0.405

  (b)

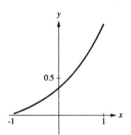

9. **(a)**

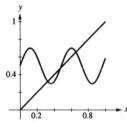

  (b)   Let $g(x) = x - f(x)$. Then $g(1) \geq 0$ and $g(0) \leq 0$; by the Intermediate Value Theorem there is a solution c in $[0,1]$ of $g(c) = 0$.

11.   If, on the contrary, $f(x_0) < 0$ for some x_0 in $[0,1]$, then by the Intermediate Value Theorem we would have a solution of $f(x) = 0$ in $[0, x_0]$, contrary to the hypothesis.

13. $f(-6) = 185$, $f(0) = -1$, $f(2) = 65$; apply Theorem 2.4.9 twice, once on $[-6, 0]$ and once on $[0, 2]$

15.   Let $\epsilon = f(x_0)/2 > 0$; then there corresponds $\delta > 0$ such that if $|x - x_0| < \delta$ then $|f(x) - f(x_0)| < \epsilon$, $-\epsilon < f(x) - f(x_0) < \epsilon$, $f(x) > f(x_0) - \epsilon = f(x_0)/2 > 0$ for $x_0 - \delta < x < x_0 + \delta$.

17. **(a)** 1.449 (x must be ≥ -1)   **(b)** $x = 0, \pm 1.896$

19. (a) $\sqrt{5}$, no limit, $\sqrt{10}$, $\sqrt{10}$, no limit, $+\infty$,   (b) $5, 10, 0, 0, 10, -\infty, +\infty$
           no limit

21. a/b   **23.** does not exist   **25.** 0   **27.** $3 - k$

29.

x	0.1	0.01	0.001	0.0001	0.00001	0.000001
$f(x)$	2.59	2.70	2.717	2.718	2.7183	2.71828

31.

x	1.1	1.01	1.001	1.0001	1.00001	1.000001
$f(x)$	0.49	0.54	0.540	0.5403	0.54030	0.54030

33.

x	100	1000	10^4	10^5	10^6	10^7
$f(x)$	0.48809	0.49611	0.49876	0.49961	0.49988	0.49996

35. $\delta = 0.07747$

37. (a) $x^3 - x - 1 = 0$, $x^3 = x + 1$, $x = \sqrt[3]{x + 1}$.   (b)

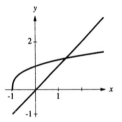

(c)

(d) $1, 1.26, 1.31, 1.322, 1.324, 1.3246, 1.3247$

39. $x = \sqrt[5]{x + 2}$; 1.267168

CHAPTER 3
The Derivative

EXERCISE SET 3.1

1. **(a)** $m_{\sec} = \dfrac{f(4) - f(3)}{4 - 3} = \dfrac{(4)^2/2 - (3)^2/2}{1} = \dfrac{7}{2}$

    (b) $m_{\tan} = \lim\limits_{x_1 \to 3} \dfrac{f(x_1) - f(3)}{x_1 - 3} = \lim\limits_{x_1 \to 3} \dfrac{x_1^2/2 - 9/2}{x_1 - 3}$

          $= \lim\limits_{x_1 \to 3} \dfrac{x_1^2 - 9}{2(x_1 - 3)} = \lim\limits_{x_1 \to 3} \dfrac{(x_1 + 3)(x_1 - 3)}{2(x_1 - 3)} = \lim\limits_{x_1 \to 3} \dfrac{x_1 + 3}{2} = 3$

    (c) $m_{\tan} = \lim\limits_{x_1 \to x_0} \dfrac{f(x_1) - f(x_0)}{x_1 - x_0}$ **(d)**

          $= \lim\limits_{x_1 \to x_0} \dfrac{x_1^2/2 - x_0^2/2}{x_1 - x_0}$

          $= \lim\limits_{x_1 \to x_0} \dfrac{x_1^2 - x_0^2}{2(x_1 - x_0)}$

          $= \lim\limits_{x_1 \to x_0} \dfrac{x_1 + x_0}{2} = x_0$

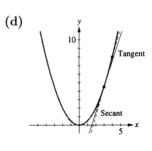

3. **(a)** $m_{\sec} = \dfrac{f(3) - f(2)}{3 - 2} = \dfrac{1/3 - 1/2}{1} = -\dfrac{1}{6}$

    (b) $m_{\tan} = \lim\limits_{x_1 \to 2} \dfrac{f(x_1) - f(2)}{x_1 - 2} = \lim\limits_{x_1 \to 2} \dfrac{1/x_1 - 1/2}{x_1 - 2}$

          $= \lim\limits_{x_1 \to 2} \dfrac{2 - x_1}{2x_1(x_1 - 2)} = \lim\limits_{x_1 \to 2} \dfrac{-1}{2x_1} = -\dfrac{1}{4}$

    (c) $m_{\tan} = \lim\limits_{x_1 \to x_0} \dfrac{f(x_1) - f(x_0)}{x_1 - x_0}$ **(d)**

          $= \lim\limits_{x_1 \to x_0} \dfrac{1/x_1 - 1/x_0}{x_1 - x_0}$

          $= \lim\limits_{x_1 \to x_0} \dfrac{x_0 - x_1}{x_0 x_1(x_1 - x_0)}$

          $= \lim\limits_{x_1 \to x_0} \dfrac{-1}{x_0 x_1} = -\dfrac{1}{x_0^2}$

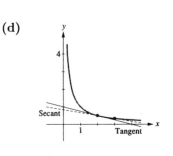

5. **(a)** $m_{\tan} = \lim\limits_{x_1 \to x_0} \dfrac{f(x_1) - f(x_0)}{x_1 - x_0} = \lim\limits_{x_1 \to x_0} \dfrac{(x_1^2 + 1) - (x_0^2 + 1)}{x_1 - x_0}$

          $= \lim\limits_{x_1 \to x_0} \dfrac{x_1^2 - x_0^2}{x_1 - x_0} = \lim\limits_{x_1 \to x_0} (x_1 + x_0) = 2x_0$

    (b) $m_{\tan} = 2(2) = 4$

7. **(a)** $m_{\tan} = \lim\limits_{x_1 \to x_0} \dfrac{f(x_1) - f(x_0)}{x_1 - x_0} = \lim\limits_{x_1 \to x_0} \dfrac{\sqrt{x_1} - \sqrt{x_0}}{x_1 - x_0}$

          $= \lim\limits_{x_1 \to x_0} \dfrac{1}{\sqrt{x_1} + \sqrt{x_0}} = \dfrac{1}{2\sqrt{x_0}}$

    (b) $m_{\tan} = \dfrac{1}{2\sqrt{1}} = \dfrac{1}{2}$

9. **(a)** $m_{\tan} = (50 - 10)/(15 - 5)$
$= 40/10$
$= 4 \text{ m/s}$

(b)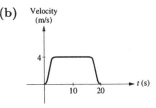

11. From the figure:

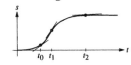

(a) The particle is moving faster at time t_0 because the slope of the tangent to the curve at t_0 is greater than that at t_2.

(b) The initial velocity is 0 because the slope of a horizontal line is 0.

(c) The particle is speeding up because the slope increases as t increases from t_0 to t_1.

(d) The particle is slowing down because the slope decreases as t increases from t_1 to t_2.

13. It is a straight line with slope equal to the velocity.

15. **(a)** 72°F at about 4:30 P.M.
(b) about $(67 - 43)/6 = 4°\text{F/h}$

(c) decreasing most rapidly at about 9 P.M.; rate of change of temperature is about $-7°\text{F/h}$ (slope of estimated tangent line to curve at 9 P.M.)

17. **(a)** during the first year after birth

(b) about 6 cm/year (slope of estimated tangent line at age 5)

(c) the growth rate is greatest at about age 14; about 10 cm/year

(d)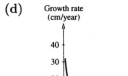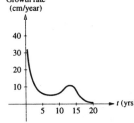

19. **(a)** $5(40)^3 = 320{,}000 \text{ ft}$

(b) $v_{\text{ave}} = 320{,}000/40 = 8{,}000 \text{ ft/s}$

(c) $5t^3 = 135$ when the rocket has gone 135 ft, so $t^3 = 27$, $t = 3$ s; $v_{\text{ave}} = 135/3 = 45 \text{ ft/s}$.

(d) $v_{\text{inst}} = \lim\limits_{t_1 \to 40} \dfrac{5t_1^3 - 5(40)^3}{t_1 - 40} = \lim\limits_{t_1 \to 40} \dfrac{5(t_1^3 - 40^3)}{t_1 - 40}$

$= \lim\limits_{t_1 \to 40} 5(t_1^2 + 40t_1 + 1600) = 24{,}000 \text{ ft/s}$

21. **(a)** $v_{\text{ave}} = \dfrac{6(4)^4 - 6(2)^4}{4 - 2} = 720 \text{ ft/min}$

(b) $v_{\text{inst}} = \lim\limits_{t_1 \to 2} \dfrac{6t_1^4 - 6(2)^4}{t_1 - 2} = \lim\limits_{t_1 \to 2} \dfrac{6(t_1^4 - 16)}{t_1 - 2}$

$= \lim\limits_{t_1 \to 2} \dfrac{6(t_1^2 + 4)(t_1^2 - 4)}{t_1 - 2} = \lim\limits_{t_1 \to 2} 6(t_1^2 + 4)(t_1 + 2) = 192 \text{ ft/min}$

EXERCISE SET 3.2

1. $f'(1) = 2,\ f'(3) = 0,\ f'(5) = -2,\ f'(6) = -1/2$

3. (b) $f'(2) = m = 3$ **(c)** the same, $f'(2) = 3$

5.

7. $y - (-1) = 5(x - 3),\ y = 5x - 16$

9. $f'(x) = \lim_{h \to 0} \dfrac{f(x+h) - f(x)}{h} = \lim_{h \to 0} \dfrac{3(x^2 + 2xh + h^2) - 3x^2}{h} = \lim_{h \to 0} 3(2x + h) = 6x;\ f(3) = 3(3)^2 = 27,$
$f'(3) = 18$ so $y - 27 = 18(x - 3),\ y = 18x - 27$

11. $f'(x) = \lim_{h \to 0} \dfrac{f(x+h) - f(x)}{h} = \lim_{h \to 0} \dfrac{(x+h)^3 - x^3}{h} = 3x^2;\ f(0) = 0^3 = 0,$
$f'(0) = 0$ so $y - 0 = (0)(x - 0),\ y = 0$

13. $f'(x) = \lim_{h \to 0} \dfrac{f(x+h) - f(x)}{h} = \lim_{h \to 0} \dfrac{\sqrt{x+1+h} - \sqrt{x+1}}{h}$

$= \lim_{h \to 0} \dfrac{\sqrt{x+1+h} - \sqrt{x+1}}{h} \dfrac{\sqrt{x+1+h} + \sqrt{x+1}}{\sqrt{x+1+h} + \sqrt{x+1}} = \lim_{h \to 0} \dfrac{1}{\sqrt{x+1+h} + \sqrt{x+1}} = \dfrac{1}{2\sqrt{x+1}};$

$f(8) = \sqrt{8+1} = 3,\ f'(8) = \dfrac{1}{6}$ so $y - 3 = \dfrac{1}{6}(x - 8),\ y = \dfrac{1}{6}x + \dfrac{5}{3}$

15. $f'(x) = \lim_{\Delta x \to 0} \dfrac{\dfrac{1}{x + \Delta x} - \dfrac{1}{x}}{\Delta x} = \lim_{\Delta x \to 0} \dfrac{\dfrac{x - (x + \Delta x)}{x(x + \Delta x)}}{\Delta x}$

$= \lim_{\Delta x \to 0} \dfrac{-\Delta x}{x \Delta x (x + \Delta x)} = \lim_{\Delta x \to 0} -\dfrac{1}{x(x + \Delta x)} = -\dfrac{1}{x^2}$

17. $f'(x) = \lim_{\Delta x \to 0} \dfrac{[a(x + \Delta x)^2 + b] - [ax^2 + b]}{\Delta x} = \lim_{\Delta x \to 0} \dfrac{ax^2 + 2ax\Delta x + a(\Delta x)^2 + b - ax^2 - b}{\Delta x}$

$= \lim_{\Delta x \to 0} \dfrac{2ax\Delta x + a(\Delta x)^2}{\Delta x} = \lim_{\Delta x \to 0} (2ax + a\Delta x) = 2ax$

19. $f'(x) = \lim_{\Delta x \to 0} \dfrac{\dfrac{1}{\sqrt{x + \Delta x}} - \dfrac{1}{\sqrt{x}}}{\Delta x} = \lim_{\Delta x \to 0} \dfrac{\sqrt{x} - \sqrt{x + \Delta x}}{\Delta x \sqrt{x}\sqrt{x + \Delta x}}$

$= \lim_{\Delta x \to 0} \dfrac{x - (x + \Delta x)}{\Delta x \sqrt{x}\sqrt{x + \Delta x}(\sqrt{x} + \sqrt{x + \Delta x})} = \lim_{\Delta x \to 0} \dfrac{-1}{\sqrt{x}\sqrt{x + \Delta x}(\sqrt{x} + \sqrt{x + \Delta x})} = -\dfrac{1}{2x^{3/2}}$

21. $f'(t) = \lim\limits_{h \to 0} \dfrac{f(t+h) - f(t)}{h} = \lim\limits_{h \to 0} \dfrac{[4(t+h)^2 + (t+h)] - [4t^2 + t]}{h}$

$= \lim\limits_{h \to 0} \dfrac{4t^2 + 8th + 4h^2 + t + h - 4t^2 - t}{h}$

$= \lim\limits_{h \to 0} \dfrac{8th + 4h^2 + h}{h} = \lim\limits_{h \to 0}(8t + 4h + 1) = 8t + 1$

23. **(a)** D **(b)** F **(c)** B **(d)** C **(e)** A **(f)** E

25. **(a)** 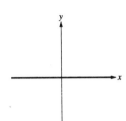 **(b)**  **(c)**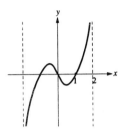

27. **(a)** $f(x) = x^2$ and $a = 3$ **(b)** $f(x) = \sqrt{x}$ and $a = 1$

29. $\dfrac{dy}{dx} = \lim\limits_{h \to 0} \dfrac{[4(x+h)^2 + 1] - [4x^2 + 1]}{h} = \lim\limits_{h \to 0} \dfrac{4x^2 + 8xh + 4h^2 + 1 - 4x^2 - 1}{h} = \lim\limits_{h \to 0}(8x + 4h) = 8x$

$\dfrac{dy}{dx}\Big|_{x=1} = 8(1) = 8$

31. $y = -2x + 1$

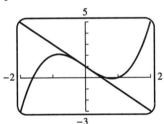

33. **(b)**

h	0.5	0.1	0.01	0.001	0.0001	0.00001
$(f(1+h) - f(1))/h$	1.6569	1.4355	1.3911	1.3868	1.3863	1.3863

35. **(a)** dollars/ft

(b) As you go deeper the price per foot may increase dramatically, so $f'(x)$ is roughly the price per additional foot.

(c) If each additional foot costs extra money (this is to be expected) then $f'(x)$ remains positive.

(d) From the approximation $1000 = f'(300) \approx \dfrac{f(301) - f(300)}{301 - 300}$ we see that $f(301) \approx f(300) + 1000$, so the extra foot will cost around \$1000.

37. **(a)** $F \approx 200$ lb, $dF/d\theta \approx 60$ lb/rad **(b)** $\mu = (dF/d\theta)/F \approx 60/200 = 0.3$

39. **(a)** $T \approx 120°F$, $dT/dt \approx -4.5°F/min$

(b) $k = (dT/dt)/(T - T_0) \approx (-4.5)/(120 - 75) = -0.1$

41. $\lim_{x\to 0} f(x) = \lim_{x\to 0} \sqrt[3]{x} = 0 = f(0)$, so f is continuous at $x = 0$.

$\lim_{h\to 0} \dfrac{f(0+h) - f(0)}{h} = \lim_{h\to 0} \dfrac{\sqrt[3]{h} - 0}{h} = \lim_{h\to 0} \dfrac{1}{h^{2/3}} = +\infty$, so $f'(0)$ does not exist.

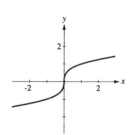

43. $\lim_{x\to 1^-} f(x) = \lim_{x\to 1^+} f(x) = f(1)$, so f is continuous at $x = 1$.

$\lim_{h\to 0^-} \dfrac{f(1+h) - f(1)}{h} = \lim_{h\to 0^-} \dfrac{[(1+h)^2 + 1] - 2}{h} = \lim_{h\to 0^-} (2 + h) = 2;$

$\lim_{h\to 0^+} \dfrac{f(1+h) - f(1)}{h} = \lim_{h\to 0^+} \dfrac{2(1+h) - 2}{h} = \lim_{h\to 0^+} 2 = 2$, so $f'(1) = 2$.

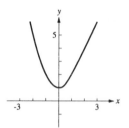

45. f is continuous at $x = 1$ because it is differentiable there, thus $\lim_{h\to 0} f(1 + h) = f(1)$ and so $f(1) = 0$ because $\lim_{h\to 0} \dfrac{f(1+h)}{h}$ exists; $f'(1) = \lim_{h\to 0} \dfrac{f(1+h) - f(1)}{h} = \lim_{h\to 0} \dfrac{f(1+h)}{h} = 5.$

47. $f'(x) = \lim_{h\to 0} \dfrac{f(x+h) - f(x)}{h} = \lim_{h\to 0} \dfrac{f(x)f(h) - f(x)}{h} = \lim_{h\to 0} \dfrac{f(x)[f(h) - 1]}{h} = f(x) \lim_{h\to 0} \dfrac{f(h) - f(0)}{h}$

$= f(x)f'(0) = f(x)$

EXERCISE SET 3.3

1. $28x^6$

3. $24x^7 + 2$

5. 0

7. $-\dfrac{1}{3}(7x^6 + 2)$

9. $3ax^2 + 2bx + c$

11. $24x^{-9} + 1/\sqrt{x}$

13. $-3x^{-4} - 7x^{-8}$

15. $f'(x) = (3x^2 + 6)\dfrac{d}{dx}\left(2x - \dfrac{1}{4}\right) + \left(2x - \dfrac{1}{4}\right)\dfrac{d}{dx}(3x^2 + 6) = (3x^2 + 6)(2) + \left(2x - \dfrac{1}{4}\right)(6x)$

$= 18x^2 - \dfrac{3}{2}x + 12$

17. $f'(x) = (x^3 + 7x^2 - 8)\dfrac{d}{dx}(2x^{-3} + x^{-4}) + (2x^{-3} + x^{-4})\dfrac{d}{dx}(x^3 + 7x^2 - 8)$

$= (x^3 + 7x^2 - 8)(-6x^{-4} - 4x^{-5}) + (2x^{-3} + x^{-4})(3x^2 + 14x) = -15x^{-2} - 14x^{-3} + 48x^{-4} + 32x^{-5}$

19. $12x(3x^2 + 1)$

21. $\dfrac{dy}{dx} = \dfrac{(5x - 3)\dfrac{d}{dx}(1) - (1)\dfrac{d}{dx}(5x - 3)}{(5x - 3)^2} = -\dfrac{5}{(5x - 3)^2};\ y'(1) = -5/4$

23. $\dfrac{dx}{dt} = \dfrac{(2t + 1)\dfrac{d}{dt}(3t) - (3t)\dfrac{d}{dt}(2t + 1)}{(2t + 1)^2} = \dfrac{(2t + 1)(3) - (3t)(2)}{(2t + 1)^2} = \dfrac{3}{(2t + 1)^2}$

25. $\dfrac{dy}{dx} = \dfrac{(x+3)\dfrac{d}{dx}(2x-1) - (2x-1)\dfrac{d}{dx}(x+3)}{(x+3)^2} = \dfrac{(x+3)(2) - (2x-1)(1)}{(x+3)^2} = \dfrac{7}{(x+3)^2}; \left.\dfrac{dy}{dx}\right|_{x=1} = \dfrac{7}{16}$

27. $\dfrac{dy}{dx} = \left(\dfrac{3x+2}{x}\right)\dfrac{d}{dx}\left(x^{-5}+1\right) + \left(x^{-5}+1\right)\dfrac{d}{dx}\left(\dfrac{3x+2}{x}\right)$

$= \left(\dfrac{3x+2}{x}\right)\left(-5x^{-6}\right) + \left(x^{-5}+1\right)\left[\dfrac{x(3) - (3x+2)(1)}{x^2}\right] = \left(\dfrac{3x+2}{x}\right)\left(-5x^{-6}\right) + \left(x^{-5}+1\right)\left(-\dfrac{2}{x^2}\right);$

$\left.\dfrac{dy}{dx}\right|_{x=1} = 5(-5) + 2(-2) = -29$

29. $32t$

31. $3\pi r^2$

33. **(a)** $\dfrac{dV}{dr} = 4\pi r^2$ **(b)** $\left.\dfrac{dV}{dr}\right|_{r=5} = 4\pi(5)^2 = 100\pi$

35. **(a)** $g'(x) = \sqrt{x}f'(x) + \dfrac{1}{2\sqrt{x}}f(x), g'(4) = (2)(-5) + \dfrac{1}{4}(3) = -37/4$

(b) $g'(x) = \dfrac{xf'(x) - f(x)}{x^2}, g'(4) = \dfrac{(4)(-5) - 3}{16} = -23/16$

37. **(a)** $F'(x) = 5f'(x) + 2g'(x), F'(2) = 5(4) + 2(-5) = 10$

(b) $F'(x) = f'(x) - 3g'(x), F'(2) = 4 - 3(-5) = 19$

(c) $F'(x) = f(x)g'(x) + g(x)f'(x), F'(2) = (-1)(-5) + (1)(4) = 9$

(d) $F'(x) = [g(x)f'(x) - f(x)g'(x)]/g^2(x), F'(2) = [(1)(4) - (-1)(-5)]/(1)^2 = -1$

39. $y - 2 = 5(x+3), y = 5x + 17$

41. **(a)** $dy/dx = 21x^2 - 10x + 1, d^2y/dx^2 = 42x - 10$

(b) $dy/dx = 24x - 2, d^2y/dx^2 = 24$

(c) $dy/dx = -1/x^2, d^2y/dx^2 = 2/x^3$

(d) $y = 35x^5 - 16x^3 - 3x, dy/dx = 175x^4 - 48x^2 - 3, d^2y/dx^2 = 700x^3 - 96x$

43. **(a)** $y' = -5x^{-6} + 5x^4, y'' = 30x^{-7} + 20x^3, y''' = -210x^{-8} + 60x^2$

(b) $y = x^{-1}, y' = -x^{-2}, y'' = 2x^{-3}, y''' = -6x^{-4}$

(c) $y' = 3ax^2 + b, y'' = 6ax, y''' = 6a$

45. **(a)** $f'(x) = 6x, f''(x) = 6, f'''(x) = 0, f'''(2) = 0$

(b) $\dfrac{dy}{dx} = 30x^4 - 8x, \dfrac{d^2y}{dx^2} = 120x^3 - 8, \left.\dfrac{d^2y}{dx^2}\right|_{x=1} = 112$

(c) $\dfrac{d}{dx}\left[x^{-3}\right] = -3x^{-4}, \dfrac{d^2}{dx^2}\left[x^{-3}\right] = 12x^{-5}, \dfrac{d^3}{dx^3}\left[x^{-3}\right] = -60x^{-6}, \dfrac{d^4}{dx^4}\left[x^{-3}\right] = 360x^{-7},$

$\left.\dfrac{d^4}{dx^4}\left[x^{-3}\right]\right|_{x=1} = 360$

47. $y' = 3x^2 + 3, y'' = 6x,$ and $y''' = 6$ so

$y''' + xy'' - 2y' = 6 + x(6x) - 2(3x^2 + 3) = 6 + 6x^2 - 6x^2 - 6 = 0$

49. $F'(x) = xf'(x) + f(x), F''(x) = xf''(x) + f'(x) + f'(x) = xf''(x) + 2f'(x)$

51. The graph has a horizontal tangent at points where $\dfrac{dy}{dx} = 0$, but $\dfrac{dy}{dx} = x^2 - 3x + 2 = (x-1)(x-2) = 0$ if $x = 1, 2$. The corresponding values of y are $5/6$ and $2/3$ so the tangent line is horizontal at $(1, 5/6)$ and $(2, 2/3)$.

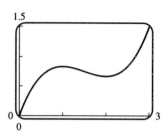

53. $f'(1) \approx \dfrac{f(1.01) - f(1)}{0.01} = \dfrac{0.999699 - (-1)}{0.01} = 0.0301$, and by differentiation, $f'(1) = 3(1)^2 - 3 = 0$

55. $f'(1) = 0$

57. The y-intercept is -2 so the point $(0, -2)$ is on the graph; $-2 = a(0)^2 + b(0) + c$, $c = -2$. The x-intercept is 1 so the point $(1, 0)$ is on the graph; $0 = a + b - 2$. The slope is $dy/dx = 2ax + b$; at $x = 0$ the slope is b so $b = -1$, thus $a = 3$. The function is $y = 3x^2 - x - 2$.

59. The points $(-1, 1)$ and $(2, 4)$ are on the secant line so its slope is $(4 - 1)/(2 + 1) = 1$. The slope of the tangent line to $y = x^2$ is $y' = 2x$ so $2x = 1$, $x = 1/2$.

61. $y' = -2x$, so at any point (x_0, y_0) on $y = 1 - x^2$ the tangent line is $y - y_0 = -2x_0(x - x_0)$, or $y = -2x_0 x + x_0^2 + 1$. The point $(2, 0)$ is to be on the line, so $0 = -4x_0 + x_0^2 + 1$, $x_0^2 - 4x_0 + 1 = 0$. Use the quadratic formula to get $x_0 = \dfrac{4 \pm \sqrt{16 - 4}}{2} = 2 \pm \sqrt{3}$.

63. $y' = 3ax^2 + b$; the tangent line at $x = x_0$ is $y - y_0 = (3ax_0^2 + b)(x - x_0)$ where $y_0 = ax_0^3 + bx_0$. Solve with $y = ax^3 + bx$ to get

$$(ax^3 + bx) - (ax_0^3 + bx_0) = (3ax_0^2 + b)(x - x_0)$$
$$ax^3 + bx - ax_0^3 - bx_0 = 3ax_0^2 x - 3ax_0^3 + bx - bx_0$$
$$x^3 - 3x_0^2 x + 2x_0^3 = 0$$
$$(x - x_0)(x^2 + xx_0 - 2x_0^2) = 0$$
$$(x - x_0)^2(x + 2x_0) = 0, \text{ so } x = -2x_0.$$

65. $y' = -\dfrac{1}{x^2}$; the tangent line at $x = x_0$ is $y - y_0 = -\dfrac{1}{x_0^2}(x - x_0)$, or $y = -\dfrac{x}{x_0^2} + \dfrac{2}{x_0}$. The tangent line crosses the x-axis at $2x_0$, the y-axis at $2/x_0$, so that the area of the triangle is $\dfrac{1}{2}(2/x_0)(2x_0) = 2$.

67. $F = GmMr^{-2}$, $\dfrac{dF}{dr} = -2GmMr^{-3} = -\dfrac{2GmM}{r^3}$

69. $f'(x) = 1 + 1/x^2 > 0$ for all x

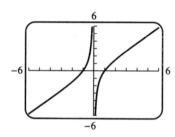

71. $(f \cdot g \cdot h)' = [(f \cdot g) \cdot h]' = (f \cdot g)h' + h(f \cdot g)' = (f \cdot g)h' + h[fg' + f'g] = fgh' + fg'h + f'gh$

73. **(a)** $2(1 + x^{-1})(x^{-3} + 7) + (2x + 1)(-x^{-2})(x^{-3} + 7) + (2x + 1)(1 + x^{-1})(-3x^{-4})$

(b) $(x^7 + 2x - 3)^3 = (x^7 + 2x - 3)(x^7 + 2x - 3)(x^7 + 2x - 3)$ so

$$\frac{d}{dx}(x^7 + 2x - 3)^3 = (7x^6 + 2)(x^7 + 2x - 3)(x^7 + 2x - 3)$$
$$+ (x^7 + 2x - 3)(7x^6 + 2)(x^7 + 2x - 3)$$
$$+ (x^7 + 2x - 3)(x^7 + 2x - 3)(7x^6 + 2)$$
$$= 3(7x^6 + 2)(x^7 + 2x - 3)^2$$

75. f is continuous at 1 because $\lim\limits_{x \to 1^-} f(x) = \lim\limits_{x \to 1^+} f(x) = f(1)$, also $\lim\limits_{x \to 1^-} f'(x) = \lim\limits_{x \to 1^-} 2x = 2$ and

$\lim\limits_{x \to 1^+} f'(x) = \lim\limits_{x \to 1^+} \dfrac{1}{2\sqrt{x}} = \dfrac{1}{2}$ so f is not differentiable at 1.

77. If f is differentiable at $x = 1$, then f is continuous there;

$\lim\limits_{x \to 1^+} f(x) = \lim\limits_{x \to 1^-} f(x) = f(1) = 3$, $a + b = 3$; $\lim\limits_{x \to 1^+} f'(x) = a$ and

$\lim\limits_{x \to 1^-} f'(x) = 6$ so $a = 6$ and $b = 3 - 6 = -3$.

79. (a) $f(x) = 3x - 2$ if $x \geq 2/3$, $f(x) = -3x + 2$ if $x < 2/3$ so f is differentiable everywhere except perhaps at $2/3$. f is continuous at $2/3$, also $\lim\limits_{x \to 2/3^-} f'(x) = \lim\limits_{x \to 2/3^-} (-3) = -3$ and $\lim\limits_{x \to 2/3^+} f'(x) = \lim\limits_{x \to 2/3^+} (3) = 3$ so f is not differentiable at $x = 2/3$.

(b) $f(x) = x^2 - 4$ if $|x| \geq 2$, $f(x) = -x^2 + 4$ if $|x| < 2$ so f is differentiable everywhere except perhaps at ± 2. f is continuous at -2 and 2, also $\lim\limits_{x \to 2^-} f'(x) = \lim\limits_{x \to 2^-} (-2x) = -4$ and $\lim\limits_{x \to 2^+} f'(x) = \lim\limits_{x \to 2^+} (2x) = 4$ so f is not differentiable at $x = 2$. Similarly, f is not differentiable at $x = -2$.

81. (a) $\dfrac{d^2}{dx^2}[cf(x)] = \dfrac{d}{dx}\left[\dfrac{d}{dx}[cf(x)]\right] = \dfrac{d}{dx}\left[c\dfrac{d}{dx}[f(x)]\right] = c\dfrac{d}{dx}\left[\dfrac{d}{dx}[f(x)]\right] = c\dfrac{d^2}{dx^2}[f(x)]$

$\dfrac{d^2}{dx^2}[f(x) + g(x)] = \dfrac{d}{dx}\left[\dfrac{d}{dx}[f(x) + g(x)]\right] = \dfrac{d}{dx}\left[\dfrac{d}{dx}[f(x)] + \dfrac{d}{dx}[g(x)]\right] = \dfrac{d^2}{dx^2}[f(x)] + \dfrac{d^2}{dx^2}[g(x)]$

(b) yes, by repeated application of the procedure illustrated in part (a)

83. (a) $f'(x) = nx^{n-1}$, $f''(x) = n(n-1)x^{n-2}$, $f'''(x) = n(n-1)(n-2)x^{n-3}, \dots,$
$f^{(n)}(x) = n(n-1)(n-2)\cdots 1$

(b) from part (a), $f^{(k)}(x) = k(k-1)(k-2)\cdots 1$ so $f^{(k+1)}(x) = 0$ thus $f^{(n)}(x) = 0$ if $n > k$

(c) from parts (a) and (b), $f^{(n)}(x) = a_n n(n-1)(n-2)\cdots 1$

85. (a) If a function is differentiable at a point then it is continuous at that point, thus f' is continuous on (a, b) and consequently so is f.

(b) f and all its derivatives up to $f^{(n-1)}(x)$ are continuous on (a, b)

EXERCISE SET 3.4

1. $f'(x) = -2\sin x - 3\cos x$

3. $f'(x) = \dfrac{x(\cos x) - \sin x(1)}{x^2} = \dfrac{x\cos x - \sin x}{x^2}$

5. $f'(x) = x^3(\cos x) + (\sin x)(3x^2) - 5(-\sin x) = x^3\cos x + (3x^2 + 5)\sin x$

7. $f'(x) = \sec x \tan x - \sqrt{2}\sec^2 x$

9. $f'(x) = \sec x(\sec^2 x) + (\tan x)(\sec x \tan x) = \sec^3 x + \sec x \tan^2 x$

11. $f'(x) = (\csc x)(-\csc^2 x) + (\cot x)(-\csc x \cot x) = -\csc^3 x - \csc x \cot^2 x$

13. $f'(x) = \dfrac{(1 + \csc x)(-\csc^2 x) - \cot x(0 - \csc x \cot x)}{(1 + \csc x)^2} = \dfrac{\csc x(-\csc x - \csc^2 x + \cot^2 x)}{(1 + \csc x)^2}$ but

$1 + \cot^2 x = \csc^2 x$ (identity) thus $\cot^2 x - \csc^2 x = -1$ so

$f'(x) = \dfrac{\csc x(-\csc x - 1)}{(1 + \csc x)^2} = -\dfrac{\csc x}{1 + \csc x}$

15. $f(x) = \sin^2 x + \cos^2 x = 1$ (identity) so $f'(x) = 0$

17. $f(x) = \dfrac{\tan x}{1 + x\tan x}$ (because $\sin x \sec x = (\sin x)(1/\cos x) = \tan x$),

$f'(x) = \dfrac{(1 + x\tan x)(\sec^2 x) - \tan x[x(\sec^2 x) + (\tan x)(1)]}{(1 + x\tan x)^2}$

$= \dfrac{\sec^2 x - \tan^2 x}{(1 + x\tan x)^2} = \dfrac{1}{(1 + x\tan x)^2}$ (because $\sec^2 x - \tan^2 x = 1$)

19. $dy/dx = -x\sin x + \cos x$,

$d^2y/dx^2 = -x\cos x - \sin x - \sin x = -x\cos x - 2\sin x$

21. $dy/dx = x(\cos x) + (\sin x)(1) - 3(-\sin x) = x\cos x + 4\sin x$,

$d^2y/dx^2 = x(-\sin x) + (\cos x)(1) + 4\cos x = -x\sin x + 5\cos x$

23. $dy/dx = (\sin x)(-\sin x) + (\cos x)(\cos x) = \cos^2 x - \sin^2 x$,

$d^2y/dx^2 = (\cos x)(-\sin x) + (\cos x)(-\sin x) - [(\sin x)(\cos x) + (\sin x)(\cos x)]$

$= -4\sin x \cos x$

27. Let $f(x) = \tan x$, then $f'(x) = \sec^2 x$.

  (a) $f(0) = 0$ and $f'(0) = 1$ so $y - 0 = (1)(x - 0)$, $y = x$.

  (b) $f\left(\dfrac{\pi}{4}\right) = 1$ and $f'\left(\dfrac{\pi}{4}\right) = 2$ so $y - 1 = 2\left(x - \dfrac{\pi}{4}\right)$, $y = 2x - \dfrac{\pi}{2} + 1$.

  (c) $f\left(-\dfrac{\pi}{4}\right) = -1$ and $f'\left(-\dfrac{\pi}{4}\right) = 2$ so $y + 1 = 2\left(x + \dfrac{\pi}{4}\right)$, $y = 2x + \dfrac{\pi}{2} - 1$.

29. (a) $f'(x) = \cos x = 0$ at $x = \pm\pi/2, \pm 3\pi/2$.

  (b) $f'(x) = 1 - \sin x = 0$ at $x = -3\pi/2, \pi/2$.

  (c) $f'(x) = \sec^2 x \geq 1$ always, so no horizontal tangent line.

  (d) $f'(x) = \sec x \tan x = 0$ when $\sin x = 0$, $x = \pm 2\pi, \pm \pi, 0$

31. $x = 10\sin\theta$, $dx/d\theta = 10\cos\theta$; if $\theta = 60°$, then

$dx/d\theta = 10(1/2) = 5$ ft/rad $= \pi/36$ ft/deg ≈ 0.087 ft/deg

33. $D = 50\tan\theta$, $dD/d\theta = 50\sec^2\theta$; if $\theta = 45°$, then

$dD/d\theta = 50(\sqrt{2})^2 = 100$ m/rad $= 5\pi/9$ m/deg ≈ 1.75 m/deg

35. (a) $\dfrac{d^4}{dx^4}\sin x = \sin x$, so $\dfrac{d^{4k}}{dx^{4k}}\sin x = \sin x$; $\dfrac{d^{87}}{dx^{87}}\sin x = \dfrac{d^3}{dx^3}\dfrac{d^{4\cdot 21}}{dx^{4\cdot 21}}\sin x = \dfrac{d^3}{dx^3}\sin x = -\cos x$

(b) $\dfrac{d^{100}}{dx^{100}}\cos x = \dfrac{d^{4k}}{dx^{4k}}\cos x = \cos x$

37. (a) all x **(b)** all x

(c) $x \neq \pi/2 + n\pi$, $n = 0, \pm 1, \pm 2, \ldots$ **(d)** $x \neq n\pi$, $n = 0, \pm 1, \pm 2, \ldots$

(e) $x \neq \pi/2 + n\pi$, $n = 0, \pm 1, \pm 2, \ldots$ **(f)** $x \neq n\pi$, $n = 0, \pm 1, \pm 2, \ldots$

(g) $x \neq (2n+1)\pi$, $n = 0, \pm 1, \pm 2, \ldots$ **(h)** $x \neq n\pi/2$, $n = 0, \pm 1, \pm 2, \ldots$

(i) all x

39. $f'(x) = -\sin x$, $f''(x) = -\cos x$, $f'''(x) = \sin x$, and $f^{(4)}(x) = \cos x$ with higher order derivatives repeating this pattern, so $f^{(n)}(x) = \sin x$ for $n = 3, 7, 11, \ldots$

41. $\displaystyle\lim_{x\to 0}\frac{\tan(x+y) - \tan y}{x} = \lim_{h\to 0}\frac{\tan(y+h) - \tan y}{h} = \frac{d}{dy}(\tan y) = \sec^2 y$

43. Let t be the radian measure, then $h = \dfrac{180}{\pi}t$ and $\cos h = \cos t$, $\sin h = \sin t$.

(a) $\displaystyle\lim_{h\to 0}\frac{\cos h - 1}{h} = \lim_{t\to 0}\frac{\cos t - 1}{180 t/\pi} = \frac{\pi}{180}\lim_{t\to 0}\frac{\cos t - 1}{t} = 0$

(b) $\displaystyle\lim_{h\to 0}\frac{\sin h}{h} = \lim_{t\to 0}\frac{\sin t}{180 t/\pi} = \frac{\pi}{180}\lim_{t\to 0}\frac{\sin t}{t} = \frac{\pi}{180}$

(c) $\dfrac{d}{dx}[\sin x] = \sin x\displaystyle\lim_{h\to 0}\frac{\cos h - 1}{h} + \cos x\lim_{h\to 0}\frac{\sin h}{h} = \sin x(0) + \cos x(\pi/180) = \dfrac{\pi}{180}\cos x$

EXERCISE SET 3.5

1. $f'(x) = 37(x^3 + 2x)^{36}\dfrac{d}{dx}(x^3 + 2x) = 37(x^3 + 2x)^{36}(3x^2 + 2)$

3. $f'(x) = -2\left(x^3 - \dfrac{7}{x}\right)^{-3}\dfrac{d}{dx}\left(x^3 - \dfrac{7}{x}\right) = -2\left(x^3 - \dfrac{7}{x}\right)^{-3}\left(3x^2 + \dfrac{7}{x^2}\right)$

5. $f(x) = 4(3x^2 - 2x + 1)^{-3}$,

$f'(x) = -12(3x^2 - 2x + 1)^{-4}\dfrac{d}{dx}(3x^2 - 2x + 1) = -12(3x^2 - 2x + 1)^{-4}(6x - 2) = \dfrac{24(1 - 3x)}{(3x^2 - 2x + 1)^4}$

7. $f'(x) = \dfrac{1}{2\sqrt{4 + 3\sqrt{x}}}\dfrac{d}{dx}(4 + 3\sqrt{x}) = \dfrac{3}{4\sqrt{x}\sqrt{4 + 3\sqrt{x}}}$

9. $f'(x) = \cos(x^3)\dfrac{d}{dx}(x^3) = 3x^2\cos(x^3)$

11. $f'(x) = \sec^2(4x^2)\dfrac{d}{dx}(4x^2) = 8x\sec^2(4x^2)$

13. $f'(x) = 20\cos^4 x\dfrac{d}{dx}(\cos x) = 20\cos^4 x(-\sin x) = -20\cos^4 x\sin x$

15. $f'(x) = \cos(1/x^2)\dfrac{d}{dx}(1/x^2) = -\dfrac{2}{x^3}\cos(1/x^2)$

17. $f'(x) = 4\sec(x^7)\dfrac{d}{dx}[\sec(x^7)] = 4\sec(x^7)\sec(x^7)\tan(x^7)\dfrac{d}{dx}(x^7) = 28x^6\sec^2(x^7)\tan(x^7)$

19. $f'(x) = \dfrac{1}{2\sqrt{\cos(5x)}}\dfrac{d}{dx}[\cos(5x)] = -\dfrac{5\sin(5x)}{2\sqrt{\cos(5x)}}$

21. $f'(x) = -3\left[x + \csc(x^3 + 3)\right]^{-4}\dfrac{d}{dx}\left[x + \csc(x^3 + 3)\right]$

$\qquad = -3\left[x + \csc(x^3 + 3)\right]^{-4}\left[1 - \csc(x^3 + 3)\cot(x^3 + 3)\dfrac{d}{dx}(x^3 + 3)\right]$

$\qquad = -3\left[x + \csc(x^3 + 3)\right]^{-4}\left[1 - 3x^2\csc(x^3 + 3)\cot(x^3 + 3)\right]$

23. $f'(x) = x^2 \cdot \dfrac{-2x}{2\sqrt{5 - x^2}} + 2x\sqrt{5 - x^2} = \dfrac{x(10 - 3x^2)}{\sqrt{5 - x^2}}$

25. $\dfrac{dy}{dx} = x^3(2\sin 5x)\dfrac{d}{dx}(\sin 5x) + 3x^2\sin^2 5x = 10x^3\sin 5x\cos 5x + 3x^2\sin^2 5x$

27. $\dfrac{dy}{dx} = x^5\sec\left(\dfrac{1}{x}\right)\tan\left(\dfrac{1}{x}\right)\dfrac{d}{dx}\left(\dfrac{1}{x}\right) + \sec\left(\dfrac{1}{x}\right)(5x^4) = x^5\sec\left(\dfrac{1}{x}\right)\tan\left(\dfrac{1}{x}\right)\left(-\dfrac{1}{x^2}\right) + 5x^4\sec\left(\dfrac{1}{x}\right)$

$\qquad = -x^3\sec\left(\dfrac{1}{x}\right)\tan\left(\dfrac{1}{x}\right) + 5x^4\sec\left(\dfrac{1}{x}\right)$

29. $\dfrac{dy}{dx} = -\sin(\cos x)\dfrac{d}{dx}(\cos x) = -\sin(\cos x)(-\sin x) = \sin(\cos x)\sin x$

31. $\dfrac{dy}{dx} = 3\cos^2(\sin 2x)\dfrac{d}{dx}[\cos(\sin 2x)] = 3\cos^2(\sin 2x)[-\sin(\sin 2x)]\dfrac{d}{dx}(\sin 2x)$
$\qquad = -6\cos^2(\sin 2x)\sin(\sin 2x)\cos 2x$

33. $\dfrac{dy}{dx} = (5x + 8)^{13}12(x^3 + 7x)^{11}\dfrac{d}{dx}(x^3 + 7x) + (x^3 + 7x)^{12}13(5x + 8)^{12}\dfrac{d}{dx}(5x + 8)$

$\qquad = 12(5x + 8)^{13}(x^3 + 7x)^{11}(3x^2 + 7) + 65(x^3 + 7x)^{12}(5x + 8)^{12}$

35. $\dfrac{dy}{dx} = 3\left[\dfrac{x - 5}{2x + 1}\right]^2\dfrac{d}{dx}\left[\dfrac{x - 5}{2x + 1}\right] = 3\left[\dfrac{x - 5}{2x + 1}\right]^2 \cdot \dfrac{11}{(2x + 1)^2} = \dfrac{33(x - 5)^2}{(2x + 1)^4}$

37. $\dfrac{dy}{dx} = \dfrac{(4x^2 - 1)^8(3)(2x + 3)^2(2) - (2x + 3)^3(8)(4x^2 - 1)^7(8x)}{(4x^2 - 1)^{16}}$

$\qquad = \dfrac{2(2x + 3)^2(4x^2 - 1)^7[3(4x^2 - 1) - 32x(2x + 3)]}{(4x^2 - 1)^{16}} = -\dfrac{2(2x + 3)^2(52x^2 + 96x + 3)}{(4x^2 - 1)^9}$

39. $\dfrac{dy}{dx} = 5\left[x\sin 2x + \tan^4(x^7)\right]^4\dfrac{d}{dx}\left[x\sin 2x\tan^4(x^7)\right]$

$\qquad = 5\left[x\sin 2x + \tan^4(x^7)\right]^4\left[x\cos 2x\dfrac{d}{dx}(2x) + \sin 2x + 4\tan^3(x^7)\dfrac{d}{dx}\tan(x^7)\right]$

$\qquad = 5\left[x\sin 2x + \tan^4(x^7)\right]^4\left[2x\cos 2x + \sin 2x + 28x^6\tan^3(x^7)\sec^2(x^7)\right]$

41. $\dfrac{dy}{dx} = x(-\sin(5x))\dfrac{d}{dx}(5x) + \cos(5x) - 2\sin x\dfrac{d}{dx}(\sin x)$
$\qquad = -5x\sin(5x) + \cos(5x) - 2\sin x\cos x = -5x\sin(5x) + \cos(5x) - \sin(2x),$

$\quad \dfrac{d^2y}{dx^2} = -5x\cos(5x)\dfrac{d}{dx}(5x) - 5\sin(5x) - \sin(5x)\dfrac{d}{dx}(5x) - \cos(2x)\dfrac{d}{dx}(2x)$

$\qquad = -25x\cos(5x) - 10\sin(5x) - 2\cos(2x)$

43. $\dfrac{dy}{dx} = \dfrac{(1-x)+(1+x)}{(1-x)^2} = \dfrac{2}{(1-x)^2} = 2(1-x)^{-2}$ and $\dfrac{d^2y}{dx^2} = -2(2)(-1)(1-x)^{-3} = 4(1-x)^{-3}$

45. $\dfrac{dy}{dx} = -3x\sin 3x + \cos 3x$; if $x = \pi$ then $y = -\pi$ and $\dfrac{dy}{dx} = -1$ so $y + \pi = -(x - \pi)$, $y = -x$

47. $\dfrac{dy}{dx} = -3\sec^3(\pi/2 - x)\tan(\pi/2 - x)$; if $x = -\pi/2$ then $y = -1$ and $\dfrac{dy}{dx} = 0$

so $y + 1 = (0)(x + \pi/2)$, $y = -1$

49. $y = \cot^3(\pi - \theta) = -\cot^3\theta$ so $dy/dx = 3\cot^2\theta\csc^2\theta$

51. $\dfrac{d}{d\omega}[a\cos^2\pi\omega + b\sin^2\pi\omega] = -2\pi a\cos\pi\omega\sin\pi\omega + 2\pi b\sin\pi\omega\cos\pi\omega$

$$= \pi(b-a)(2\sin\pi\omega\cos\pi\omega) = \pi(b-a)\sin 2\pi\omega$$

53. **(a)**

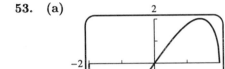

(c) $f'(x) = x\dfrac{-x}{\sqrt{4-x^2}} + \sqrt{4-x^2} = \dfrac{4 - 2x^2}{\sqrt{4-x^2}}$

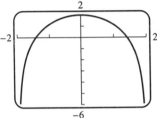

(d) $f(1) = \sqrt{3}$ and $f'(1) = \dfrac{2}{\sqrt{3}}$ so the tangent line has the equation $y - \sqrt{3} = \dfrac{2}{\sqrt{3}}(x - 1)$.

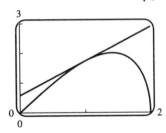

55. **(a)** $dy/dt = -A\omega\sin\omega t, d^2y/dt^2 = -A\omega^2\cos\omega t = -\omega^2 y$

(b) one complete oscillation occurs when ωt increases over an interval of length 2π, or if t increases over an interval of length $2\pi/\omega$

(c) $f = 1/T$

(d) amplitude $= 0.6$ cm, $\quad T = 2\pi/15$ s/oscillation, $\quad f = 15/(2\pi)$ oscillations/s

57. **(a)** $p \approx 10$ lb/in^2, $dp/dh \approx -2$ lb/in^2/mi

(b) $\dfrac{dp}{dt} = \dfrac{dp}{dh}\dfrac{dh}{dt} \approx (-2)(0.3) = -0.6$ lb/in^2/s

59. With $u = \sin x$, $\dfrac{d}{dx}(|\sin x|) = \dfrac{d}{dx}(|u|) = \dfrac{d}{du}(|u|)\dfrac{du}{dx} = \dfrac{d}{du}(|u|)\cos x = \begin{cases} \cos x, & u > 0 \\ -\cos x, & u < 0 \end{cases}$

$$= \begin{cases} \cos x, & \sin x > 0 \\ -\cos x, & \sin x < 0 \end{cases} = \begin{cases} \cos x, & 0 < x < \pi \\ -\cos x, & -\pi < x < 0 \end{cases}$$

61. **(a)** for $x \neq 0$, $f'(x) = x\left(\cos\dfrac{1}{x}\right)\left(-\dfrac{1}{x^2}\right) + \sin\dfrac{1}{x} = -\dfrac{1}{x}\cos\dfrac{1}{x} + \sin\dfrac{1}{x}$

(b) $\displaystyle\lim_{x\to 0} x\sin\dfrac{1}{x} = 0 = f(0)$

(c) $\displaystyle\lim_{h\to 0}\dfrac{f(0+h)-f(0)}{h} = \lim_{h\to 0}\dfrac{h\sin\dfrac{1}{h}}{h} = \lim_{h\to 0}\sin\dfrac{1}{h}$, which does not exist

63. **(a)** $g'(x) = 3[f(x)]^2 f'(x)$, $g'(2) = 3[f(2)]^2 f'(2) = 3(1)^2(7) = 21$

(b) $h'(x) = f'(x^3)(3x^2)$, $h'(2) = f'(8)(12) = (-3)(12) = -36$

65. $(f\circ g)'(x) = f'(g(x))g'(x)$ so $(f\circ g)'(0) = f'(g(0))g'(0) = f'(0)(3) = (2)(3) = 6$

67. $F'(x) = f'(g(x))g'(x) = f'(\sqrt{3x-1})\dfrac{3}{2\sqrt{3x-1}} = \dfrac{\sqrt{3x-1}}{(3x-1)+1}\dfrac{3}{2\sqrt{3x-1}} = \dfrac{1}{2x}$

69. $\dfrac{d}{dx}[f(3x)] = f'(3x)\dfrac{d}{dx}(3x) = 3f'(3x) = 6x$, so $f'(3x) = 2x$. Let $u = 3x$ to get $f'(u) = \dfrac{2}{3}u$;

$\dfrac{d}{dx}[f(x)] = f'(x) = \dfrac{2}{3}x$.

71. For an even function, the graph is symmetric about the y-axis; the slope of the tangent line at $(a, f(a))$ is the negative of the slope of the tangent line at $(-a, f(-a))$. For an odd function, the graph is symmetric about the origin; the slope of the tangent line at $(a, f(a))$ is the same as the slope of the tangent line at $(-a, f(-a))$.

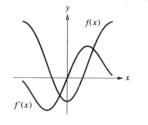 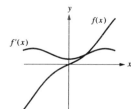

73. $\dfrac{d}{dx}[f(g(h(x)))] = \dfrac{d}{dx}[f(g(u))], \quad u = h(x)$

$= \dfrac{d}{du}[f(g(u))]\dfrac{du}{dx} = f'(g(u))g'(u)\dfrac{du}{dx} = f'(g(h(x)))g'(h(x))h'(x)$

EXERCISE SET 3.6

1. **(a)** $dy = f'(x)dx = 2xdx = 4(1) = 4$ and
$\Delta y = (x+\Delta x)^2 - x^2 = (2+1)^2 - 2^2 = 5$

(b)

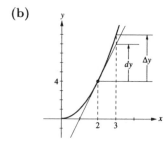

3. (a) $dy = (-1/x^2)dx = (-1)(-0.5) = 0.5$ and
$$\Delta y = 1/(x + \Delta x) - 1/x = 1/(1 - 0.5) - 1/1 = 2 - 1 = 1$$

(b)

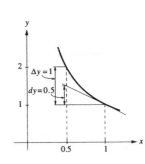

5. $dy = 3x^2 dx;$
$$\Delta y = (x + \Delta x)^3 - x^3 = x^3 + 3x^2\Delta x + 3x(\Delta x)^2 + (\Delta x)^3 - x^3 = 3x^2\Delta x + 3x(\Delta x)^2 + (\Delta x)^3$$

7. $dy = (2x - 2)dx;$
$$\Delta y = [(x + \Delta x)^2 - 2(x + \Delta x) + 1] - [x^2 - 2x + 1]$$
$$= x^2 + 2x\,\Delta x + (\Delta x)^2 - 2x - 2\Delta x + 1 - x^2 + 2x - 1 = 2x\,\Delta x + (\Delta x)^2 - 2\Delta x$$

9. (a) $dy = (12x^2 - 14x)dx$

(b) $dy = x\,d(\cos x) + \cos x\,dx = x(-\sin x)dx + \cos x dx = (-x\sin x + \cos x)dx$

11. (a) $dy = \left(\sqrt{1-x} - \dfrac{x}{2\sqrt{1-x}}\right)dx = \dfrac{2 - 3x}{2\sqrt{1-x}}dx$

(b) $dy = -17(1 + x)^{-18}dx$

13. (a) $f(x) \approx f(1) + f'(1)(x - 1) = 1 + 3(x - 1)$ **(b)** $f(1 + \Delta x) \approx f(1) + f'(1)\Delta x = 1 + 3\Delta x$

(c) From part (a), $(1.02)^3 \approx 1 + 3(0.02) = 1.06$. From part (b), $(1.02)^3 \approx 1 + 3(0.02) = 1.06$.

15. (a) $f(x) \approx f(x_0) + f'(x_0)(x - x_0) = 1 + (1/(2\sqrt{1})(x - 0) = 1 + (1/2)x$, so with $x_0 = 0$ and
$x = -0.1$, we have $\sqrt{0.9} = f(-0.1) \approx 1 + (1/2)(-0.1) = 1 - 0.05 = 0.95$. With $x = 0.1$ we have
$\sqrt{1.1} = f(0.1) \approx 1 + (1/2)(0.1) = 1.05$.

(b)

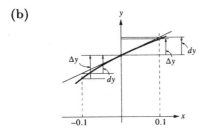

17. $f(x) = (1 + x)^{15}$ and $x_0 = 0$. Thus $(1 + x)^{15} \approx f(x_0) + f'(x_0)(x - x_0) = 1 + 15(1)^{14}(x - 0) = 1 + 15x$.

19. $\tan x \approx \tan(0) + \sec^2(0)(x - 0) = x$

21. $x^4 \approx (1)^4 + 4(1)^3(x - 1)$. Set $\Delta x = x - 1$; then $x = \Delta + 1$ and $(1 + \Delta x)^4 = 1 + 4\Delta x$.

23. $\dfrac{1}{2 + x} = \dfrac{1}{2 + 1} - \dfrac{1}{(2 + 1)^2}(x - 1)$, and $2 + x = 3 + \Delta x$, so $\dfrac{1}{3 + \Delta x} = \dfrac{1}{3} - \dfrac{1}{9}\Delta x$

25. (a) The local linear approximation $\sin x \approx x$ gives $\sin 1° = \sin(\pi/180) \approx \pi/180 = 0.0174533$ and
a calculator gives $\sin 1° = 0.0174524$. The relative error $|\sin(\pi/180) - (\pi/180)|/(\sin \pi/180) = 0.000051$ is very small, so for such a small value of x the approximation is very good.

(b) Use $x_0 = 45°$ (this assumes you know, or can approximate, $\sqrt{2}/2$).

(c) $44° = \dfrac{44\pi}{180}$ radians, and $45° = \dfrac{45\pi}{180} = \dfrac{\pi}{4}$ radians. With $x = \dfrac{44\pi}{180}$ and $x_0 = \dfrac{\pi}{4}$ we obtain

$\sin 44° = \sin\dfrac{44\pi}{180} \approx \sin\dfrac{\pi}{4} + \left(\cos\dfrac{\pi}{4}\right)\left(\dfrac{44\pi}{180} - \dfrac{\pi}{4}\right) = \dfrac{\sqrt{2}}{2} + \dfrac{\sqrt{2}}{2}\left(\dfrac{-\pi}{180}\right) = 0.694765.$ With a calculator, $\sin 44° = 0.694658.$

27. $f(x) = x^4$, $f'(x) = 4x^3$, $x_0 = 3$, $\Delta x = 0.02$; $(3.02)^4 \approx 3^4 + (108)(0.02) = 81 + 2.16 = 83.16$

29. $f(x) = \sqrt{x}$, $f'(x) = \dfrac{1}{2\sqrt{x}}$, $x_0 = 64$, $\Delta x = 1$; $\sqrt{65} \approx \sqrt{64} + \dfrac{1}{16}(1) = 8 + \dfrac{1}{16} = 8.0625$

31. $f(x) = \sqrt{x}$, $f'(x) = \dfrac{1}{2\sqrt{x}}$, $x_0 = 81$, $\Delta x = -0.1$; $\sqrt{80.9} \approx \sqrt{81} + \dfrac{1}{18}(-0.1) \approx 8.9944$

33. $f(x) = \sin x$, $f'(x) = \cos x$, $x_0 = 0$, $\Delta x = 0.1$; $\sin 0.1 \approx \sin 0 + (\cos 0)(0.1) = 0.1$

35. $f(x) = \cos x$, $f'(x) = -\sin x$, $x_0 = \pi/6$, $\Delta x = \pi/180$;

$\cos 31° \approx \cos 30° + \left(-\dfrac{1}{2}\right)\left(\dfrac{\pi}{180}\right) = \dfrac{\sqrt{3}}{2} - \dfrac{\pi}{360} \approx 0.8573$

37. $f(x) = \sqrt{x+3}$ and $x_0 = 0$, so

$\sqrt{x+3} \approx \sqrt{3} + \dfrac{1}{2\sqrt{3}}(x-0) = \sqrt{3} + \dfrac{1}{2\sqrt{3}}x,$ and

$\left|f(x) - \left(\sqrt{3} + \dfrac{1}{2\sqrt{3}}x\right)\right| < 0.1$ if $|x| < 1.692.$

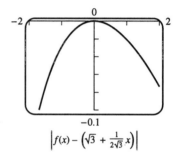

$\left|f(x) - \left(\sqrt{3} + \frac{1}{2\sqrt{3}}x\right)\right|$

39. $\tan x \approx \tan 0 + (\sec^2 0)(x-0) = x$, and $|\tan x - x| < 0.1$ if $|x| < 0.6316$

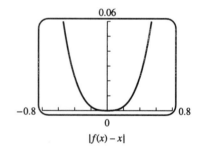

$|f(x) - x|$

41. $dy = \dfrac{3}{2\sqrt{3x-2}}dx$, $x = 2$, $dx = 0.03$; $\Delta y \approx dy = \dfrac{3}{4}(0.03) = 0.0225$

43. $dy = \dfrac{1-x^2}{(x^2+1)^2}dx$, $x = 2$, $dx = -0.04$; $\Delta y \approx dy = \left(-\dfrac{3}{25}\right)(-0.04) = 0.0048$

45. **(a)** $A = x^2$ where x is the length of a side; $dA = 2x\,dx = 2(10)(\pm 0.1) = \pm 2$ ft^2.

(b) relative error in x is $\approx \dfrac{dx}{x} = \dfrac{\pm 0.1}{10} = \pm 0.01$ so percentage error in x is $\approx \pm 1\%$; relative error in A is $\approx \dfrac{dA}{A} = \dfrac{2x\,dx}{x^2} = 2\dfrac{dx}{x} = 2(\pm 0.01) = \pm 0.02$ so percentage error in A is $\approx \pm 2\%$

47. **(a)** $x = 10\sin\theta$, $y = 10\cos\theta$ (see figure),

$$dx = 10\cos\theta d\theta = 10\left(\cos\frac{\pi}{6}\right)\left(\pm\frac{\pi}{180}\right) = 10\left(\frac{\sqrt{3}}{2}\right)\left(\pm\frac{\pi}{180}\right)$$
$$\approx \pm 0.151 \text{ in},$$
$$dy = -10(\sin\theta)d\theta = -10\left(\sin\frac{\pi}{6}\right)\left(\pm\frac{\pi}{180}\right) = -10\left(\frac{1}{2}\right)\left(\pm\frac{\pi}{180}\right)$$
$$\approx \pm 0.087 \text{ in}$$

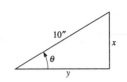

(b) relative error in x is $\approx \dfrac{dx}{x} = (\cot\theta)d\theta = \left(\cot\dfrac{\pi}{6}\right)\left(\pm\dfrac{\pi}{180}\right) = \sqrt{3}\left(\pm\dfrac{\pi}{180}\right) \approx \pm 0.030$

so percentage error in x is $\approx \pm 3.0\%$;

relative error in y is $\approx \dfrac{dy}{y} = -\tan\theta d\theta = -\left(\tan\dfrac{\pi}{6}\right)\left(\pm\dfrac{\pi}{180}\right) = -\dfrac{1}{\sqrt{3}}\left(\pm\dfrac{\pi}{180}\right) \approx \pm 0.010$

so percentage error in y is $\approx \pm 1.0\%$

49. $\dfrac{dR}{R} = \dfrac{(-2k/r^3)dr}{(k/r^2)} = -2\dfrac{dr}{r}$, but $\dfrac{dr}{r} \approx \pm 0.05$ so $\dfrac{dR}{R} \approx -2(\pm 0.05) = \pm 0.10$; percentage error in R is $\approx \pm 10\%$

51. $A = \dfrac{1}{4}(4)^2\sin 2\theta = 4\sin 2\theta$ thus $dA = 8\cos 2\theta d\theta$ so, with $\theta = 30° = \pi/6$ radians and

$d\theta = \pm 15' = \pm 1/4° = \pm\pi/720$ radians, $dA = 8\cos(\pi/3)(\pm\pi/720) = \pm\pi/180 \approx \pm 0.017$ cm^2

53. $V = x^3$ where x is the length of a side; $\dfrac{dV}{V} = \dfrac{3x^2 dx}{x^3} = 3\dfrac{dx}{x}$, but $\dfrac{dx}{x} \approx \pm 0.02$

so $\dfrac{dV}{V} \approx 3(\pm 0.02) = \pm 0.06$; percentage error in V is $\approx \pm 6\%$.

55. $A = \dfrac{1}{4}\pi D^2$ where D is the diameter of the circle; $\dfrac{dA}{A} = \dfrac{(\pi D/2)dD}{\pi D^2/4} = 2\dfrac{dD}{D}$, but $\dfrac{dA}{A} \approx \pm 0.01$ so

$2\dfrac{dD}{D} \approx \pm 0.01$, $\dfrac{dD}{D} \approx \pm 0.005$; maximum permissible percentage error in D is $\approx \pm 0.5\%$.

57. V = volume of cylindrical rod $= \pi r^2 h = \pi r^2(15) = 15\pi r^2$; approximate ΔV by dV if $r = 2.5$ and $dr = \Delta r = 0.001$. $dV = 30\pi r\, dr = 30\pi(2.5)(0.001) \approx 0.236$ cm^3.

59. **(a)** $\alpha = \Delta L/(L\Delta T) = 0.006/(40 \times 10) = 1.5 \times 10^{-5}/°C$

(b) $\Delta L = 2.3 \times 10^{-5}(180)(25) \approx 0.1$ cm, so the pole is about 180.1 cm long.

CHAPTER 3 SUPPLEMENTARY EXERCISES

5. Set $f'(x) = 0$: $f'(x) = 6(2)(2x + 7)^5(x - 2)^5 + 5(2x + 7)^6(x - 2)^4 = 0$, so $2x + 7 = 0$ or $x - 2 = 0$ or, factoring out $(2x + 7)^5(x - 2)^4$, $12(x - 2) + 5(2x + 7) = 0$. This reduces to $x = -7/2$, $x = 2$, or $22x + 11 = 0$, so the tangent line is horizontal at $x = -7/2, 2, -1/2$.

7. Set $f'(x) = \dfrac{3}{2\sqrt{3x + 1}}(x - 1)^2 + 2\sqrt{3x + 1}(x - 1) = 0$. If $x = 1$ then $y' = 0$. If $x \neq 1$ then divide out $x - 1$ and multiply through by $2\sqrt{3x + 1}$ (at points where f is differentiable we must have $\sqrt{3x + 1} \neq 0$) to obtain $3(x - 1) + 4(3x + 1) = 0$, or $15x + 1 = 0$. So the tangent line is horizontal at $x = 1, -1/15$.

9. **(a)** $x = -2, -1, 1, 3$ **(b)** $(-\infty, -2), (-1, 1), (3, +\infty)$ **(c)** $(-2, -1), (1, 3)$

(d) $g''(x) = f''(x)\sin x + 2f'(x)\cos x - f(x)\sin x$; $g''(0) = 2f'(0)\cos 0 = 2(2)(1) = 4$

11.   The equations of such a line has the form $y = mx$. The points (x_0, y_0) which lie on both the line and the parabola and for which the slopes of both curves are equal satisfy $y_0 = mx_0 = x_0^3 - 9x_0^2 - 16x_0$, so that $m = x_0^2 - 9x_0 - 16$. By differentiating, the slope is also given by $m = 3x_0^2 - 18x_0 - 16$. Equating, we have $x_0^2 - 9x_0 - 16 = 3x_0^2 - 18x_0 - 16$, or $2x_0^2 - 9x_0 = 0$. The root $x_0 = 0$ corresponds to $m = -16, y_0 = 0$ and the root $x_0 = 9/2$ corresponds to $m = -145/4, y_0 = -1305/8$. So the line $y = -16x$ is tangent to the curve at the point $(0, 0)$, and the line $y = -145x/4$ is tangent to the curve at the point $(9/2, -1305/8)$.

13.   The line $y - x = 2$ has slope $m_1 = 1$ so we set $m_2 = \dfrac{d}{dx}(3x - \tan x) = 3 - \sec^2 x = 1$, or $\sec^2 x = 2$, $\sec x = \pm\sqrt{2}$ so $x = n\pi \pm \pi/4$ where $n = 0, \pm 1, \pm 2, \dots$.

15.   The slope of the tangent line is the derivative

$y' = 2x\Big|_{x=\frac{1}{2}(a+b)} = a + b$. The slope of the secant is

$\dfrac{a^2 - b^2}{a - b} = a + b$, so they are equal.

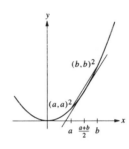

17.   **(a)** $\Delta x = 1.5 - 2 = -0.5$; $dy = \dfrac{-1}{(x-1)^2}\Delta x = \dfrac{-1}{(2-1)^2}(-0.5) = 0.5$; and

   $\Delta y = \dfrac{1}{(1.5 - 1)} - \dfrac{1}{(2-1)} = 2 - 1 = 1$.

   (b) $\Delta x = 0 - (-\pi/4) = \pi/4$; $dy = \left(\sec^2(-\pi/4)\right)(\pi/4) = \pi/2$; and $\Delta y = \tan 0 - \tan(-\pi/4) = 1$.

   (c) $\Delta x = 3 - 0 = 3$; $dy = \dfrac{-x}{\sqrt{25 - x^2}} = \dfrac{-0}{\sqrt{25 - (0)^2}}(3) = 0$; and

   $\Delta y = \sqrt{25 - 3^2} - \sqrt{25 - 0^2} = 4 - 5 = -1$.

19.   **(a)** $\dfrac{dW}{dt} = 200(t - 15)$; at $t = 5$, $\dfrac{dW}{dt} = -2000$; the water is running out at the rate of 2000 gal/min.

   (b) $\dfrac{W(5) - W(0)}{5 - 0} = \dfrac{10000 - 22500}{5} = -2500$; the average rate of flow out is 2500 gal/min.

21.   **(a)** $h = 115\tan\phi$, $dh = 115\sec^2\phi\,d\phi$; with $\phi = 51° = \dfrac{51}{180}\pi$ radians and $d\phi = \pm0.5° = \pm0.5\left(\dfrac{\pi}{180}\right)$ radians, $h \pm dh = 115(1.2349) \pm 2.5340 = 142.0135 \pm 2.5340$, so the height lies between 139.48 m and 144.55 m.

   (b)   If $|dh| \leq 5$ then $|d\phi| \leq \frac{5}{115}\cos^2\frac{51}{180}\pi \approx 0.017$ radians, or $|d\phi| \leq 0.98°$.

23.   **(a)** $f'(x) = 2x, f'(1.8) = 3.6$

   (b) $f'(x) = (x^2 - 4x)/(x - 2)^2, f'(3.5) \approx -0.777778$

25. $f'(x) = 2^x \ln 2$; $f'(2) \approx 2.772589$

27. $v_{\text{inst}} = \displaystyle\lim_{h \to 0} \dfrac{3(h+1)^{2.5} + 580h - 3}{10h} = 58 + \dfrac{1}{10}\dfrac{d}{dx}3x^{2.5}\Big|_{x=1} = 58 + \dfrac{1}{10}(2.5)(3)(1)^{1.5} = 58.75$ ft/s

29.   Solve $3x^2 - \cos x = 0$ to get $x = \pm0.535428$.

31.   **(a)** $f'(x) = 5x^4$ **(b)** $f'(x) = -1/x^2$ **(c)** $f'(x) = -1/2x^{3/2}$

   (d) $f'(x) = -3/(x - 1)^2$ **(e)** $f'(x) = 3x/\sqrt{3x^2 + 5}$ **(f)** $f'(x) = 3\cos 3x$

33. $f'(x) = \dfrac{1 - 2\sqrt{x}\sin 2x}{2\sqrt{x}}$

35. $f'(x) = \dfrac{(1 + x^2)\sec^2 x - 2x\tan x}{(1 + x^2)^2}$

37. $f'(x) = \dfrac{-2x^5\sin x - 2x^4\cos x + 4x^4 + 6x^2\sin x + 6x - 3x\cos x - 4x\sin x + 4\cos x - 8}{2x^2\sqrt{x^4 - 3} + 2(2 - \cos x)^2}$

CHAPTER 3 HORIZON MODULE

1. $x_1 = l_1\cos\theta_1, x_2 = l_2\cos(\theta_1 + \theta_2)$, so $x = x_1 + x_2 = l_1\cos\theta_1 + l_2\cos(\theta_1 + \theta_2)$ (see Figure 3 in text); similarly $y_1 = l_1\sin\theta_1 + l_2\sin(\theta_1 + \theta_2)$.

3. $(x, y) = (l_1\cos\theta + l_2\cos(\theta_1 + \theta_2), l_1\sin\theta_1 + l_2\sin(\theta_1 + \theta_2))$

$$= (\cos(\pi/4) + 3\cos(5\pi/12), \sin(\pi/4) + 3\sin(5\pi/12)) = \left(\frac{\sqrt{2} + 3\sqrt{6}}{4}, \frac{7\sqrt{2} + 3\sqrt{6}}{4}\right)$$

5.

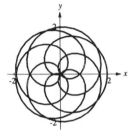

$\omega_1 = 3, \omega_2 = 5$

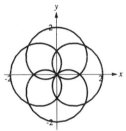

$\omega_1 = 1, \omega_2 = 4$

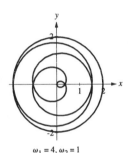

$\omega_1 = 4, \omega_2 = 1$

7. **(a)** $9 = [3\sin(\theta_1 + \theta_2)]^2 + [3\cos(\theta_1 + \theta_2)]^2 = [5 - 3\sin\theta_1]^2 + [3 - 3\cos\theta_1]^2$
$= 25 - 30\sin\theta_1 + 9\sin^2\theta_1 + 9 - 18\cos\theta_1 + 9\cos^2\theta_1 = 43 - 30\sin\theta_1 - 18\cos\theta_1$,
so $15\sin\theta_1 + 9\cos\theta_1 = 17$

(b) $1 = \sin^2\theta_1 + \cos^2\theta_2 = \left(\dfrac{17 - 9\cos\theta_1}{15}\right)^2 + \cos\theta_1$, or $306\cos^2\theta_1 - 306\cos\theta_1 = -64$

(c) $\cos\theta_1 = \left(153 \pm \sqrt{(153)^2 - 4(153)(32)}\right)/306 = \dfrac{1}{2} \pm \dfrac{5\sqrt{17}}{102}$

(e) If $\theta_1 = 0.792436$ rad, then $\theta_2 = 0.475882$ rad $\approx 27.2660°$;
if $\theta_1 = 1.26832$ rad, then $\theta_2 = -0.475882$ rad $\approx -27.2660°$.

9. **(a)** $x = 3\cos(\pi/3) + 3\cos(-\pi/3) = 6\dfrac{1}{2} = 3$ and $y = 3\sin(\pi/3) - 3\sin(\pi/3) = 0$; equations (4)
become $3\sin(\pi/3)\dfrac{d\theta_2}{dt} = 0$, $3\dfrac{d\theta_1}{dt} + 3\cos(\pi/3)\dfrac{d\theta_2}{dt} = 1$ with solution $d\theta_2/dt = 0$, $d\theta_1/dt = 1/3$.

(b) $x = -3$, $y = 3$, so $-3\dfrac{d\theta_1}{dt} = 0$ and $-3\dfrac{d\theta_1}{dt} - 3\dfrac{d\theta_2}{dt} = 1$, with solution $d\theta_1/dt = 0$, $d\theta_2/dt = -1/3$.

CHAPTER 4

Logarithmic and Exponential Functions

EXERCISE SET 4.1

1. **(a)** $f(g(x)) = 4(x/4) = x$, $g(f(x)) = (4x)/4 = x$, f and g are inverse functions

   (b) $f(g(x)) = 3(3x - 1) + 1 = 9x - 2 \neq x$ so f and g are not inverse functions

   (c) $f(g(x)) = \sqrt[3]{(x^3 + 2) - 2} = x$, $g(f(x)) = (x - 2) + 2 = x$, f and g are inverse functions

   (d) $f(g(x)) = (x^{1/4})^4 = x$, $g(f(x)) = (x^4)^{1/4} = |x| \neq x$, f and g are not inverse functions

3. **(a)** yes; all outputs (the elements of row two) are distinct

   (b) no; $f(1) = f(6)$

5. **(a)** yes   **(b)** yes   **(c)** no   **(d)** yes   **(e)** no   **(f)** no

7. **(a)** no, the horizontal line test fails

   (b) no, the horizontal line test fails

   (c) yes, horizontal line test

9. **(a)** f has an inverse because the graph passes the horizontal line test. To compute $f^{-1}(2)$ start at 2 on the y-axis and go to the curve and then down, so $f^{-1}(2) = 8$; similarly, $f^{-1}(-1) = -1$ and $f^{-1}(0) = 0$.

   (b) domain of f^{-1} is $[-2, 2]$, range is $[-8, 8]$ **(c)**

   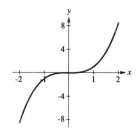

11. **(a)** $f'(x) = 2x + 8$; $f' < 0$ on $(-\infty, -4)$ and $f' > 0$ on $(-4, +\infty)$; not one-to-one

    (b) $f'(x) = 10x^4 + 3x^2 + 3 \geq 3 > 0$; $f'(x)$ is positive for all x, so f is one-to-one

    (c) $f'(x) = 2 + \cos x \geq 1 > 0$ for all x, so f is one-to-one

13. $y = f^{-1}(x)$, $x = f(y) = y^5$, $y = x^{1/5} = f^{-1}(x)$

15. $y = f^{-1}(x)$, $x = f(y) = 7y - 6$, $y = \dfrac{1}{7}(x + 6) = f^{-1}(x)$

17. $y = f^{-1}(x)$, $x = f(y) = 3y^3 - 5$, $y = \sqrt[3]{(x + 5)/3} = f^{-1}(x)$

19. $y = f^{-1}(x)$, $x = f(y) = \sqrt[3]{2y - 1}$, $y = (x^3 + 1)/2 = f^{-1}(x)$

21. $y = f^{-1}(x)$, $x = f(y) = 3/y^2$, $y = -\sqrt{3/x} = f^{-1}(x)$

23. $y = f^{-1}(x), x = f(y) = \begin{cases} 5/2 - y, & y < 2 \\ 1/y, & y \geq 2 \end{cases}$, $y = f^{-1}(x) = \begin{cases} 5/2 - x, & x > 1/2 \\ 1/x, & 0 < x \leq 1/2 \end{cases}$

25. $y = f^{-1}(x)$, $x = f(y) = (y + 2)^4$ for $y \geq 0$, $y = f^{-1}(x) = x^{1/4} - 2$ for $x \geq 16$

27. $y = f^{-1}(x)$, $x = f(y) = -\sqrt{3 - 2y}$ for $y \leq 3/2$, $y = f^{-1}(x) = (3 - x^2)/2$ for $x \leq 0$

29. $y = f^{-1}(x)$, $x = f(y) = y - 5y^2$ for $y \geq 1$, $5y^2 - y + x = 0$ for $y \geq 1$,

$y = f^{-1}(x) = (1 + \sqrt{1 - 20x})/10$ for $x \leq -4$

31. **(a)** $y = f(x) = (6.214 \times 10^{-4})x$ 　　　　　　**(b)** $x = f^{-1}(y) = \dfrac{10^4}{6.214}y$

　　　(c) how many meters in y miles

33. **(a)** $f(g(x)) = f(\sqrt{x})$

　　　　　$= (\sqrt{x})^2 = x, x > 1;$

　　　$g(f(x)) = g(x^2)$

　　　　　$= \sqrt{x^2} = x, x > 1$

(b)

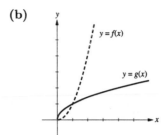

　　　(c) no, because $f(g(x)) = x$ for every x in the domain of g is not satisfied (the domain of g is $x \geq 0$)

35. **(a)** $f(f(x)) = \dfrac{3 - \dfrac{3 - x}{1 - x}}{1 - \dfrac{3 - x}{1 - x}} = \dfrac{3 - 3x - 3 + x}{1 - x - 3 + x} = x$ so $f = f^{-1}$

　　　(b) symmetric about the line $y = x$

37. **(a)** $f(x) = x^3 - 3x^2 + 2x = x(x - 1)(x - 2)$ so $f(0) = f(1) = f(2) = 0$ thus f is not one-to-one.

　　　(b) $f'(x) = 3x^2 - 6x + 2$, $f'(x) = 0$ when $x = \dfrac{6 \pm \sqrt{36 - 24}}{6} = 1 \pm \sqrt{3}/3$. $f'(x) > 0$ (f is increasing) if $x < 1 - \sqrt{3}/3$, $f'(x) < 0$ (f is decreasing) if $1 - \sqrt{3}/3 < x < 1 + \sqrt{3}/3$, so $f(x)$ takes on values less than $f(1 - \sqrt{3}/3)$ on both sides of $1 - \sqrt{3}/3$ thus $1 - \sqrt{3}/3$ is the largest value of k.

39. if $f^{-1}(x) = 1$, then $x = f(1) = 2(1)^3 + 5(1) + 3 = 10$

41. 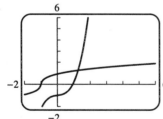　　　　　　**43.**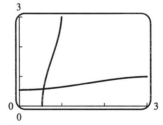

45. $f(f(x)) = x$ thus $f = f^{-1}$ so the graph is symmetric about $y = x$.

47.

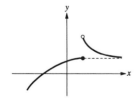

49. $F'(x) = 2f'(2g(x))g'(x)$ so $F'(3) = 2f'(2g(3))g'(3)$. By inspection $f(1) = 3$, so $g(3) = f^{-1}(3) = 1$ and $g'(3) = (f^{-1})'(3) = 1/f'(f^{-1}(3)) = 1/f'(1) = 1/7$ because $f'(x) = 4x^3 + 3x^2$. Thus $F'(3) = 2f'(2)(1/7) = 2(44)(1/7) = 88/7$.

EXERCISE SET 4.2

1. (a) -4 (b) 4 (c) $1/4$

3. (a) 2.9690 (b) 0.0341

5. (a) $\log_2 16 = \log_2(2^4) = 4$ (b) $\log_2\left(\dfrac{1}{32}\right) = \log_2(2^{-5}) = -5$

    (c) $\log_4 4 = 1$ (d) $\log_9 3 = \log_9(9^{1/2}) = 1/2$

7. (a) 1.3655 (b) -0.3011

9. (a) $2\ln a + \dfrac{1}{2}\ln b + \dfrac{1}{2}\ln c = 2r + s/2 + t/2$ (b) $\ln b - 3\ln a - \ln c = s - 3r - t$

11. (a) $1 + \log x + \dfrac{1}{2}\log(x-3)$ (b) $2\ln|x| + 3\ln\sin x - \dfrac{1}{2}\ln(x^2+1)$

13. $\log\dfrac{2^4(16)}{3} = \log(256/3)$ 15. $\ln\dfrac{\sqrt[3]{x}(x+1)^2}{\cos x}$

17. $\sqrt{x} = 10^{-1} = 0.1,\ x = 0.01$ 19. $1/x = e^{-2},\ x = e^2$

21. $2x = 8,\ x = 4$

23. $\log_{10} x = 5,\ x = 10^5$

25. $\ln 2x^2 = \ln 3,\ 2x^2 = 3,\ x^2 = 3/2,\ x = \sqrt{3/2}$ (we discard $-\sqrt{3/2}$ because it does not satisfy the original equation)

27. $\ln 5^{-2x} = \ln 3,\ -2x\ln 5 = \ln 3,\ x = -\dfrac{\ln 3}{2\ln 5}$

29. $e^{3x} = 7/2,\ 3x = \ln(7/2),\ x = \dfrac{1}{3}\ln(7/2)$

31. $e^{-x}(x+2) = 0$ so $e^{-x} = 0$ (impossible) or $x + 2 = 0,\ x = -2$

33. $e^{-2x} - 3e^{-x} + 2 = (e^{-x} - 2)(e^{-x} - 1) = 0$ so $e^{-x} = 2,\ x = -\ln 2$ or $e^{-x} = 1,\ x = 0$

35. (a)   (b)

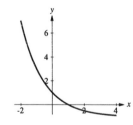   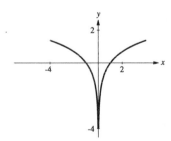

37. $\log_2 7.35 = (\log 7.35)/(\log 2) = (\ln 7.35)/(\ln 2) \approx 2.8777$;
     $\log_5 0.6 = (\log 0.6)/(\log 5) = (\ln 0.6)/(\ln 5) \approx -0.3174$

39.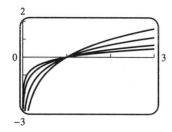

41. $x = 3.6541, y = 1.2958$

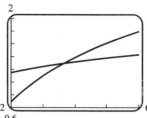

43. **(a)** no, the curve passes through the origin **(b)** $y = 2^{x/4}$
   (c) $y = 2^{-x}$ **(d)** $y = (\sqrt{5})^x$

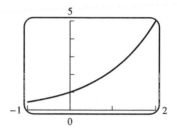

45. $\log(1/2) < 0$ so $3\log(1/2) < 2\log(1/2)$

47. $75e^{-t/125} = 15, t = -125\ln(1/5) = 125\ln 5 \approx 201$ days.

49. **(a)** 7.4; basic **(b)** 4.2; acidic **(c)** 6.4; acidic **(d)** 5.9; acidic

51. **(a)** 140 dB; damage **(b)** 120 dB; damage
   (c) 80 dB; no damage **(d)** 75 dB; no damage

53. Let I_A and I_B be the intensities of the automobile and blender, respectively. Then
   $\log_{10} I_A/I_0 = 7$ and $\log_{10} I_B/I_0 = 9.3$, $I_A = 10^7 I_0$ and $I_B = 10^{9.3} I_0$, so $I_B/I_A = 10^{2.3} \approx 200$.

55. **(a)** $\log E = 4.4 + 1.5(8.2) = 16.7, E = 10^{16.7} \approx 5 \times 10^{16}$ J
   (b) Let M_1 and M_2 be the magnitudes of earthquakes with energies of E and $10E$,
      respectively. Then $1.5(M_2 - M_1) = \log(10E) - \log E = \log 10 = 1$,
      $M_2 - M_1 = 1/1.5 = 2/3 \approx 0.67$.

57. If $t = -2x$, then $x = -t/2$ and $\lim_{x \to 0}(1 - 2x)^{1/x} = \lim_{t \to 0}(1 + t)^{-2/t} = \lim_{t \to 0}[(1 + t)^{1/t}]^{-2} = e^{-2}$.

EXERCISE SET 4.3

1. $y = (2x - 5)^{1/3}; dy/dx = \dfrac{2}{3}(2x - 5)^{-2/3}$

3. $dy/dx = \dfrac{3}{2}\left[\dfrac{x-1}{x+2}\right]^{1/2} \dfrac{d}{dx}\left[\dfrac{x-1}{x+2}\right] = \dfrac{9}{2(x+2)^2}\left[\dfrac{x-1}{x+2}\right]^{1/2}$

5. $dy/dx = x^3\left(-\dfrac{2}{3}\right)(5x^2 + 1)^{-5/3}(10x) + 3x^2(5x^2 + 1)^{-2/3} = \dfrac{1}{3}x^2(5x^2 + 1)^{-5/3}(25x^2 + 9)$

7. $dy/dx = \dfrac{5}{2}[\sin(3/x)]^{3/2}[\cos(3/x)](-3/x^2) = -\dfrac{15[\sin(3/x)]^{3/2}\cos(3/x)}{2x^2}$

9. (a) $3x^2 + x\dfrac{dy}{dx} + y - 2 = 0$, $\dfrac{dy}{dx} = \dfrac{2 - 3x^2 - y}{x}$

   (b) $y = \dfrac{1 + 2x - x^3}{x} = \dfrac{1}{x} + 2 - x^2$ so $\dfrac{dy}{dx} = -\dfrac{1}{x^2} - 2x$

   (c) from part (a), $\dfrac{dy}{dx} = \dfrac{2 - 3x^2 - y}{x} = \dfrac{2 - 3x^2 - (1/x + 2 - x^2)}{x} = -2x - \dfrac{1}{x^2}$

11. $2x + 2y\dfrac{dy}{dx} = 0$ so $\dfrac{dy}{dx} = -\dfrac{x}{y}$

13. $x^2\dfrac{dy}{dx} + 2xy + 3x(3y^2)\dfrac{dy}{dx} + 3y^3 - 1 = 0$

   $(x^2 + 9xy^2)\dfrac{dy}{dx} = 1 - 2xy - 3y^3$ so $\dfrac{dy}{dx} = \dfrac{1 - 2xy - 3y^3}{x^2 + 9xy^2}$

15. $-\dfrac{1}{y^2}\dfrac{dy}{dx} - \dfrac{1}{x^2} = 0$ so $\dfrac{dy}{dx} = -\dfrac{y^2}{x^2}$

17. $\cos(x^2y^2)\left[x^2(2y)\dfrac{dy}{dx} + 2xy^2\right] = 1$, $\dfrac{dy}{dx} = \dfrac{1 - 2xy^2\cos(x^2y^2)}{2x^2y\cos(x^2y^2)}$

19. $3\tan^2(xy^2 + y)\sec^2(xy^2 + y)\left(2xy\dfrac{dy}{dx} + y^2 + \dfrac{dy}{dx}\right) = 1$

   so $\dfrac{dy}{dx} = \dfrac{1 - 3y^2\tan^2(xy^2 + y)\sec^2(xy^2 + y)}{3(2xy + 1)\tan^2(xy^2 + y)\sec^2(xy^2 + y)}$

21. $\dfrac{dy}{dx} = \dfrac{3x}{4y}$, $\dfrac{d^2y}{dx^2} = \dfrac{(4y)(3) - (3x)(4\,dy/dx)}{16y^2} = \dfrac{12y - 12x(3x/(4y))}{16y^2} = \dfrac{12y^2 - 9x^2}{16y^3} = \dfrac{-3(3x^2 - 4y^2)}{16y^3}$, but

   $3x^2 - 4y^2 = 7$ so $\dfrac{d^2y}{dx^2} = \dfrac{-3(7)}{16y^3} = -\dfrac{21}{16y^3}$

23. $\dfrac{dy}{dx} = -\dfrac{y}{x}$, $\dfrac{d^2y}{dx^2} = -\dfrac{x(dy/dx) - y(1)}{x^2} = -\dfrac{x(-y/x) - y}{x^2} = \dfrac{2y}{x^2}$

25. $\dfrac{dy}{dx} = (1 + \cos y)^{-1}$, $\dfrac{d^2y}{dx^2} = -(1 + \cos y)^{-2}(-\sin y)\dfrac{dy}{dx} = \dfrac{\sin y}{(1 + \cos y)^3}$

27. By implicit differentiation, $2x + 2y(dy/dx) = 0$, $\dfrac{dy}{dx} = -\dfrac{x}{y}$; at $(1/\sqrt{2}, 1/\sqrt{2})$, $\dfrac{dy}{dx} = -1$; at $(1/\sqrt{2}, -1/\sqrt{2})$,

   $\dfrac{dy}{dx} = +1$. Directly, at the upper point $y = \sqrt{1 - x^2}$, $\dfrac{dy}{dx} = \dfrac{-x}{\sqrt{1 - x^2}} = -1$ and at the lower point

   $y = -\sqrt{1 - x^2}$, $\dfrac{dy}{dx} = \dfrac{x}{\sqrt{1 - x^2}} = +1$.

29. $4x^3 + 4y^3\dfrac{dy}{dx} = 0$, so $\dfrac{dy}{dx} = -\dfrac{x^3}{y^3} = -\dfrac{1}{15^{3/4}} \approx -0.1312$.

31. $4(x^2 + y^2)\left(2x + 2y\dfrac{dy}{dx}\right) = 25\left(2x - 2y\dfrac{dy}{dx}\right),$

$\dfrac{dy}{dx} = \dfrac{x[25 - 4(x^2 + y^2)]}{y[25 + 4(x^2 + y^2)]};$ at $(3,1)$ $\dfrac{dy}{dx} = -9/13$

35. **(a)**

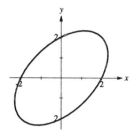

(b) ± 1.1547

(c) Implicit differentiation yields $2x - x\dfrac{dy}{dx} - y + 2y\dfrac{dy}{dx} = 0.$ Solve for $\dfrac{dy}{dx} = \dfrac{y - 2x}{2y - x}.$ If $\dfrac{dy}{dx} = 0$ then

$y - 2x = 0$ or $y = 2x.$ Thus $4 = x^2 - xy + y^2 = x^2 - 2x^2 + 4x^2 = 3x^2,$ $x = \pm\dfrac{2}{\sqrt{3}}.$

37. $4a^3\dfrac{da}{dt} - 4t^3 = 6\left(a^2 + 2at\dfrac{da}{dt}\right),$ solve for $\dfrac{da}{dt}$ to get $\dfrac{da}{dt} = \dfrac{2t^3 + 3a^2}{2a^3 - 6at}$

39. $2a^2\omega\dfrac{d\omega}{d\lambda} + 2b^2\lambda = 0$ so $\dfrac{d\omega}{d\lambda} = -\dfrac{b^2\lambda}{a^2\omega}$

41. The point $(1,1)$ is on the graph, so $1 + a = b.$ The slope of the tangent line at $(1,1)$ is $-4/3;$ use implicit differentiation to get $\dfrac{dy}{dx} = -\dfrac{2xy}{x^2 + 2ay}$ so at $(1,1),$ $-\dfrac{2}{1 + 2a} = -\dfrac{4}{3},$ $1 + 2a = 3/2,$ $a = 1/4$ and hence $b = 1 + 1/4 = 5/4.$

43. Let $P(x_0, y_0)$ be a point where a line through the origin is tangent to the curve $x^2 - 4x + y^2 + 3 = 0.$ Implicit differentiation applied to the equation of the curve gives $dy/dx = (2 - x)/y.$ At P the slope of the curve must equal the slope of the line so $(2 - x_0)/y_0 = y_0/x_0,$ or $y_0^2 = 2x_0 - x_0^2.$ But $x_0^2 - 4x_0 + y_0^2 + 3 = 0$ because (x_0, y_0) is on the curve, and elimination of y_0^2 in the latter two equations gives $x_0^2 - 4x_0 + (2x_0 - x_0^2) + 3 = 0,$ $x_0 = 3/2$ which when substituted into $y_0^2 = 2x_0 - x_0^2$ yields $y_0^2 = 3/4,$ so $y_0 = \pm\sqrt{3}/2.$ The slopes of the lines are $(\pm\sqrt{3}/2)/(3/2) = \pm\sqrt{3}/3$ and their equations are $y = (\sqrt{3}/3)x$ and $y = -(\sqrt{3}/3)x.$

45. By the chain rule, $\dfrac{dy}{dx} = \dfrac{dy}{dt}\dfrac{dt}{dx}.$ Use implicit differentiation on $2y^3t + t^3y = 1$ to get $\dfrac{dy}{dt} = -\dfrac{2y^3 + 3t^2y}{6ty^2 + t^3},$ but $\dfrac{dt}{dx} = \dfrac{1}{\cos t}$ so $\dfrac{dy}{dx} = -\dfrac{2y^3 + 3t^2y}{(6ty^2 + t^3)\cos t}.$

47. $2xy\dfrac{dy}{dt} = y^2\dfrac{dx}{dt} = 3(\cos 3x)\dfrac{dx}{dt},\ \dfrac{dy}{dt} = \dfrac{3\cos 3x - y^2}{2xy}\dfrac{dx}{dt}$

49. $y' = rx^{r-1},\ y'' = r(r-1)x^{r-2}$ so $3x^2\left[r(r-1)x^{r-2}\right] + 4x\left(rx^{r-1}\right) - 2x^r = 0,$

$3r(r-1)x^r + 4rx^r - 2x^r = 0,\ (3r^2 + r - 2)x^r = 0,$

$3r^2 + r - 2 = 0,\ (3r - 2)(r + 1) = 0;\ r = -1, 2/3$

51. We shall find when the curves intersect and check that the slopes are negative reciprocals. For the intersection solve the simultaneous equations $x^2 + (y - c)^2 = c^2$ and $(x - k)^2 + y^2 = k^2$ to obtain $cy = kx = \dfrac{1}{2}(x^2 + y^2)$. Thus $x^2 + y^2 = cy + kx$, or $y^2 - cy = -x^2 + kx$, and $\dfrac{y - c}{x} = -\dfrac{x - k}{y}$. Differentiating the two families yields (black) $\dfrac{dy}{dx} = -\dfrac{x}{y - c}$, and (gray) $\dfrac{dy}{dx} = -\dfrac{x - k}{y}$. But it was proven that these quantities are negative reciprocals of each other.

53. $y = f^{-1}(x)$, $x = f(y) = 5y^3 + y - 7$, $\dfrac{dx}{dy} = 15y^2 + 1$, $\dfrac{dy}{dx} = \dfrac{1}{15y^2 + 1}$;

check: $1 = 15y^2\dfrac{dy}{dx} + \dfrac{dy}{dx}$, $\dfrac{dy}{dx} = \dfrac{1}{15y^2 + 1}$

55. $y = f^{-1}(x)$, $x = f(y) = 2y^5 + y^3 + 1$, $\dfrac{dx}{dy} = 10y^4 + 3y^2$, $\dfrac{dy}{dx} = \dfrac{1}{10y^4 + 3y^2}$;

check: $1 = 10y^4\dfrac{dy}{dx} + 3y^2\dfrac{dy}{dx}$, $\dfrac{dy}{dx} = \dfrac{1}{10y^4 + 3y^2}$

EXERCISE SET 4.4

1. $\dfrac{1}{2x}(2) = 1/x$

3. $2(\ln x)\left(\dfrac{1}{x}\right) = \dfrac{2\ln x}{x}$

5. $\dfrac{1}{\tan x}(\sec^2 x) = \dfrac{\sec^2 x}{\tan x}$

7. $\dfrac{1}{x/(1 + x^2)}\left[\dfrac{(1 + x^2)(1) - x(2x)}{(1 + x^2)^2}\right] = \dfrac{1 - x^2}{x(1 + x^2)}$

9. $\dfrac{3x^2 - 14x}{x^3 - 7x^2 - 3}$

11. $\dfrac{1}{2}(\ln x)^{-1/2}\left(\dfrac{1}{x}\right) = \dfrac{1}{2x\sqrt{\ln x}}$

13. $-\dfrac{1}{x}\sin(\ln x)$

15. $3x^2\log_2(3 - 2x) + \dfrac{-2x^3}{(\ln 2)(3 - 2x)}$

17. $\dfrac{2x(1 + \log x) - x/(\ln 10)}{(1 + \log x)^2}$

19. $7e^{7x}$

21. $x^3 e^x + 3x^2 e^x = x^2 e^x(x + 3)$

23. $\dfrac{dy}{dx} = \dfrac{(e^x + e^{-x})(e^x + e^{-x}) - (e^x - e^{-x})(e^x - e^{-x})}{(e^x + e^{-x})^2}$

$= \dfrac{(e^{2x} + 2 + e^{-2x}) - (e^{2x} - 2 + e^{-2x})}{(e^x + e^{-x})^2} = 4/(e^x + e^{-x})^2$

25. $(x\sec^2 x + \tan x)e^{x\tan x}$

27. $(1 - 3e^{3x})e^{(x - e^{3x})}$

29. $\dfrac{(x - 1)e^{-x}}{1 - xe^{-x}} = \dfrac{x - 1}{e^x - x}$

31. $\dfrac{dy}{dx} + \dfrac{1}{xy}\left(x\dfrac{dy}{dx} + y\right) = 0$, $\dfrac{dy}{dx} = -\dfrac{y}{x(y + 1)}$

33. $\dfrac{d}{dx}\left[\ln\cos x - \dfrac{1}{2}\ln(4 - 3x^2)\right] = -\tan x + \dfrac{3x}{4 - 3x^2}$

35. $\ln|y| = \ln|x| + \dfrac{1}{3}\ln|1+x^2|, \dfrac{dy}{dx} = x\sqrt[3]{1+x^2}\left[\dfrac{1}{x} + \dfrac{2x}{3(1+x^2)}\right]$

37. $\ln|y| = \dfrac{1}{3}\ln|x^2 - 8| + \dfrac{1}{2}\ln|x^3 + 1| - \ln|x^6 - 7x + 5|$

$\dfrac{dy}{dx} = \dfrac{(x^2 - 8)^{1/3}\sqrt{x^3 + 1}}{x^6 - 7x + 5}\left[\dfrac{2x}{3(x^2 - 8)} + \dfrac{3x^2}{2(x^3 + 1)} - \dfrac{6x^5 - 7}{x^6 - 7x + 5}\right]$

39. $f'(x) = 2^x \ln 2;\ y = 2^x,\ \ln y = x\ln 2,\ \dfrac{1}{y}y' = \ln 2,\ y' = y\ln 2 = 2^x\ln 2$

41. $f'(x) = \pi^{\sin x}(\ln \pi)\cos x;$

$y = \pi^{\sin x},\ \ln y = (\sin x)\ln \pi,\ \dfrac{1}{y}y' = (\ln \pi)\cos x,\ y' = \pi^{\sin x}(\ln \pi)\cos x$

43. $\ln y = (\ln x)\ln(x^3 - 2x),\ \dfrac{1}{y}\dfrac{dy}{dx} = \dfrac{3x^2 - 2}{x^3 - 2x}\ln x + \dfrac{1}{x}\ln(x^3 - 2x),$

$\dfrac{dy}{dx} = (x^3 - 2x)^{\ln x}\left[\dfrac{3x^2 - 2}{x^3 - 2x}\ln x + \dfrac{1}{x}\ln(x^3 - 2x)\right]$

45. $\ln y = (\tan x)\ln(\ln x),\ \dfrac{1}{y}\dfrac{dy}{dx} = \dfrac{1}{x\ln x}\tan x + (\sec^2 x)\ln(\ln x),$

$\dfrac{dy}{dx} = (\ln x)^{\tan x}\left[\dfrac{\tan x}{x\ln x} + (\sec^2 x)\ln(\ln x)\right]$

47. $y = Ae^{2x} + Be^{-4x},\ y' = 2Ae^{2x} - 4Be^{-4x},\ y'' = 4Ae^{2x} + 16Be^{-4x}$ so

$y'' + 2y' - 8y = (4Ae^{2x} + 16Be^{-4x}) + 2(2Ae^{2x} - 4Be^{-4x}) - 8(Ae^{2x} + Be^{-4x}) = 0$

49. **(a)** $f'(x) = ke^{kx},\ f''(x) = k^2 e^{kx},\ f'''(x) = k^3 e^{kx}, \ldots, f^{(n)}(x) = k^n e^{kx}$

(b) $f'(x) = -ke^{-kx},\ f''(x) = k^2 e^{-kx},\ f'''(x) = -k^3 e^{-kx}, \ldots, f^{(n)}(x) = (-1)^n k^n e^{-kx}$

51. $f'(x) = \dfrac{1}{\sqrt{2\pi}\sigma}\exp\left[-\dfrac{1}{2}\left(\dfrac{x-\mu}{\sigma}\right)^2\right]\dfrac{d}{dx}\left[-\dfrac{1}{2}\left(\dfrac{x-\mu}{\sigma}\right)^2\right]$

$= \dfrac{1}{\sqrt{2\pi}\sigma}\exp\left[-\dfrac{1}{2}\left(\dfrac{x-\mu}{\sigma}\right)^2\right]\left[-\left(\dfrac{x-\mu}{\sigma}\right)\left(\dfrac{1}{\sigma}\right)\right]$

$= -\dfrac{1}{\sqrt{2\pi}\sigma^3}(x-\mu)\exp\left[-\dfrac{1}{2}\left(\dfrac{x-\mu}{\sigma}\right)^2\right]$

53. **(a)** $\log_x e = \dfrac{\ln e}{\ln x} = \dfrac{1}{\ln x},\ \dfrac{d}{dx}[\log_x e] = -\dfrac{1}{x(\ln x)^2}$

(b) $\log_x 2 = \dfrac{\ln 2}{\ln x},\ \dfrac{d}{dx}[\log_x 2] = -\dfrac{\ln 2}{x(\ln x)^2}$

55. $\dfrac{dk}{dT} = k_0\exp\left[-\dfrac{q(T-T_0)}{2T_0 T}\right]\left(-\dfrac{q}{2T^2}\right) = -\dfrac{qk_0}{2T^2}\exp\left[-\dfrac{q(T-T_0)}{2T_0 T}\right]$

57. $f'(x) = ex^{e-1}$

59. **(a)** $f(x) = \ln x;\ f'(1) = \lim\limits_{h\to 0}\dfrac{\ln(1+h) - \ln 1}{h} = \lim\limits_{h\to 0}\dfrac{\ln(1+h)}{h} = \dfrac{1}{x}\bigg|_{x=1} = 1$

(b) $f(x) = 10^x; \ f'(0) = \lim_{h \to 0} \dfrac{10^h - 1}{h} = \dfrac{d}{dx}(10^x)\Big|_{x=0} = 10^x \ln 10 \Big|_{x=0} = \ln 10$

61. **(b)**

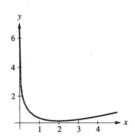

(c) $\dfrac{dy}{dx} = \dfrac{1}{2} - \dfrac{1}{x}$ so $\dfrac{dy}{dx} < 0$ at

$x = 1$ and $\dfrac{dy}{dx} > 0$ at $x = e$

(d) The slope is a continuous function which goes from a negative value to a positive value; therefore it must take the value zero in between, by the Intermediate Value Theorem.

(e) $\dfrac{dy}{dx} = 0$ when $x = 2$

63. **(a)** $e^x \cos \pi x$ oscillates between $+e^x$ and $-e^x$ as $\cos \pi x$ oscillates between -1 and $+1$.

(b)

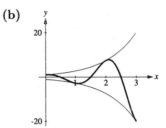

65. **(a)**

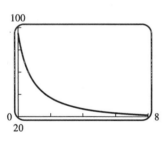

(b) as t tends to $+\infty$, the population tends to 19

$\lim_{t \to +\infty} P(t) = \lim_{t \to +\infty} \dfrac{95}{5 - 4e^{-t/4}} = \dfrac{95}{5 - 4 \lim_{t \to +\infty} e^{-t/4}} = \dfrac{95}{5} = 19$

(c) the rate of population growth tends to zero

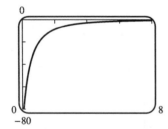

EXERCISE SET 4.5

1. **(a)** $-\pi/2$ **(b)** π **(c)** $-\pi/4$ **(d)** 0

3. $\theta = -\pi/3$; $\cos\theta = 1/2$, $\tan\theta = -\sqrt{3}$, $\cot\theta = -1/\sqrt{3}$, $\sec\theta = 2$, $\csc\theta = -2/\sqrt{3}$

5. $\tan\theta = 4/3$, $0 < \theta < \pi/2$; use the triangle shown to get $\sin\theta = 4/5$, $\cos\theta = 3/5$, $\cot\theta = 3/4$, $\sec\theta = 5/3$, $\csc\theta = 5/4$

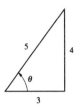

7. **(a)** $\pi/7$ **(b)** $\sin^{-1}(\sin\pi) = \sin^{-1}(\sin 0) = 0$

     (c) $\sin^{-1}(\sin(5\pi/7)) = \sin^{-1}(\sin(2\pi/7)) = 2\pi/7$

     (d) Note that $\pi/2 < 630 - 200\pi < \pi$ so
$\sin(630) = \sin(630 - 200\pi) = \sin(\pi - (630 - 200\pi)) = \sin(201\pi - 630)$
where $0 < 201\pi - 630 < \pi/2$; $\sin^{-1}(\sin 630) = \sin^{-1}(\sin(201\pi - 630)) = 201\pi - 630$.

9. **(a)** $0 \le x \le \pi$ **(b)** $-1 \le x \le 1$
    (c) $-\pi/2 < x < \pi/2$ **(d)** $-\infty < x < +\infty$

11. Let $\theta = \cos^{-1}(3/5)$, $\sin 2\theta = 2\sin\theta\cos\theta = 2(4/5)(3/5) = 24/25$

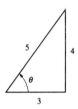

13. **(a)** $\cos(\tan^{-1}x) = \dfrac{1}{\sqrt{1+x^2}}$ **(b)** $\tan(\cot^{-1}x) = \dfrac{1}{x}$

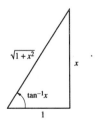   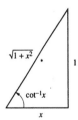

     (c) $\sin(\sec^{-1}x) = \dfrac{\sqrt{x^2-1}}{x}$ **(d)** $\cot(\csc^{-1}x) = \sqrt{x^2-1}$

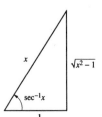   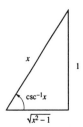

15. (a)

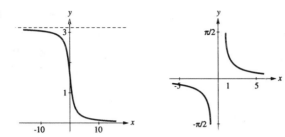

(b) The domain of $\cot^{-1} x$ is $(-\infty, +\infty)$, the range is $(0, \pi)$; the domain of $\csc^{-1} x$ is $(-\infty, -1] \cup [1, +\infty)$, the range is $[-\pi/2, 0) \cup (0, \pi/2]$.

17. (a) $55.0°$ **(b)** $33.6°$ **(c)** $25.8°$

19. (a) $x = \pi + \cos^{-1}(0.85) \approx 3.6964$ rad **(b)** $\theta = -\cos^{-1}(0.23) \approx -76.7°$

21. (a) $\dfrac{1}{\sqrt{1 - x^2/9}}(1/3) = 1/\sqrt{9 - x^2}$ **(b)** $-2/\sqrt{1 - (2x + 1)^2}$

23. (a) $\dfrac{1}{x^7\sqrt{x^{14} - 1}}(7x^6) = \dfrac{7}{x\sqrt{x^{14} - 1}}$ **(b)** $-1/\sqrt{e^{2x} - 1}$

25. (a) $\dfrac{1}{\sqrt{1 - 1/x^2}}(-1/x^2) = -\dfrac{1}{|x|\sqrt{x^2 - 1}}$ **(b)** $\dfrac{\sin x}{\sqrt{1 - \cos^2 x}} = \dfrac{\sin x}{|\sin x|} = \begin{cases} 1, & \sin x > 0 \\ -1, & \sin x < 0 \end{cases}$

27. (a) $\dfrac{e^x}{x\sqrt{x^2 - 1}} + e^x \sec^{-1} x$ **(b)** $\dfrac{3x^2(\sin^{-1} x)^2}{\sqrt{1 - x^2}} + 2x(\sin^{-1} x)^3$

29. $x^3 + x\tan^{-1} y = e^y$, $3x^2 + \dfrac{x}{1 + y^2}y' + \tan^{-1} y = e^y y'$, $y' = \dfrac{(3x^2 + \tan^{-1} y)(1 + y^2)}{(1 + y^2)e^y - x}$

31. (a)

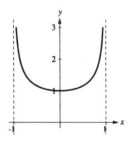

33. (a)

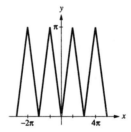

35. (a)

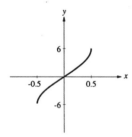

(b)

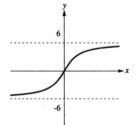

37. (b) $\theta = \sin^{-1}\dfrac{R}{R + h} = \sin^{-1}\dfrac{6378}{16,378} \approx 23°$

39. $\sin 2\theta = gR/v^2 = (9.8)(18)/(14)^2 = 0.9$, $2\theta = \sin^{-1}(0.9)$ or $2\theta = 180° - \sin^{-1}(0.9)$ so
$\theta = \frac{1}{2}\sin^{-1}(0.9) \approx 32°$ or $\theta = 90° - \frac{1}{2}\sin^{-1}(0.9) \approx 58°$. The ball will have a lower
parabolic trajectory for $\theta = 32°$ and hence will result in the shorter time of flight.

41. $y = 0$ when $x^2 = 6000v^2/g$, $x = 10v\sqrt{60/g} = 1000\sqrt{30}$ for $v = 400$ and $g = 32$;
$\tan\theta = 3000/x = 3/\sqrt{30}$, $\theta = \tan^{-1}(3/\sqrt{30}) \approx 29°$.

43.   **(a)**   Let $\theta = \sin^{-1}(-x)$ then $\sin\theta = -x$, $-\pi/2 \le \theta \le \pi/2$. But $\sin(-\theta) = -\sin\theta$ and
            $-\pi/2 \le -\theta \le \pi/2$ so $\sin(-\theta) = -(-x) = x$, $-\theta = \sin^{-1}x$, $\theta = -\sin^{-1}x$.

       (b)   proof is similar to that in part (a)

45.   **(a)** $\sin^{-1}x = \tan^{-1}\dfrac{x}{\sqrt{1-x^2}}$

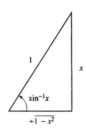

       (b) $\sin^{-1}x + \cos^{-1}x = \pi/2$; $\cos^{-1}x = \pi/2 - \sin^{-1}x = \pi/2 - \tan^{-1}\dfrac{x}{\sqrt{1-x^2}}$

47.   **(a)** $\tan^{-1}\dfrac{1}{2} + \tan^{-1}\dfrac{1}{3} = \tan^{-1}\dfrac{1/2 + 1/3}{1 - (1/2)(1/3)} = \tan^{-1}1 = \pi/4$

       (b) $2\tan^{-1}\dfrac{1}{3} = \tan^{-1}\dfrac{1}{3} + \tan^{-1}\dfrac{1}{3} = \tan^{-1}\dfrac{1/3 + 1/3}{1 - (1/3)(1/3)} = \tan^{-1}\dfrac{3}{4}$,

             $2\tan^{-1}\dfrac{1}{3} + \tan^{-1}\dfrac{1}{7} = \tan^{-1}\dfrac{3}{4} + \tan^{-1}\dfrac{1}{7} = \tan^{-1}\dfrac{3/4 + 1/7}{1 - (3/4)(1/7)} = \tan^{-1}1 = \pi/4$

EXERCISE SET 4.6

1.   **(b)** $A = x^2$ **(c)** $\dfrac{dA}{dt} = 2x\dfrac{dx}{dt}$

       (d)   Find $\dfrac{dA}{dt}\bigg|_{x=3}$ given that $\dfrac{dx}{dt}\bigg|_{x=3} = 2$. From part (c), $\dfrac{dA}{dt}\bigg|_{x=3} = 2(3)(2) = 12$ ft^2/min.

3.   **(a)** $V = \pi r^2 h$, so $\dfrac{dV}{dt} = \pi\left(r^2\dfrac{dh}{dt} + 2rh\dfrac{dr}{dt}\right)$.

       (b)   Find $\dfrac{dV}{dt}\bigg|_{\substack{h=6, \\ r=10}}$ given that $\dfrac{dh}{dt}\bigg|_{\substack{h=6, \\ r=10}} = 1$ and $\dfrac{dr}{dt}\bigg|_{\substack{h=6, \\ r=10}} = -1$. From part (a),

            $\dfrac{dV}{dt}\bigg|_{\substack{h=6, \\ r=10}} = \pi[10^2(1) + 2(10)(6)(-1)] = -20\pi$ in^3/s; the volume is decreasing.

5. (a) $\tan\theta = \dfrac{y}{x}$, so $\sec^2\theta\dfrac{d\theta}{dt} = \dfrac{x\dfrac{dy}{dt} - y\dfrac{dx}{dt}}{x^2}$, $\dfrac{d\theta}{dt} = \dfrac{\cos^2\theta}{x^2}\left(x\dfrac{dy}{dt} - y\dfrac{dx}{dt}\right)$

(b) Find $\dfrac{d\theta}{dt}\Big|_{\substack{x=2,\\y=2}}$ given that $\dfrac{dx}{dt}\Big|_{\substack{x=2,\\y=2}} = 1$ and $\dfrac{dy}{dt}\Big|_{\substack{x=2,\\y=2}} = -\dfrac{1}{4}$.

When $x = 2$ and $y = 2$, $\tan\theta = 2/2 = 1$ so $\theta = \dfrac{\pi}{4}$ and $\cos\theta = \cos\dfrac{\pi}{4} = \dfrac{1}{\sqrt{2}}$. Thus

from part (a), $\dfrac{d\theta}{dt}\Big|_{\substack{x=2,\\y=2}} = \dfrac{(1/\sqrt{2})^2}{2^2}\left[2\left(-\dfrac{1}{4}\right) - 2(1)\right] = -\dfrac{5}{16}$ rad/s; θ is decreasing.

7. Let A be the area swept out, and θ the angle through which the minute hand has rotated.
Find $\dfrac{dA}{dt}$ given that $\dfrac{d\theta}{dt} = \dfrac{\pi}{30}$ rad/min; $A = \dfrac{1}{2}r^2\theta = 8\theta$, so $\dfrac{dA}{dt} = 8\dfrac{d\theta}{dt} = \dfrac{4\pi}{15}$ in^2/min.

9. Find $\dfrac{dr}{dt}\Big|_{A=9}$ given that $\dfrac{dA}{dt} = 6$. From $A = \pi r^2$ we get $\dfrac{dA}{dt} = 2\pi r\dfrac{dr}{dt}$ so $\dfrac{dr}{dt} = \dfrac{1}{2\pi r}\dfrac{dA}{dt}$. If $A = 9$ then

$\pi r^2 = 9$, $r = 3/\sqrt{\pi}$ so $\dfrac{dr}{dt}\Big|_{A=9} = \dfrac{1}{2\pi(3/\sqrt{\pi})}(6) = 1/\sqrt{\pi}$ mi/h.

11. Find $\dfrac{dV}{dt}\Big|_{r=9}$ given that $\dfrac{dr}{dt} = -15$. From $V = \dfrac{4}{3}\pi r^3$ we get $\dfrac{dV}{dt} = 4\pi r^2\dfrac{dr}{dt}$ so

$\dfrac{dV}{dt}\Big|_{r=9} = 4\pi(9)^2(-15) = -4860\pi$. Air must be removed at the rate of 4860π cm^3/min.

13. Find $\dfrac{dx}{dt}\Big|_{y=5}$ given that $\dfrac{dy}{dt} = -2$. From $x^2 + y^2 = 13^2$ we get

$2x\dfrac{dx}{dt} + 2y\dfrac{dy}{dt} = 0$ so $\dfrac{dx}{dt} = -\dfrac{y}{x}\dfrac{dy}{dt}$. Use $x^2 + y^2 = 169$ to find that

$x = 12$ when $y = 5$ so $\dfrac{dx}{dt}\Big|_{y=5} = -\dfrac{5}{12}(-2) = \dfrac{5}{6}$ ft/s.

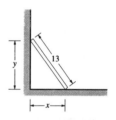

15. Let x denote the distance from first base and y the distance from
home plate. Then $x^2 + 60^2 = y^2$ and $2x\dfrac{dx}{dt} = 2y\dfrac{dy}{dt}$. When $x = 50$

then $y = 10\sqrt{61}$ so $\dfrac{dy}{dt} = \dfrac{x}{y}\dfrac{dx}{dt} = \dfrac{50}{10\sqrt{61}}(25) = \dfrac{125}{\sqrt{61}}$ ft/s.

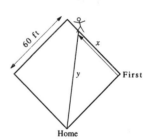

17. Find $\dfrac{dy}{dt}\Big|_{x=4000}$ given that $\dfrac{dx}{dt}\Big|_{x=4000} = 880$. From $y^2 = x^2 + 3000^2$
we get $2y\dfrac{dy}{dt} = 2x\dfrac{dx}{dt}$ so $\dfrac{dy}{dt} = \dfrac{x}{y}\dfrac{dx}{dt}$. If $x = 4000$, then $y = 5000$ so

$\dfrac{dy}{dt}\Big|_{x=4000} = \dfrac{4000}{5000}(880) = 704$ ft/s.

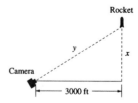

19. (a) If x denotes the altitude, then $r - x = 3960$, the radius of the Earth. $\theta = 0$ at perigee, so
$r = 4995/1.12 \approx 4460$; the altitude is $x = 4460 - 3960 = 500$ miles. $\theta = \pi$ at apogee, so
$r = 4995/0.88 \approx 5676$; the altitude is $x = 5676 - 3960 = 1716$ miles.

(b) If $\theta = 120°$, then $r = 4995/0.94 \approx 5314$; the altitude is $5314 - 3960 = 1354$ miles. The rate of change of the altitude is given by

$$\frac{dx}{dt} = \frac{dr}{dt} = \frac{dr}{d\theta}\frac{d\theta}{dt} = \frac{4995(0.12\sin\theta)}{(1 + 0.12\cos\theta)^2}\frac{d\theta}{dt}.$$

Use $\theta = 120°$ and $d\theta/dt = 2.7°/\text{min} = (2.7)(\pi/180)$ rad/min to get $dr/dt \approx 27.7$ mi/min.

21. Find $\left.\dfrac{dh}{dt}\right|_{h=16}$ given that $\dfrac{dV}{dt} = 20$. The volume of water in the tank

at a depth h is $V = \dfrac{1}{3}\pi r^2 h$. Use similar triangles (see figure) to get

$\dfrac{r}{h} = \dfrac{10}{24}$ so $r = \dfrac{5}{12}h$ thus $V = \dfrac{1}{3}\pi\left(\dfrac{5}{12}h\right)^2 h = \dfrac{25}{432}\pi h^3$,

$\dfrac{dV}{dt} = \dfrac{25}{144}\pi h^2\dfrac{dh}{dt}; \dfrac{dh}{dt} = \dfrac{144}{25\pi h^2}\dfrac{dV}{dt}, \left.\dfrac{dh}{dt}\right|_{h=16} = \dfrac{144}{25\pi(16)^2}(20) = \dfrac{9}{20\pi}$

ft/min.

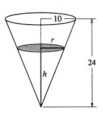

23. Find $\left.\dfrac{dV}{dt}\right|_{h=10}$ given that $\dfrac{dh}{dt} = 5$. $V = \dfrac{1}{3}\pi r^2 h$, but $r = \dfrac{1}{2}h$ so

$V = \dfrac{1}{3}\pi\left(\dfrac{h}{2}\right)^2 h = \dfrac{1}{12}\pi h^3$,

$\dfrac{dV}{dt} = \dfrac{1}{4}\pi h^2\dfrac{dh}{dt}, \left.\dfrac{dV}{dt}\right|_{h=10} = \dfrac{1}{4}\pi(10)^2(5) = 125\pi$ ft^3/min.

25. With s and h as shown in the figure, we want to find $\dfrac{dh}{dt}$ given that

$\dfrac{ds}{dt} = 500$. From the figure, $h = s\sin 30° = \dfrac{1}{2}s$ so

$\dfrac{dh}{dt} = \dfrac{1}{2}\dfrac{ds}{dt} = \dfrac{1}{2}(500) = 250$ mi/h.

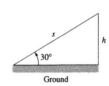

27. Find $\dfrac{dy}{dt}$ given that $\left.\dfrac{dx}{dt}\right|_{y=125} = -12$. From $x^2 + 10^2 = y^2$ we get

$2x\dfrac{dx}{dt} = 2y\dfrac{dy}{dt}$ so $\dfrac{dy}{dt} = \dfrac{x}{y}\dfrac{dx}{dt}$. Use $x^2 + 100 = y^2$ to find that

$x = \sqrt{15,525} = 15\sqrt{69}$ when $y = 125$ so

$\dfrac{dy}{dt} = \dfrac{15\sqrt{69}}{125}(-12) = -\dfrac{36\sqrt{69}}{25}$. The rope must be pulled at the rate

of $\dfrac{36\sqrt{69}}{25}$ ft/min.

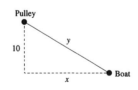

29. Find $\left.\dfrac{dx}{dt}\right|_{\theta=\pi/4}$ given that $\dfrac{d\theta}{dt} = \dfrac{2\pi}{10} = \dfrac{\pi}{5}$ rad/s. Then

$x = 4\tan\theta$ (see figure) so $\dfrac{dx}{dt} = 4\sec^2\theta\dfrac{d\theta}{dt}$,

$\left.\dfrac{dx}{dt}\right|_{\theta=\pi/4} = 4\left(\sec^2\dfrac{\pi}{4}\right)\left(\dfrac{\pi}{5}\right) = 8\pi/5$ km/s.

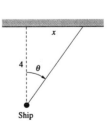

31. We wish to find $\dfrac{dz}{dt}\Big|_{\substack{x=2,\\y=4}}$ given $\dfrac{dx}{dt} = -600$ and $\dfrac{dy}{dt}\Big|_{\substack{x=2,\\y=4}} = -1200$ (see

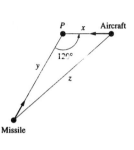

figure). From the law of cosines,
$z^2 = x^2 + y^2 - 2xy\cos 120° = x^2 + y^2 - 2xy(-1/2) = x^2 + y^2 + xy$, so
$2z\dfrac{dz}{dt} = 2x\dfrac{dx}{dt} + 2y\dfrac{dy}{dt} + x\dfrac{dy}{dt} + y\dfrac{dx}{dt}$,
$\dfrac{dz}{dt} = \dfrac{1}{2z}\left[(2x+y)\dfrac{dx}{dt} + (2y+x)\dfrac{dy}{dt}\right]$. When $x=2$ and $y=4$,
$z^2 = 2^2 + 4^2 + (2)(4) = 28$, so $z = \sqrt{28} = 2\sqrt{7}$, thus
$\dfrac{dz}{dt}\Big|_{\substack{x=2,\\y=4}} = \dfrac{1}{2(2\sqrt{7})}[(2(2)+4)(-600) + (2(4)+2)(-1200)] = -\dfrac{4200}{\sqrt{7}} =$
$-600\sqrt{7}$ mi/h; the distance between missile and aircraft is
decreasing at the rate of $600\sqrt{7}$ mi/h.

33. **(a)** We want $\dfrac{dy}{dt}\Big|_{\substack{x=1,\\y=2}}$ given that $\dfrac{dx}{dt}\Big|_{\substack{x=1,\\y=2}} = 6$. For convenience, first rewrite the equation as

$xy^3 = \dfrac{8}{5} + \dfrac{8}{5}y^2$ then $3xy^2\dfrac{dy}{dt} + y^3\dfrac{dx}{dt} = \dfrac{16}{5}y\dfrac{dy}{dt}$, $\dfrac{dy}{dt} = \dfrac{y^3}{\dfrac{16}{5}y - 3xy^2}\dfrac{dx}{dt}$ so

$\dfrac{dy}{dt}\Big|_{\substack{x=1,\\y=2}} = \dfrac{2^3}{\dfrac{16}{5}(2) - 3(1)2^2}(6) = -60/7$ units/s.

(b) falling, because $\dfrac{dy}{dt} < 0$

35. The coordinates of P are $(x, 2x)$, so the distance between P and the point $(3,0)$ is

$D = \sqrt{(x-3)^2 + (2x-0)^2} = \sqrt{5x^2 - 6x + 9}$. Find $\dfrac{dD}{dt}\Big|_{x=3}$ given that $\dfrac{dx}{dt}\Big|_{x=3} = -2$.

$\dfrac{dD}{dt} = \dfrac{5x-3}{\sqrt{5x^2 - 6x + 9}}\dfrac{dx}{dt}$, so $\dfrac{dD}{dt}\Big|_{x=3} = \dfrac{12}{\sqrt{36}}(-2) = -4$ units/s.

37. Solve $\dfrac{dy}{dt} = 3\dfrac{dx}{dt}$ given $y = x\ln x$. Then $\dfrac{dy}{dt} = \dfrac{dy}{dx}\dfrac{dx}{dt} = (1 + \ln x)\dfrac{dx}{dt}$, so $1 + \ln x = 3$, $\ln x = 2$, $x = e^2$.

39. Find $\dfrac{dS}{dt}\Big|_{s=10}$ given that $\dfrac{ds}{dt}\Big|_{s=10} = -2$. From $\dfrac{1}{s} + \dfrac{1}{S} = \dfrac{1}{6}$ we get $-\dfrac{1}{s^2}\dfrac{ds}{dt} - \dfrac{1}{S^2}\dfrac{dS}{dt} = 0$, so
$\dfrac{dS}{dt} = -\dfrac{S^2}{s^2}\dfrac{ds}{dt}$. If $s = 10$, then $\dfrac{1}{10} + \dfrac{1}{S} = \dfrac{1}{6}$ which gives $S = 15$. So $\dfrac{dS}{dt}\Big|_{s=10} = -\dfrac{225}{100}(-2) = 4.5$ cm/s.
The image is moving away from the lens.

41. Let r be the radius, V the volume, and A the surface area of a sphere. Show that $\dfrac{dr}{dt}$ is a constant
given that $\dfrac{dV}{dt} = -kA$, where k is a positive constant. Because $V = \dfrac{4}{3}\pi r^3$,

$$\dfrac{dV}{dt} = 4\pi r^2\dfrac{dr}{dt} \qquad\qquad (1)$$

But it is given that $\dfrac{dV}{dt} = -kA$ or, because $A = 4\pi r^2$, $\dfrac{dV}{dt} = -4\pi r^2 k$ which when substituted into
equation (1) gives $-4\pi r^2 k = 4\pi r^2\dfrac{dr}{dt}$, $\dfrac{dr}{dt} = -k$.

43. Extend sides of cup to complete the cone and let V_0 be the volume
of the portion added, then (see figure) $V = \dfrac{1}{3}\pi r^2 h - V_0$ where

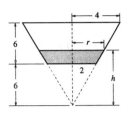

$$\dfrac{r}{h} = \dfrac{4}{12} = \dfrac{1}{3} \text{ so } r = \dfrac{1}{3}h \text{ and } V = \dfrac{1}{3}\pi\left(\dfrac{h}{3}\right)^2 h - V_0 = \dfrac{1}{27}\pi h^3 - V_0,$$

$$\dfrac{dV}{dt} = \dfrac{1}{9}\pi h^2 \dfrac{dh}{dt}, \ \dfrac{dh}{dt} = \dfrac{9}{\pi h^2}\dfrac{dV}{dt}, \ \dfrac{dh}{dt}\Big|_{h=9} = \dfrac{9}{\pi(9)^2}(20) = \dfrac{20}{9\pi} \text{ cm/s}.$$

EXERCISE SET 4.7

1. (a) $\displaystyle\lim_{x\to 2}\frac{x^2-4}{x^2+2x-8} = \lim_{x\to 2}\frac{(x-2)(x+2)}{(x+4)(x-2)} = \lim_{x\to 2}\frac{x+2}{x+4} = \frac{2}{3}$

(b) $\displaystyle\lim_{x\to +\infty}\frac{2x-5}{3x+7} = \frac{2 - \displaystyle\lim_{x\to +\infty}\frac{5}{x}}{3 + \displaystyle\lim_{x\to +\infty}\frac{7}{x}} = \frac{2}{3}$

3. $\displaystyle\lim_{x\to 1}\frac{1/x}{1} = 1$ $\qquad\qquad$ **5.** $\displaystyle\lim_{x\to 0}\frac{e^x}{\cos x} = 1$

7. $\displaystyle\lim_{\theta\to 0}\frac{\sec^2\theta}{1} = 1$ $\qquad\qquad$ **9.** $\displaystyle\lim_{x\to \pi^+}\frac{\cos x}{1} = -1$

11. $\displaystyle\lim_{x\to +\infty}\frac{1/x}{1} = 0$

13. $\displaystyle\lim_{x\to 0^+}\frac{-\csc^2 x}{1/x} = \lim_{x\to 0^+}\frac{-x}{\sin^2 x} = \lim_{x\to 0^+}\frac{-1}{2\sin x\cos x} = -\infty$

15. $\displaystyle\lim_{x\to +\infty}\frac{100x^{99}}{e^x} = \lim_{x\to +\infty}\frac{(100)(99)x^{98}}{e^x} = \cdots = \lim_{x\to +\infty}\frac{(100)(99)(98)\cdots(1)}{e^x} = 0$

17. $\displaystyle\lim_{x\to 0}\frac{2/\sqrt{1-4x^2}}{1} = 2$ $\qquad\qquad$ **19.** $\displaystyle\lim_{x\to +\infty} xe^{-x} = \lim_{x\to +\infty}\frac{x}{e^x} = \lim_{x\to +\infty}\frac{1}{e^x} = 0$

21. $\displaystyle\lim_{x\to +\infty} x\sin(\pi/x) = \lim_{x\to +\infty}\frac{\sin(\pi/x)}{1/x} = \lim_{x\to +\infty}\frac{(-\pi/x^2)\cos(\pi/x)}{-1/x^2} = \lim_{x\to +\infty}\pi\cos(\pi/x) = \pi$

23. $\displaystyle\lim_{x\to (\pi/2)^-}\sec 3x\cos 5x = \lim_{x\to (\pi/2)^-}\frac{\cos 5x}{\cos 3x} = \lim_{x\to (\pi/2)^-}\frac{-5\sin 5x}{-3\sin 3x} = \frac{-5(+1)}{(-3)(-1)} = -\frac{5}{3}$

25. $y = (1-3/x)^x$, $\displaystyle\lim_{x\to +\infty}\ln y = \lim_{x\to +\infty}\frac{\ln(1-3/x)}{1/x} = \lim_{x\to +\infty}\frac{-3}{1-3/x} = -3$, $\displaystyle\lim_{x\to +\infty} y = e^{-3}$

27. $y = (e^x+x)^{1/x}$, $\displaystyle\lim_{x\to 0}\ln y = \lim_{x\to 0}\frac{\ln(e^x+x)}{x} = \lim_{x\to 0}\frac{e^x+1}{e^x+x} = 2$, $\displaystyle\lim_{x\to 0} y = e^2$

29. $y = (2-x)^{\tan(\pi x/2)}$, $\displaystyle\lim_{x\to 1}\ln y = \lim_{x\to 1}\frac{\ln(2-x)}{\cot(\pi x/2)} = \lim_{x\to 1}\frac{2\sin^2(\pi x/2)}{\pi(2-x)} = 2/\pi$, $\displaystyle\lim_{x\to 1} y = e^{2/\pi}$

31. $\displaystyle\lim_{x\to 0}\left(\frac{1}{\sin x} - \frac{1}{x}\right) = \lim_{x\to 0}\frac{x-\sin x}{x\sin x} = \lim_{x\to 0}\frac{1-\cos x}{x\cos x+\sin x} = \lim_{x\to 0}\frac{\sin x}{2\cos x - x\sin x} = 0$

33. $\displaystyle\lim_{x\to+\infty}\frac{(x^2+x)-x^2}{\sqrt{x^2+x}+x}=\lim_{x\to+\infty}\frac{x}{\sqrt{x^2+x}+x}=\lim_{x\to+\infty}\frac{1}{\sqrt{1+1/x}+1}=1/2$

35. $\displaystyle\lim_{x\to+\infty}[x-\ln(x^2+1)]=\lim_{x\to+\infty}[\ln e^x-\ln(x^2+1)]=\lim_{x\to+\infty}\ln\frac{e^x}{x^2+1},$

$\displaystyle\lim_{x\to+\infty}\frac{e^x}{x^2+1}=\lim_{x\to+\infty}\frac{e^x}{2x}=\lim_{x\to+\infty}\frac{e^x}{2}=+\infty$ so $\displaystyle\lim_{x\to+\infty}[x-\ln(x^2+1)]=+\infty$

39. **(a)** L'Hôpital's Rule does not apply to the problem $\displaystyle\lim_{x\to1}\frac{3x^2-2x+1}{3x^2-2x}$ because it is not a $\dfrac{0}{0}$ form

  (b) $\displaystyle\lim_{x\to1}\frac{3x^2-2x+1}{3x^2-2x}=2$

41. $\displaystyle\lim_{x\to+\infty}\frac{1/(x\ln x)}{1/(2\sqrt{x})}=\lim_{x\to+\infty}\frac{2}{\sqrt{x}\ln x}=0$

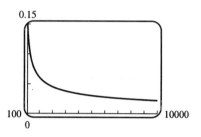

43. $y=(\sin x)^{3/\ln x},\ \displaystyle\lim_{x\to0^+}\ln y=\lim_{x\to0^+}\frac{3\ln\sin x}{\ln x}=\lim_{x\to0^+}(3\cos x)\frac{x}{\sin x}=3,$

  $\displaystyle\lim_{x\to0^+}y=e^3$

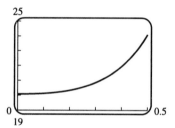

45. $\ln x-e^x=\ln x-\dfrac{1}{e^{-x}}=\dfrac{e^{-x}\ln x-1}{e^{-x}};$

  $\displaystyle\lim_{x\to+\infty}e^{-x}\ln x=\lim_{x\to+\infty}\frac{\ln x}{e^x}=\lim_{x\to+\infty}\frac{1/x}{e^x}=0$ by L'Hôpital's Rule, so

  $\displaystyle\lim_{x\to+\infty}[\ln x-e^x]=\lim_{x\to+\infty}\frac{e^{-x}\ln x-1}{e^{-x}}=-\infty$

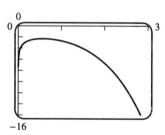

47. $y=(\ln x)^{1/x},\ \displaystyle\lim_{x\to+\infty}\ln y=\lim_{x\to+\infty}\frac{\ln(\ln x)}{x}=\lim_{x\to+\infty}\frac{1}{x\ln x}=0;$

  $\displaystyle\lim_{x\to+\infty}y=1,\ y=1$ is the horizontal asymptote

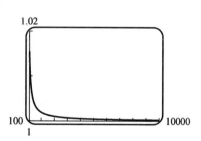

49. **(a)** 0   **(b)** $+\infty$ **(c)** 0   **(d)** $-\infty$ **(e)** $+\infty$ **(f)** $-\infty$

51. $\displaystyle\lim_{x\to+\infty}\frac{1+2\cos 2x}{1}$ does not exist, nor is it $\pm\infty$; $\displaystyle\lim_{x\to+\infty}\frac{x+\sin 2x}{x}=\lim_{x\to+\infty}\left(1+\frac{\sin 2x}{x}\right)=1$

53. $\displaystyle\lim_{x\to+\infty}(2+x\cos 2x+\sin 2x)$ does not exist, nor is it $\pm\infty$; $\displaystyle\lim_{x\to+\infty}\frac{x(2+\sin 2x)}{x+1}=\lim_{x\to+\infty}\frac{2+\sin 2x}{1+1/x}$, which
does not exist because $\sin 2x$ oscillates between -1 and 1 as $x\to+\infty$

55. $\displaystyle\lim_{R\to 0^+}\frac{\frac{Vt}{L}e^{-Rt/L}}{1}=\frac{Vt}{L}$

57. **(b)** $\displaystyle\lim_{x\to+\infty}x(k^{1/x}-1)=\lim_{t\to 0^+}\frac{k^t-1}{t}=\lim_{t\to 0^+}\frac{(\ln k)k^t}{1}=\ln k$

     (c) $\ln 0.3=-1.20397$, $1024\left(\sqrt[1024]{0.3}-1\right)=-1.20327$; $\ln 2=0.69315$, $1024\left(\sqrt[1024]{2}-1\right)=0.69338$

59. If $k\neq -1$ then $\displaystyle\lim_{x\to 0}(k+\cos \ell x)=k+1\neq 0$, so $\displaystyle\lim_{x\to 0}\frac{k+\cos\ell x}{x^2}=\pm\infty$. Hence $k=-1$, and by the rule
$\displaystyle\lim_{x\to 0}\frac{-1+\cos\ell x}{x^2}=\lim_{x\to 0}\frac{-\ell\sin\ell x}{2x}=\lim_{x\to 0}\frac{-\ell^2\cos\ell x}{2}=-\frac{\ell^2}{2}=4$ if $\ell=\pm 2\sqrt{2}$.

61. $\displaystyle\lim_{x\to 0^+}\frac{\sin(1/x)}{(\sin x)/x}$, $\displaystyle\lim_{x\to 0^+}\frac{\sin x}{x}=1$ but $\displaystyle\lim_{x\to 0^+}\sin(1/x)$ does not exist because $\sin(1/x)$ oscillates between -1
and 1 as $x\to+\infty$, so $\displaystyle\lim_{x\to 0^+}\frac{x\sin(1/x)}{\sin x}$ does not exist.

CHAPTER 4 SUPPLEMENTARY EXERCISES

1. **(a)** $f(g(x))=x$ for all x in the domain of g, and $g(f(x))=x$ for all x in the domain of f.

     (b) They are reflections of each other through the line $y=x$.

     (c) The domain of one is the range of the other and vice versa.

     (d) The equation $y=f(x)$ can always be solved for x as a function of y. Functions with no inverses include $y=x^2$, $y=\sin x$.

     (e) Yes, g is continuous; this is evident from the statement about the graphs in part (b) above.

     (f) Yes, g must be differentiable (where $f'\neq 0$); this can be inferred from the graphs. Note that if $f'=0$ at a point then g' cannot exist (infinite slope).

3. **(a)** when the limit takes the form $0/0$ or ∞/∞

     (b) Not necessarily; only if $\lim f(x)=0$. Consider $g(x)=x$; $\displaystyle\lim_{x\to 0}g(x)=0$. For $f(x)$ choose $\cos x$, x^2, and $|x|^{1/2}$. There are three possibilities; $\displaystyle\lim_{x\to 0}\frac{\cos x}{x}$ does not exist; $\displaystyle\lim_{x\to 0}\frac{x^2}{x}=0$, and $\displaystyle\lim_{x\to 0}\frac{|x|^{1/2}}{x^2}=+\infty$.

5. **(a)** $x=f(y)=8y^3-1$; $y=f^{-1}(x)=\left(\dfrac{x+1}{8}\right)^{1/3}=\dfrac{1}{2}(x+1)^{1/3}$

     (b) $f(x)=(x-1)^2$; f does not have an inverse because f is not one-to-one, for example $f(0)=f(2)=1$.

     (c) $x=f(y)=(e^y)^2+1$; $y=f^{-1}(x)=\ln\sqrt{x-1}=\frac{1}{2}\ln(x-1)$

     (d) $x=f(y)=\dfrac{y+2}{y-1}$; $y=f^{-1}(x)=\dfrac{x+2}{x-1}$

7. (a) Differentiating, $\frac{2}{3}x^{-1/3} - \frac{2}{3}y^{-1/3}y' - y' = 0$. At $x = 1$ and $y = -1$, $y' = 2$. The tangent line is $y + 1 = 2(x - 1)$.

(b) $(xy' + y)\cos xy = y'$. With $x = \pi/2$ and $y = 1$ this becomes $y' = 0$, so the equation of the tangent line is $y - 1 = 0(x - \pi/2)$ or $y = 1$.

9. $3\ln\left(e^{2x}(e^x)^3\right) + 2\exp(\ln 1) = 3\ln e^{2x} + 3\ln(e^x)^3 + 2 \cdot 1 = 3(2x) + (3 \cdot 3)x + 2 = 15x + 2$

11. (a) $\lim\limits_{x \to +\infty}(e^x - x^2) = \lim\limits_{x \to +\infty} x^2(e^x/x^2 - 1)$, but $\lim\limits_{x \to +\infty} \frac{e^x}{x^2} = \lim\limits_{x \to +\infty} \frac{e^x}{2x} = \lim\limits_{x \to +\infty} \frac{e^x}{2} = +\infty$

so $\lim\limits_{x \to +\infty}(e^x/x^2 - 1) = +\infty$ and thus $\lim\limits_{x \to +\infty} x^2(e^x/x^2 - 1) = +\infty$

(b) $\lim\limits_{x \to 1} \frac{\ln x}{x^4 - 1} = \lim\limits_{x \to 1} \frac{1/x}{4x^3} = \frac{1}{4}$; $\lim\limits_{x \to 1}\sqrt{\frac{\ln x}{x^4 - 1}} = \sqrt{\lim\limits_{x \to 1} \frac{\ln x}{x^4 - 1}} = \frac{1}{2}$

(c) $\lim\limits_{x \to 0} a^x \ln a = \ln a$

13. $\sin(\tan^{-1}x) = x/\sqrt{1 + x^2}$ and $\cos(\tan^{-1}x) = 1/\sqrt{1 + x^2}$, and $y' = \frac{1}{1 + x^2}$, $y'' = \frac{-2x}{(1 + x^2)^2}$, hence

$$y'' + 2\sin y \cos^3 y = \frac{-2x}{(1 + x^2)^2} + 2\frac{x}{\sqrt{1 + x^2}}\frac{1}{(1 + x^2)^{3/2}} = 0.$$

15. Find $\left.\dfrac{d\theta}{dt}\right|_{\substack{x=1 \\ y=1}}$ given $\dfrac{dz}{dt} = a$ and $\dfrac{dy}{dt} = -b$. From the figure

$\sin\theta = y/z$; when $x = y = 1$, $z = \sqrt{2}$. So $\theta = \sin^{-1}(y/z)$ and

$$\frac{d\theta}{dt} = \frac{1}{\sqrt{1 - y^2/z^2}}\left(\frac{1}{z}\frac{dy}{dt} - \frac{y}{z^2}\frac{dz}{dt}\right) = -b - \frac{a}{\sqrt{2}}$$ when $x = y = 1$.

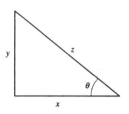

17. (a)

(b) The curve $y = e^{-x/2}\sin 2x$ has x-intercepts at $x = 0, \pi/2$. It intersects the curve $y = e^{-x/2}$ at $x = \pi/4$, and it intersects the curve $y = -e^{-x/2}$ at $x = -\pi/4, 3\pi/4$.

19. (a) $\ln y = \dfrac{\ln(1 + x)}{x}$, $\dfrac{y'}{y} = \dfrac{x/(1 + x) - \ln(1 + x)}{x^2} = \dfrac{1}{x(1 + x)} - \dfrac{\ln(1 + x)}{x^2}$,

$$\frac{dy}{dx} = \frac{1}{x}(1 + x)^{(1/x) - 1} - \frac{(1 + x)^{(1/x)}}{x^2}\ln(1 + x)$$

(b) $\ln y = e^x \ln x$, $\dfrac{y'}{y} = e^x\left(\dfrac{1}{x} + \ln x\right)$, $\dfrac{dy}{dx} = x^{e^x}e^x\left(\dfrac{1}{x} + \ln x\right) = e^x\left[x^{e^x - 1} + x^{e^x}\ln x\right]$

(c) $y = x^3 + 1$ so $y' = 3x^2$.

(d) $y' = \dfrac{abe^{-x}}{(1 + be^{-x})^2}$

(e) $\dfrac{2}{3}xy^{-1/3}\dfrac{dy}{dx} + y^{2/3} + \dfrac{2}{3}yx^{-1/3} + x^{2/3}\dfrac{dy}{dx} = 2x$. Multiply by $3x^{1/3}y^{1/3}$:

$$2x^{4/3}\frac{dy}{dx} + 3x^{1/3}y + 2y^{4/3} + 3xy^{1/3}\frac{dy}{dx} = 6x^{4/3}y^{1/3}. \text{ Regroup:}$$

$$\frac{dy}{dx}\left(2x^{4/3} + 3xy^{1/3}\right) = 6x^{4/3}y^{1/3} - 3x^{1/3}y - 2y^{4/3}, \quad \frac{dy}{dx} = \frac{6x^{4/3}y^{1/3} - 3x^{1/3}y - 2y^{4/3}}{2x^{4/3} + 3xy^{1/3}}.$$

(f) $y = \dfrac{1}{2}\ln x + \dfrac{1}{3}\ln(x+1) - \ln\sin x + \ln\cos x$, so

$$y' = \frac{1}{2x} + \frac{1}{3(x+1)} - \frac{\cos x}{\sin x} - \frac{\sin x}{\cos x} = \frac{5x+3}{6x(x+1)} - \cot x - \tan x.$$

21. **(a)** The function $\ln x - x^{0.2}$ is negative at $x = 1$ and positive at $x = 4$, so it must be zero in between (IVT).

   (b) $x = 3.654$

23. Set $y = \log_b x$ and solve $y' = 1$: $y' = \dfrac{1}{x\ln b} = 1$ so $x = \dfrac{1}{\ln b}$. The curves intersect when (x, x) lies on the graph of $y = \log_b x$, so $x = \log_b x$. From Formula (9), Section 4.2, $\log_b x = \dfrac{\ln x}{\ln b}$ from which $\ln x = 1$, $x = e$, $\ln b = 1/e$, $b = e^{1/e} \approx 1.4447$.

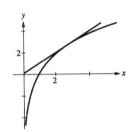

Analysis of Functions and Their Graphs

EXERCISE SET 5.1

1. **(a)** $f' > 0$ and $f'' > 0$

    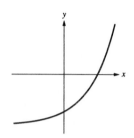

    (b) $f' > 0$ and $f'' < 0$

    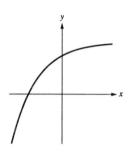

    (c) $f' < 0$ and $f'' > 0$

    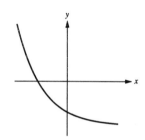

    (d) $f' < 0$ and $f'' < 0$

    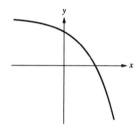

3. A: $dy/dx < 0$, $d^2y/dx^2 > 0$
    B: $dy/dx > 0$, $d^2y/dx^2 < 0$
    C: $dy/dx < 0$, $d^2y/dx^2 < 0$

5. An inflection point occurs when f'' changes sign: at $x = -1, 0, 1$ and 2.

7. **(a)** $[4,6]$ **(b)** $[1,4]$ and $[6,7]$ **(c)** $(1,2)$ and $(3,5)$
    (d) $(2,3)$ and $(5,7)$ **(e)** $x = 2, 3, 5$

9. $f'(x) = 2x - 5$ **(a)** $[5/2, +\infty)$ **(b)** $(-\infty, 5/2]$
    $f''(x) = 2$ **(c)** $(-\infty, +\infty)$ **(d)** none
         (e) none

11. $f'(x) = 3(x+2)^2$ **(a)** $(-\infty, +\infty)$ **(b)** none
    $f''(x) = 6(x+2)$ **(c)** $(-2, +\infty)$ **(d)** $(-\infty, -2)$
         (e) -2

13. $f'(x) = 12x^2(x-1)$ **(a)** $[1, +\infty)$ **(b)** $(-\infty, 1]$
    $f''(x) = 36x(x - 2/3)$ **(c)** $(-\infty, 0), (2/3, +\infty)$ **(d)** $(0, 2/3)$
         (e) $0, 2/3$

15. $f'(x) = \dfrac{4x}{(x^2+2)^2}$ $f''(x) = -4\dfrac{3x^2 - 2}{(x^2+2)^3}$
    (a) $[0, +\infty)$ **(b)** $(-\infty, 0]$ **(c)** $(-\sqrt{2/3}, +\sqrt{2/3})$
    (d) $(-\infty, -\sqrt{2/3}), (+\sqrt{2/3}, +\infty)$ **(e)** $-\sqrt{2/3}, \sqrt{2/3}$

17. $f'(x) = \frac{1}{3}(x+2)^{-2/3}$

　　　$f''(x) = -\frac{2}{9}(x+2)^{-5/3}$

(a) $(-\infty, +\infty)$ 　　**(b)** none

(c) $(-\infty, -2)$ 　　**(d)** $(-2, +\infty)$

(e) -2

19. $f'(x) = \dfrac{4(x+1)}{3x^{2/3}}$

　　　$f''(x) = \dfrac{4(x-2)}{9x^{5/3}}$

(a) $[-1, +\infty)$ 　　**(b)** $(-\infty, -1]$

(c) $(-\infty, 0), (2, +\infty)$ 　　**(d)** $(0, 2)$

(e) $0, 2$

21. $f'(x) = -xe^{-x^2/2}$

　　　$f''(x) = (-1 + x^2)e^{-x^2/2}$

(a) $(-\infty, 0]$ 　　**(b)** $[0, +\infty)$

(c) $(-\infty, -1), (1, +\infty)$ 　　**(d)** $(-1, 1)$

(e) $-1, 1$

23. $f'(x) = \dfrac{2x}{1 + x^2}$

　　　$f''(x) = 2\dfrac{1 - x^2}{(1 + x^2)^2}$

(a) $[0, +\infty)$ 　　**(b)** $(-\infty, 0]$

(c) $(-1, 1)$ 　　**(d)** $(-\infty, -1), (1, +\infty)$

(e) $-1, 1$

25. $f'(x) = -\sin x$

　　　$f''(x) = -\cos x$

(a) $[\pi, 2\pi]$ 　　**(b)** $[0, \pi]$

(c) $(\pi/2, 3\pi/2)$ 　　**(d)** $(0, \pi/2), (3\pi/2, 2\pi)$

(e) $\pi/2, 3\pi/2$

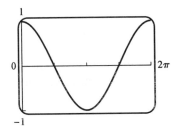

27. $f'(x) = \sec^2 x$

　　　$f''(x) = 2\sec^2 x \tan x$

(a) $(-\pi/2, \pi/2)$ 　　**(b)** none

(c) $(0, \pi/2)$ 　　**(d)** $(-\pi/2, 0)$

(e) 0

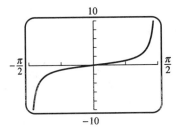

29. $f'(x) = \cos 2x$

　　　$f''(x) = -2\sin 2x$

(a) $[0, \pi/4], [3\pi/4, \pi]$ 　　**(b)** $[\pi/4, 3\pi/4]$

(c) $(\pi/2, \pi)$ 　　**(d)** $(0, \pi/2)$

(e) $\pi/2$

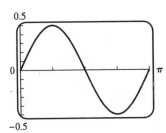

31. **(a)**

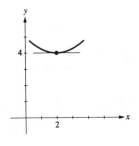

(b)

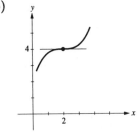

(c)

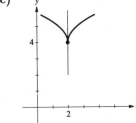

33. **(a)** $f'(x) = 3(x-a)^2$, $f''(x) = 6(x-a)$; inflection point is $(a, 0)$

(b) $f'(x) = 4(x-a)^3$, $f''(x) = 12(x-a)^2$; no inflection points

35. $f'(x) = 1/3 - 1/[3(1+x)^{2/3}]$ so f is increasing on $[0, +\infty)$ thus if $x > 0$, then $f(x) > f(0) = 0$, $1 + x/3 - \sqrt[3]{1+x} > 0$, $\sqrt[3]{1+x} < 1 + x/3$.

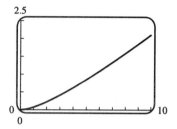

37. $x \geq \sin x$ on $[0, +\infty)$: let $f(x) = x - \sin x$. Then $f(0) = 0$ and $f'(x) = 1 - \cos x \geq 0$, so $f(x)$ is increasing on $[0, +\infty)$.

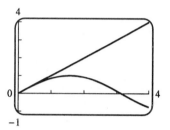

39. Points of inflection at $x = -2, +2$. Concave up on $(-5, -2)$ and $(2, 5)$; concave down on $(-2, 2)$. Increasing on $[-3.5829, 0.2513]$ and $[3.3316, 5]$, and decreasing on $[-5, -3.5829]$ and $[0.2513, 3.3316]$.

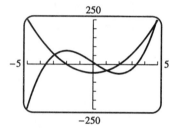

41. Break the interval $[-5, 5]$ into ten subintervals and check $f''(x)$ at each endpoint. We find $f''(-1) > 0$ and $f''(0) < 0$. Refine $[-1, 0]$ into ten subintervals; $f''(-0.2) > 0$, $f''(-0.1) < 0$; repeat, $f''(-0.18) > 0$, $f''(-0.17) < 0$, so $x = -0.175$ is correct to two decimal places. Note also that $f''(1) = 0$ so there are two inflection points.

43. $f''(x) = 2\dfrac{90x^3 - 81x^2 - 585x + 397}{(3x^2 - 5x + 8)^3}$. The denominator has complex roots, so is always positive; hence the x-coordinates of the points of inflection of $f(x)$ are the roots of the numerator (if it changes sign). A plot of the numerator over $[-5, 5]$ shows roots lying in $[-3, -2]$, $[0, 1]$, and $[2, 3]$. Breaking each of these intervals into ten subintervals locates the roots in $[-2.5, -2.4]$, $[0.6, 0.7]$ and $[2.7, 2.8]$. Thus to one decimal place the roots are $x = -2.45, 0.65, 2.75$.

45. $f(x_1) - f(x_2) = x_1^2 - x_2^2 = (x_1 + x_2)(x_1 - x_2) < 0$ if $x_1 < x_2$ for x_1, x_2 in $[0, +\infty)$, so $f(x_1) < f(x_2)$ and f is thus increasing.

47. **(a)** If $x_1 < x_2$ where x_1 and x_2 are in I, then $f(x_1) < f(x_2)$ and $g(x_1) < g(x_2)$, so $f(x_1) + g(x_1) < f(x_2) + g(x_2)$, $(f + g)(x_1) < (f + g)(x_2)$. Thus $f + g$ is increasing on I.

(b) Case I: If f and g are ≥ 0 on I, and if $x_1 < x_2$ where x_1 and x_2 are in I, then $0 < f(x_1) < f(x_2)$ and $0 < g(x_1) < g(x_2)$, so $f(x_1)g(x_1) < f(x_2)g(x_2)$, $(f \cdot g)(x_1) < (f \cdot g)(x_2)$. Thus $f \cdot g$ is increasing on I.
Case II: If f and g are not necessarily positive on I then no conclusion can be drawn: for example, $f(x) = g(x) = x$ are both increasing on $(-\infty, 0)$, but $(f \cdot g)(x) = x^2$ is decreasing there.

49. **(a)** $f''(x) = 6ax + 2b = 6a(x + \dfrac{b}{3a})$, $f''(x) = 0$ when $x = -\dfrac{b}{3a}$. f changes its direction of concavity at $x = -\dfrac{b}{3a}$ so $-\dfrac{b}{3a}$ is an inflection point.

(b) If $f(x) = ax^3 + bx^2 + cx + d$ has three x-intercepts, then it has three roots, say x_1, x_2 and x_3, so we can write $f(x) = a(x - x_1)(x - x_2)(x - x_3) = ax^3 + bx^2 + cx + d$, from which it follows that $b = -a(x_1 + x_2 + x_3)$. Thus $-\dfrac{b}{3a} = \dfrac{1}{3}(x_1 + x_2 + x_3)$, which is the average.

(c) $f(x) = x(x^2 - 3x^2 + 2) = x(x - 1)(x - 2)$ so the intercepts are 0, 1, and 2 and the average is 1. $f''(x) = 6x - 6 = 6(x - 1)$ changes sign at $x = 1$.

51. (a) Let $x_1 < x_2$ belong to (a, b). If both belong to $(a, c]$ or both belong to $[c, b)$ then we have $f(x_1) < f(x_2)$ by hypothesis. So assume $x_1 < c < x_2$. We know by hypothesis that $f(x_1) < f(c)$, and $f(c) < f(x_2)$. We conclude that $f(x_1) < f(x_2)$.

(b) Use the same argument as in part (a), but with inequalities reversed.

53. $t = 7.67$

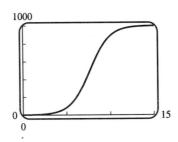

55.

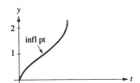

EXERCISE SET 5.2

1. (a)

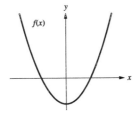

(b)

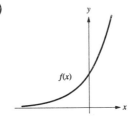

(c)

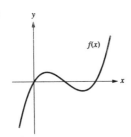

(d)

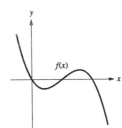

3. (a) $f'(x) = 6x - 6$ and $f''(x) = 6$, with $f'(1) = 0$. For the first derivative test, $f' < 0$ for $x < 1$ and $f' > 0$ for $x > 1$. For the second derivative test, $f''(1) > 0$.

(b) $f'(x) = 3x^2 - 3$ and $f''(x) = 6x$. $f'(x) = 0$ at $x = \pm 1$. First derivative test: $f' > 0$ for $x < -1$ and $x > 1$, and $f' < 0$ for $-1 < x < 1$, so there is a relative maximum at $x = -1$, and a relative minimum at $x = 1$. Second derivative test: $f'' < 0$ at $x = -1$, a relative maximum; and $f'' > 0$ at $x = 1$, a relative minimum.

5. (a) $f'(x) = 4(x-1)^3$, $g'(x) = 3x^2 - 6x + 3$ so $f'(1) = g'(1) = 0$.

   (b) $f''(x) = 12(x-1)^2$, $g''(x) = 6x - 6$, so $f''(1) = g''(1) = 0$, which yields no information.

   (c) $f' < 0$ for $x < 1$ and $f' > 0$ for $x > 1$, so there is a relative minimum at $x = 1$; $g'(x) = 3(x-1)^2 > 0$ on both sides of $x = 1$, so there is no relative extremum at $x = 1$.

7. (a) $f'(x) = 3x^2 + 6x - 9 = 3(x+3)(x-1)$, $f'(x) = 0$ when $x = -3, 1$ (stationary points).

   (b) $f'(x) = 4x(x^2 - 3)$, $f'(x) = 0$ when $x = 0, \pm\sqrt{3}$ (stationary points).

9. (a) $f'(x) = (2 - x^2)/(x^2 + 2)^2$, $f'(x) = 0$ when $x = \pm\sqrt{2}$ (stationary points).

   (b) $f'(x) = \frac{2}{3}x^{-1/3} = 2/(3x^{1/3})$, $f'(x)$ does not exist when $x = 0$.

11. (a) $f'(x) = \frac{4(x+1)}{3x^{2/3}}$, $f'(x) = 0$ when $x = -1$ (stationary point), $f'(x)$ does not exist when $x = 0$.

   (b) $f'(x) = -3\sin 3x$, $f'(x) = 0$ when $\sin 3x = 0, 3x = n\pi, n = 0, \pm 1, \pm 2, \cdots$
   $x = n\pi/3, n = 0, \pm 1, \pm 2, \cdots$ (stationary points)

13. (a) $x = 2$ because $f'(x)$ changes sign from $-$ to $+$ there.

   (b) $x = 0$ because $f'(x)$ changes sign from $+$ to $-$ there.

   (c) $x = 1, 3$ because $f''(x)$ (the slope of the graph of $f'(x)$) changes sign at these points.

15. (a) critical points $x = 0, \pm\sqrt{5}$; f':
   $$\begin{array}{ccccc} - - & 0 + + & 0 - - & 0 + + \\ \hline & -\sqrt{5} & 0 & \sqrt{5} \end{array}$$

   $x = 0$: relative maximum; $x = \pm\sqrt{5}$: relative minimum

   (b) critical point $x = 0$; f':
   $$\begin{array}{cc} - - - & 0 \quad + + + \\ \hline & 0 \end{array}$$

   $x = 0$: relative minimum

17. $f'(x) = -2(x+2)$; critical point $x = -2$; $f'(x)$:
   $$\begin{array}{cc} + + + & 0 \quad - - - \\ \hline & -2 \end{array}$$

   $f''(x) = -2$; $f''(-2) < 0$, $f(-2) = 5$; relative max of 5 at $x = -2$

19. $f'(x) = 2\sin x \cos x = \sin 2x$; critical points $x = \pi/2, \pi, 3\pi/2$; $f'(x)$:
   $$\begin{array}{cccc} + + & 0 - - & 0 + + & 0 - - \\ \hline \frac{\pi}{2} & \pi & \frac{3\pi}{2} \end{array}$$

   $f''(x) = 2\cos 2x$; $f''(\pi/2) < 0$, $f''(\pi) > 0$, $f''(3\pi/2) < 0$, $f(\pi/2) = f(3\pi/2) = 1$, $f(\pi) = 0$; relative min of 0 at $x = \pi$, relative max of 1 at $x = \pi/2, 3\pi/2$

21. $f'(x) = 3x^2 + 5$; no relative extrema because there are no critical points.

23. $f'(x) = (x-1)(3x-1)$; critical points $x = 1, 1/3$
   $f''(x) = 6x - 4$; $f''(1) > 0$, $f''(1/3) < 0$
   relative min of 0 at $x = 1$, relative max of 4/27 at $x = 1/3$

25. $f'(x) = 4x(1 - x^2)$; critical points $x = 0, 1, -1$
   $f''(x) = 4 - 12x^2$; $f''(0) > 0$, $f''(1) < 0$, $f''(-1) < 0$
   relative min of 0 at $x = 0$, relative max of 1 at $x = 1, -1$

27. $f'(x) = \frac{4}{5}x^{-1/5}$; critical point $x = 0$; relative min of 0 at $x = 0$ (first derivative test)
   relative min of 0 at $x = 0$, relative max of 1/27 at $x = -1/27$

29. $f'(x) = 2x/(x^2 + 1)^2$; critical point $x = 0$; relative min of 0 at $x = 0$

31. $f'(x) = 2x/(1 + x^2)$; critical point at $x = 0$; relative min of 0 at $x = 0$ (first derivative test)

33. $f'(x) = 2x$ if $|x| > 2$, $f'(x) = -2x$ if $|x| < 2$,
$f'(x)$ does not exist when $x = \pm 2$; critical points $x = 0, 2, -2$
relative min of 0 at $x = 2, -2$, relative max of 4 at $x = 0$

35. $f'(x) = 2\cos 2x$ if $\sin 2x > 0$, $f'(x) = -2\cos 2x$ if $\sin 2x < 0$,
$f'(x)$ does not exist when $x = \pi/2, \pi, 3\pi/2$;
critical points $x = \pi/4, 3\pi/4, 5\pi/4, 7\pi/4, \pi/2, \pi, 3\pi/2$
relative min of 0 at $x = \pi/2, \pi, 3\pi/2$; relative max of 1 at
$x = \pi/4, 3\pi/4, 5\pi/4, 7\pi/4$

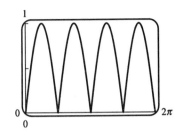

37. $f'(x) = -\sin 2x$; critical points $x = \pi/2, \pi, 3\pi/2$
relative min of 0 at $x = \pi/2, 3\pi/2$; relative max of 1 at $x = \pi$

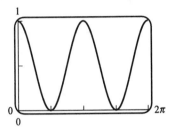

39. $f'(x) = \ln x + 1$, $f''(x) = 1/x$; $f'(1/e) = 0$, $f''(1/e) > 0$;
relative min of $-1/e$ at $x = 1/e$

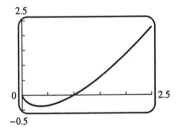

41. $f'(x) = 2x(1-x)e^{-2x} = 0$ at $x = 0, 1$. $f''(x) = (4x^2 - 8x + 2)e^{-2x}$;
$f''(0) > 0$ and $f''(1) < 0$, so a relative min of 0 at $x = 0$ and a
relative max of $1/e^2$ at $x = 1$.

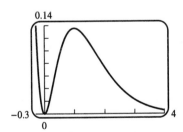

43. Relative minima at $x = -3.58, 3.33$; relative max at $x = 0.25$

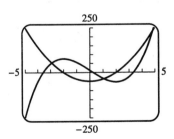

45. relative max at $x = 0.255$

47. Relative min at $x = -1.20$ and a relative max at $x = 1.80$

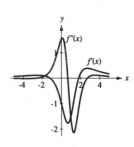

49. **(a)** Let $f(x) = x^2 + \dfrac{k}{x}$, then $f'(x) = 2x - \dfrac{k}{x^2} = \dfrac{2x^3 - k}{x^2}$. f has a relative extremum when $2x^3 - k = 0$, so $k = 2x^3 = 2(3)^3 = 54$.

(b) Let $f(x) = \dfrac{x}{x^2 + k}$, then $f'(x) = \dfrac{k - x^2}{(x^2 + k)^2}$. f has a relative extremum when $k - x^2 = 0$, so $k = x^2 = 3^2 = 9$.

51. **(a)** $f'(x) = -xf(x)$. Since $f(x)$ is always positive, $f'(x) = 0$ at $x = 0$, $f'(x) > 0$ for $x < 0$ and $f'(x) < 0$ for $x > 0$, so $x = 0$ is a maximum.

(b)

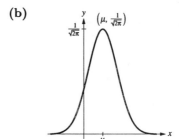

53. $f'(x) = 3ax^2 + 2bx + c$ and $f'(x)$ has roots at $x = 0, 1$, so $f'(x)$ must be of the form $f'(x) = 3ax(x - 1)$; thus $c = 0$ and $2b = -3a$, $b = -3a/2$. $f''(x) = 6ax + 2b = 6ax - 3a$, so $f''(0) > 0$ and $f''(1) < 0$ provided $a < 0$. Finally $f(0) = d$, so $d = 0$; and $f(1) = a + b + c + d = a + b = -a/2$ so $a = -2$. Thus $f(x) = -2x^3 + 3x^2$.

55. **(a)**

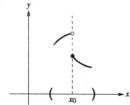

$f(x_0)$ is not an extreme value.

(b)

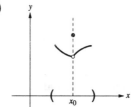

$f(x_0)$ is a relative maximum.

(c)

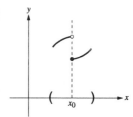

$f(x_0)$ is a relative minimum.

EXERCISE SET 5.3

1. $y = x^2 - 2x - 3$;
$y' = 2(x - 1)$;
$y'' = 2$

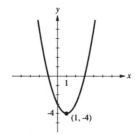

3. $y = x^3 - 3x + 1$;

$y' = 3(x^2 - 1)$;

$y'' = 6x$

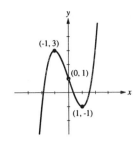

5. $y = x^4 + 2x^3 - 1$;

$y' = 4x^2(x + 3/2)$;

$y'' = 12x(x + 1)$

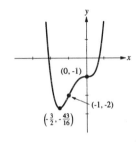

7. $y = x^3(3x^2 - 5)$;

$y' = 15x^2(x^2 - 1)$;

$y'' = 30x(2x^2 - 1)$

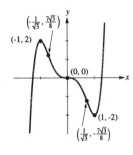

9. $y = x(x - 1)^3$;

$y' = (4x - 1)(x - 1)^2$;

$y'' = 6(2x - 1)(x - 1)$

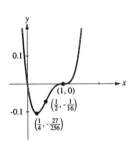

11. $y = 2x/(x - 3)$;

$y' = -6/(x - 3)^2$;

$y'' = 12/(x - 3)^3$

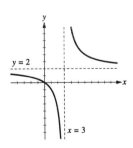

13. $y = \dfrac{x^2}{x^2 - 1}$;

$y' = -\dfrac{2x}{(x^2 - 1)^2}$;

$y'' = \dfrac{2(3x^2 + 1)}{(x^2 - 1)^3}$

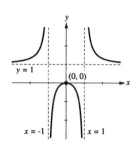

15. $y = x^2 - \dfrac{1}{x} = \dfrac{x^3 - 1}{x}$;

$y' = \dfrac{2x^3 + 1}{x^2}$,

$y' = 0$ when $x = -\sqrt[3]{\dfrac{1}{2}} \approx -0.8$;

$y'' = \dfrac{2(x^3 - 1)}{x^3}$

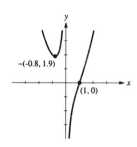

17. $y = \dfrac{x^3 - 1}{x^3 + 1}$;

$y' = \dfrac{6x^2}{(x^3 + 1)^2}$;

$y'' = \dfrac{12x(1 - 2x^3)}{(x^3 + 1)^3}$

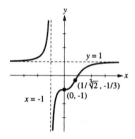

19. $y = \dfrac{x - 1}{x^2 - 4}$;

$y' = -\dfrac{x^2 - 2x + 4}{(x^2 - 4)^2}$

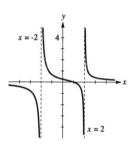

21. $y = \dfrac{(x - 1)^2}{x^2}$;

$y' = \dfrac{2(x - 1)}{x^3}$;

$y'' = \dfrac{2(3 - 2x)}{x^4}$

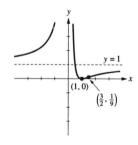

23. (a) VI   (b) I   (c) III   (d) V   (e) IV   (f) II

25. $y = \sqrt{x^2 - 1}$;
$y' = \dfrac{x}{\sqrt{x^2 - 1}}$;
$y'' = -\dfrac{1}{(x^2 - 1)^{3/2}}$

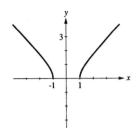

27. $y = 2x + 3x^{2/3}$;
$y' = 2 + 2x^{-1/3}$;
$y'' = -\dfrac{2}{3}x^{-4/3}$

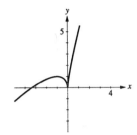

29. $y = x(3 - x)^{1/2}$;
$y' = \dfrac{3(2 - x)}{2\sqrt{3 - x}}$;
$y'' = \dfrac{3(x - 4)}{4(3 - x)^{3/2}}$

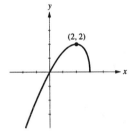

31. $y = \dfrac{8(\sqrt{x} - 1)}{x}$;
$y' = \dfrac{4(2 - \sqrt{x})}{x^2}$;
$y'' = \dfrac{2(3\sqrt{x} - 8)}{x^3}$

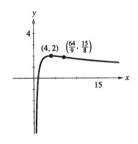

33. $y = x + \sin x$;
$y' = 1 + \cos x$, $y' = 0$ when $x = \pi + 2n\pi$;
$y'' = -\sin x$; $y'' = 0$ when $x = n\pi$
$n = 0, \pm 1, \pm 2, \ldots$

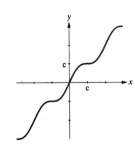

35. $y = \sin x + \cos x$;

     $y' = \cos x - \sin x$;

     $y' = 0$ when $x = \pi/4 + n\pi$;

     $y'' = -\sin x - \cos x$;

     $y'' = 0$ when $x = 3\pi/4 + n\pi$

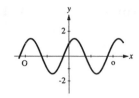

37. $y = \sin^2 x,\ 0 \le x \le 2\pi$;

     $y' = 2 \sin x \cos x = \sin 2x$;

     $y'' = 2 \cos 2x$

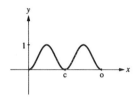

39. **(a)** $\lim\limits_{x \to +\infty} xe^x = +\infty,\ \lim\limits_{x \to -\infty} xe^x = 0$

      (b) $y = xe^x$;

           $y' = (x + 1)e^x$;

           $y'' = (x + 2)e^x$

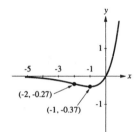

41. **(a)** $\lim\limits_{x \to +\infty} \dfrac{x^2}{e^{2x}} = 0,\ \lim\limits_{x \to -\infty} \dfrac{x^2}{e^{2x}} = +\infty$

      (b) $y = x^2/e^{2x} = x^2 e^{-2x}$;

           $y' = 2x(1 - x)e^{-2x}$;

           $y'' = 2(2x^2 - 4x + 1)e^{-2x}$;

           $y'' = 0$ if $2x^2 - 4x + 1 = 0$, when

           $x = \dfrac{4 \pm \sqrt{16 - 8}}{4} = 1 \pm \sqrt{2}/2 \approx 0.29, 1.71$

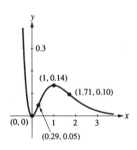

43. **(a)** $\lim\limits_{x \to +\infty} f(x) = +\infty,\ \lim\limits_{x \to -\infty} f(x) = -\infty$

      (b) $y = xe^{x^2}$;

           $y' = (1 + 2x^2)e^{x^2}$;

           $y'' = 2x(3 + 2x^2)e^{x^2}$

           no relative extrema, inflection point at $(0, 0)$

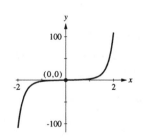

45. **(a)** $\lim_{x\to 0^+} y = \lim_{x\to 0^+} x\ln x = \lim_{x\to 0^+} \frac{\ln x}{1/x} = \lim_{x\to 0^+} \frac{1/x}{-1/x^2} = 0;$

$\lim_{x\to +\infty} y = +\infty$

(b) $y = x\ln x,$

$y' = 1 + \ln x, \ y'' = 1/x,$

$y' = 0$ when $x = e^{-1}$

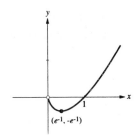

$(e^{-1}, -e^{-1})$

47. **(a)** $\lim_{x\to 0^+} y = \lim_{x\to 0^+} \frac{\ln x}{x^2} = -\infty;$

$\lim_{x\to +\infty} y = \lim_{x\to +\infty} \frac{\ln x}{x^2} = \lim_{x\to +\infty} \frac{1/x}{2x} = 0$

(b) $y = \frac{\ln x}{x^2}, y' = \frac{1 - 2\ln x}{x^3},$

$y'' = \frac{6\ln x - 5}{x^4},$

$y' = 0$ if $x = e^{1/2},$

$y'' = 0$ if $x = e^{5/6}$

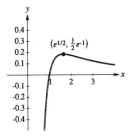

$(e^{1/2}, \tfrac{1}{2}e^{-1})$

49. **(a)** $\lim_{x\to -\infty} y = -\infty, \ \lim_{x\to +\infty} y = +\infty;$

curve crosses x-axis at $x = 0, 1, -1$

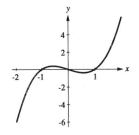

(b) $\lim_{x\to \pm\infty} y = +\infty;$

curve never crosses x-axis

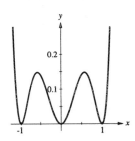

(c) $\lim_{x\to -\infty} y = -\infty, \ \lim_{x\to +\infty} y = +\infty;$

curve crosses x-axis at $x = -1$

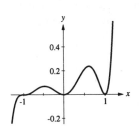

(d) $\lim\limits_{x \to \pm\infty} y = +\infty;$
curve crosses x-axis at $x = 0, 1$

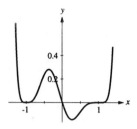

51.   **(a)**   horizontal asymptote $y = 3$ as $x \to \pm\infty$, vertical asymptotes of
$x = \pm 2$

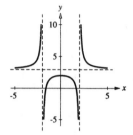

(b)   horizontal asymptote of $y = 1$ as $x \to \pm\infty$, vertical asymptotes
at $x = \pm 1$

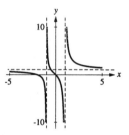

(c)   horizontal asymptote of $y = -1$ as $x \to \pm\infty$, vertical
asymptotes at $x = -2, 1$

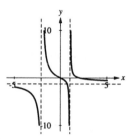

(d)   horizontal asymptote of $y = 1$ as $x \to \pm\infty$,
vertical asymptote at $x = -1, 2$

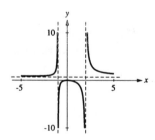

53. **(a)**

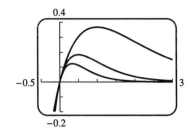

(b) $y' = (1 - bx)e^{-bx}$, $y'' = b^2(x - 2/b)e^{-bx}$; relative max at $x = 1/b$, $y = 1/be$; point of inflection at $x = 2/b$, $y = 2/be^2$. Increasing b moves the relative max and the point of inflection to the left and down, i.e. towards the origin.

55. **(a)** The oscillations of $e^x \cos x$ about zero increase as $x \to \pm\infty$ so the limit does not exist.

(b)

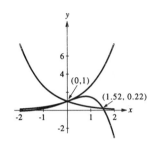

(c) The curve $y = e^{ax} \cos bx$ oscillates between $y = e^{ax}$ and $y = -e^{ax}$. The frequency of oscillation increases when b increases.

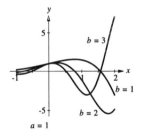

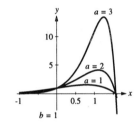

57. $y = \dfrac{x^2 - 2}{x} = x - \dfrac{2}{x}$ so
$y = x$ is an oblique asymptote;
$y' = \dfrac{x^2 + 2}{x^2}$,
$y'' = -\dfrac{4}{x^3}$

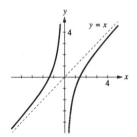

59. $y = \dfrac{(x - 2)^3}{x^2} = x - 6 + \dfrac{12x - 8}{x^2}$ so
$y = x - 6$ is an oblique asymptote;
$y' = \dfrac{(x - 2)^2(x + 4)}{x^3}$,
$y'' = \dfrac{24(x - 2)}{x^4}$

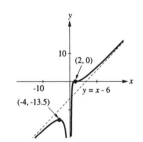

61. $y = x + 1 - \dfrac{1}{x} - \dfrac{1}{x^2} = \dfrac{(x-1)(x+1)^2}{x^2}$,

$y = x + 1$ is an oblique asymptote;

$y' = \dfrac{(x+1)(x^2 - x + 2)}{x^3}$,

$y'' = -\dfrac{2(x+3)}{x^4}$

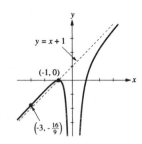

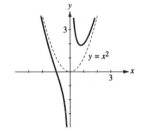

63. $\displaystyle\lim_{x \to \pm\infty} [f(x) - x^2] = \lim_{x \to \pm\infty} (1/x) = 0$

$y = x^2 + \dfrac{1}{x} = \dfrac{x^3 + 1}{x}$, $y' = 2x - \dfrac{1}{x^2} = \dfrac{2x^3 - 1}{x^2}$,

$y'' = 2 + \dfrac{2}{x^3} = \dfrac{2(x^3 + 1)}{x^3}$, $y' = 0$ when $x = 1/\sqrt[3]{2} \approx 0.8$,

$y = 3\sqrt[3]{2}/2 \approx 1.9$; $y'' = 0$ when $x = -1, y = 0$

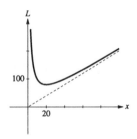

65. Let y be the length of the other side of the rectangle, then

$L = 2x + 2y$ and $xy = 400$ so $y = 400/x$ and hence $L = 2x + 800/x$.

$L = 2x$ is an oblique asymptote (see Exercise 48)

$L = 2x + \dfrac{800}{x} = \dfrac{2(x^2 + 400)}{x}$, $L' = 2 - \dfrac{800}{x^2} = \dfrac{2(x^2 - 400)}{x^2}$,

$L'' = \dfrac{1600}{x^3}$, $L' = 0$ when $x = 20, L = 80$

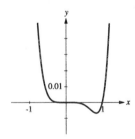

67. $y' = 0.1x^4(6x - 5)$;

critical points: $x = 0$, $x = 5/6$;

relative minimum at $x = 5/6$,

$y \approx -6.7 \times 10^{-3}$

69. **(a)** $P'(t) = \dfrac{kL^2 A e^{-kLt}}{(1 + Ae^{-kLt})^2} S$, so $P'(0) = \dfrac{kL^2 A}{(1 + A)^2}$

(b) The rate of growth increases to its maximum, which occurs when P is halfway between 0 and L, or when $t = \dfrac{1}{Lk} \ln A$; it then decreases back towards zero.

(c) From (6) one sees that $\dfrac{dP}{dt}$ is maximized when P lies half way between 0 and L, i.e. $P = L/2$. This follows since the right side of (6) is a parabola (with P as independent variable) with P-intercepts $P = 0, L$. The value $P = L/2$ corresponds to $t = \dfrac{1}{Lk} \ln A$, from (8).

SUPPLEMENTARY EXERCISES FOR CHAPTER 5

7. **(a)** $f'(x) = \dfrac{7(x-7)(x-1)}{3x^{2/3}}$; critical points at $x = 0, 1, 7$;
neither at $x = 0$, relative max at $x = 1$, relative min at $x = 7$ (first derivative test)

(b) $f'(x) = 2\cos x(1 + 2\sin x)$; critical points at $x = \pi/2, 3\pi/2, 7\pi/6, 11\pi/6$;
relative max at $x = \pi/2, 3\pi/2$, relative min at $x = 7\pi/6, 11\pi/6$

(c) $f'(x) = 3 - \dfrac{3\sqrt{x-1}}{2}$; critical points at $x = 5$; relative max at $x = 5$

9. $\lim\limits_{x\to-\infty} f(x) = +\infty$, $\lim\limits_{x\to+\infty} f(x) = +\infty$
$f'(x) = x(4x^2 - 9x + 6)$, $f''(x) = 6(2x - 1)(x - 1)$
relative min at $x = 0$,
points of inflection when $x = 1/2, 1$,
no asymptotes

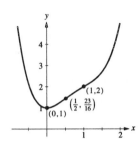

11. $\lim\limits_{x\to\pm\infty} f(x)$ doesn't exist
$f'(x) = 2x\sec^2(x^2 + 1)$,
$f''(x) = 2\sec^2(x^2 + 1)\left[1 + 4x^2\tan(x^2 + 1)\right]$
critical point at $x = 0$; relative min at $x = 0$
point of inflection when $1 + 4x^2\tan(x^2 + 1) = 0$
vertical asymptotes at $x = \pm\sqrt{\pi(n + \frac{1}{2}) - 1}$, $n = 0, 1, 2, \ldots$

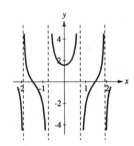

13. $f'(x) = 2\dfrac{x(x + 5)}{(x^2 + 2x + 5)^2}$, $f''(x) = -2\dfrac{2x^3 + 15x^2 - 25}{(x^2 + 2x + 5)^3}$
critical points at $x = -5, 0$;
relative max at $x = -5$,
relative min at $x = 0$
points of inflection at $x = -7.26, -1.44, 1.20$
horizontal asymptote $y = 1$ as $x \to \pm\infty$

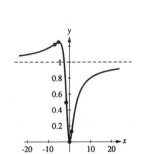

15. $\lim\limits_{x\to-\infty} f(x) = +\infty$, $\lim\limits_{x\to+\infty} f(x) = -\infty$
$f'(x) = \begin{cases} x \\ -2x \end{cases}$ if $\begin{cases} x \le 0 \\ x > 0 \end{cases}$
critical point at $x = 0$, no extrema
inflection point at $x = 0$ (f changes concavity)
no asymptotes

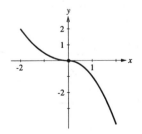

17. $\lim\limits_{x \to +\infty} f(x) = +\infty$

$f'(x) = 1 + \ln x$, $f''(x) = 1/x$

$\lim\limits_{x \to 0^+} f(x) = 0$, $\lim\limits_{x \to 0^+} f'(x) = -\infty$

critical point at $x = 1/e$;

relative min at $x = 1/e$

no points of inflection, no asymptotes

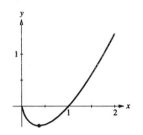

19. $f'(x) = \dfrac{1 - 2\ln x}{x^3}$, $f''(x) = \dfrac{6\ln x - 5}{x^4}$

critical point at $x = e^{1/2}$,

relative max at $x = e^{1/2}$

point of inflection at $x = e^{5/6}$

horizontal asymptote $y = 0$ as $x \to +\infty$

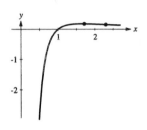

21. $\lim\limits_{x \to +\infty} f(x) = +\infty$

$f'(x) = e^x \dfrac{x - 1}{x^2}$, $f''(x) = e^x \dfrac{x^2 - 2x + 2}{x^3}$

critical point at $x = 1$;

relative min at $x = 1$

no points of inflection

vertical asymptote $x = 0$,

horizontal asymptote $y = 0$ for $x \to -\infty$

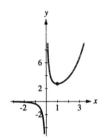

23. $f'(x) = x(2 - x)e^{1-x}$, $f''(x) = (x^2 - 4x + 2)e^{1-x}$

critical points at $x = 0, 2$;

relative min at $x = 0$,

relative max at $x = 2$

points of inflection at $x = 2 \pm \sqrt{2}$

horizontal asymptote $y = 0$ as $x \to +\infty$,

$\lim\limits_{x \to -\infty} f(x) = +\infty$

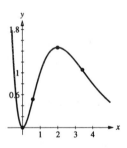

25. (a)

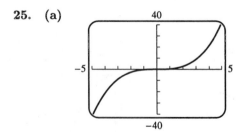

(b) $f'(x) = x^2 - \dfrac{1}{400}$, $f''(x) = 2x$

critical points at $x = \pm\dfrac{1}{20}$;

relative max at $x = -\dfrac{1}{20}$,

relative min at $x = \dfrac{1}{20}$

(c) The finer details can be seen when graphing over a much smaller x-window.

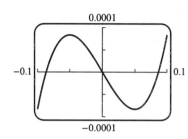

27. (a)

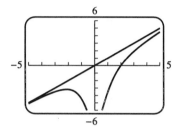

(b) Divide $y = x^2 + 1$ into $y = x^3 - 8$ to get the asymptote $ax + b = x$

29. $f'(x) = 4x^3 - 18x^2 + 24x - 8$, $f''(x) = 12(x-1)(x-2)$
$f''(1) = 0$, $f'(1) = 2$, $f(1) = 2$; $f''(2) = 0$, $f'(2) = 0$, $f(2) = 3$,
so the tangent lines at the inflection points are $y = 2x$ and $y = 3$.

31. $f(x) = \dfrac{(2x-1)(x^2+x-7)}{(2x-1)(3x^2+x-1)} = \dfrac{x^2+x-7}{3x^2+x-1}, \qquad x \neq 1/2$
horizontal asymptote: $y = 1/3$,
vertical asymptotes: $x = (-1 \pm \sqrt{13})/6$

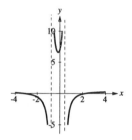

33. (a) $\sin x = -1$ yields the smallest values, and $\sin x = +1$ yields the largest

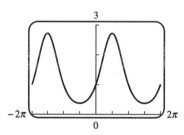

(b) $f'(x) = e^{\sin x} \cos x$; relative maxima at $x = 2n\pi + \pi/2$, $y = e$; relative minima at $x = 2n\pi - \pi/2$, $y = 1/e$; $n = 0, \pm 1, \pm 2, \ldots$ (first derivative test)

(c) $f''(x) = (1 - \sin x - \sin^2 x)e^{\sin x}$; $f''(x) = 0$ when $\sin x = t$, a root of $t^2 + t - 1 = 0$,
$t = \dfrac{-1 \pm \sqrt{5}}{2}$; $\sin x = \dfrac{-1 - \sqrt{5}}{2}$ is impossible. So the points of inflection on $0 < x < 2\pi$ occur
when $\sin x = \dfrac{-1 + \sqrt{5}}{2}$, or $x = 0.66624, 2.47535$

35. **(a)** relative minimum -0.232466 at $x = 0.450184$

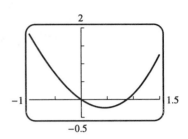

(b) relative maximum 0 at $x = 0$;
relative minimum -0.107587 at $x = \pm 0.674841$

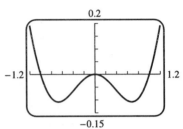

(c) relative maximum 0.876839; at $x = 0.886352$;
relative minimum -0.355977 at $x = -1.244155$

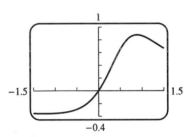

37. **(a)**

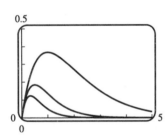

(b) $y = 0$ at $x = 0$; $\displaystyle\lim_{x \to +\infty} y = 0$

(c) relative max at $x = 1/a$, inflection point at $x = 2/a$

(d) As a increases, the x-coordinate of the maximum and the inflection point move towards the origin.

39. $f'(x) = \ln(1 + 1/x) - \dfrac{1}{x}$ and $f''(x) = \dfrac{1}{x^2(x+1)}$; so $f'' > 0$ if $x > 1$ and therefore f' is increasing on $[1, +\infty)$. Next, $f'(1) = \ln 2 - 1 < 0$. Then by L'Hôpital's Rule,

$$\lim_{x \to +\infty} x \ln(1 + 1/x) = \lim_{x \to +\infty} \frac{\ln(1 + 1/x)}{1/x} = \lim_{x \to +\infty} \frac{-1/x^2}{(1 + 1/x)(-1/x^2)} = 1$$

and thus $\displaystyle\lim_{x \to +\infty} f'(x) = \lim_{x \to +\infty} \frac{x \ln(1 + 1/x) - 1}{x}$ is indeterminate.

By L'Hôpital's Rule $\displaystyle\lim_{x \to +\infty} f'(x) = \lim_{x \to +\infty} \left[\ln\left(1 + \frac{1}{x}\right) - \frac{1}{x+1} \right] = 0.$

Thus on $[1, +\infty)$ the function f' starts negative and increases towards zero, so it is negative on the whole interval. So $f(x)$ is decreasing, and $f(x) > f(x + 1)$. Set $x = n$ and obtain $\ln(1 + 1/n)^{n+1} > \ln(1 + 1/(n+1))^{n+2}$. Since $\ln x$ and its inverse function e^x are both increasing, it follows that $(1 + 1/n)^{n+1} > (1 + 1/(n+1))^{n+2}$.

CALCULUS HORIZON MODULE CHAPTER 5

1. The sum of the squares for the residuals for line I is approximately $1^2+1^2+1^2+0^2+2^2+1^2+1^2+1^2 = 10$, and the same for line II is approximately $0^2 + (0.4)^2 + (1.2)^2 + 0^2 + (2.2)^2 + (0.6)^2 + (0.2)^2 + 0^2 = 6.84$; line II is the regression line.

5. **(a)** $S = 2.155239850t + 190.3600714$; $r = 0.9569426456$

    (b) yes, because r is close to 1

    (c) 244.241068 mi/h

    (d) It is assumed that the line still gives a good estimate in the year 2000.

7. **(a)** $y = 3.923208367 + e^{0.2934589528x}$ **(b)**

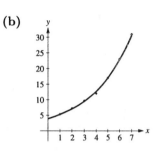

9. **(a)** $T = 27 + 57.8\,e^{-0.046t}$ **(b)** $T_0 = 84.9°C$ **(c)** 53.19 min

CHAPTER 6

Applications of the Derivative

EXERCISE SET 6.1

1. relative maxima at $x = 2, 6$; absolute maximum at $x = 6$; relative and absolute minimum at $x = 4$

3. (a) 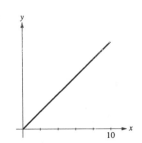   (b) 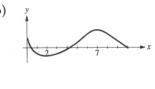   (c)

5. $f'(x) = 8x - 4$, $f'(x) = 0$ when $x = 1/2$; $f(0) = 1$, $f(1/2) = 0$, $f(1) = 1$ so the maximum value is 1 at $x = 0, 1$ and the minimum value is 0 at $x = 1/2$.

7. $f'(x) = 3(x-1)^2$, $f'(x) = 0$ when $x = 1$; $f(0) = -1$, $f(1) = 0$, $f(4) = 27$ so the maximum value is 27 at $x = 4$ and the minimum value is -1 at $x = 0$.

9. $f'(x) = 3/(4x^2 + 1)^{3/2}$, no critical points; $f(-1) = -3/\sqrt{5}$, $f(1) = 3/\sqrt{5}$ so the maximum value is $3/\sqrt{5}$ at $x = 1$ and the minimum value is $-3/\sqrt{5}$ at $x = -1$.

11. $f'(x) = 1 - \sec^2 x$, $f'(x) = 0$ for x in $(-\pi/4, \pi/4)$ when $x = 0$; $f(-\pi/4) = 1 - \pi/4$, $f(0) = 0$, $f(\pi/4) = \pi/4 - 1$ so the maximum value is $1 - \pi/4$ at $x = -\pi/4$ and the minimum value is $\pi/4 - 1$ at $x = \pi/4$.

13. $f(x) = 1 + |9 - x^2| = \begin{cases} 10 - x^2, & |x| \le 3 \\ -8 + x^2, & |x| > 3 \end{cases}$, $f'(x) = \begin{cases} -2x, & |x| < 3 \\ 2x, & |x| > 3 \end{cases}$ thus $f'(x) = 0$ when $x = 0$, $f'(x)$ does not exist for x in $(-5, 1)$ when $x = -3$ because $\lim\limits_{x \to -3^-} f'(x) \ne \lim\limits_{x \to -3^+} f'(x)$ (see Theorem preceding Exercise 75, Section 3.3); $f(-5) = 17$, $f(-3) = 1$, $f(0) = 10$, $f(1) = 9$ so the maximum value is 17 at $x = -5$ and the minimum value is 1 at $x = -3$.

15. $f'(x) = 2x - 3$; critical point $x = 3/2$. Minimum value $f(3/2) = -13/4$, no maximum.

17. $f'(x) = 12x^2(1 - x)$; critical points $x = 0, 1$. Maximum value $f(1) = 1$, no minimum because $\lim\limits_{x \to +\infty} f(x) = -\infty$.

19. No maximum or minimum because $\lim\limits_{x \to +\infty} f(x) = +\infty$ and $\lim\limits_{x \to -\infty} f(x) = -\infty$.

21. $f'(x) = x(x+2)/(x+1)^2$; critical point $x = -2$ in $(-5, -1)$. Maximum value $f(-2) = -4$, no minimum.

23. $(x^2 - 1)^2$ can never be less than zero because it is the square of $x^2 - 1$; the minimum value is 0 for $x = \pm 1$, no maximum because $\lim\limits_{x \to +\infty} f(x) = +\infty$.

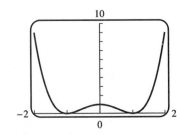

25. $f'(x) = \dfrac{5(8-x)}{3x^{1/3}}$, $f'(x) = 0$ when $x = 8$ and $f'(x)$ does not exist when $x = 0$; $f(-1) = 21$, $f(0) = 0$, $f(8) = 48$, $f(20) = 0$ so the maximum value is 48 at $x = 8$ and the minimum value is 0 at $x = 0, 20$.

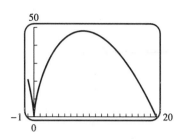

27. $f'(x) = -1/x^2$; no maximum or minimum because there are no critical points in $(0, +\infty)$.

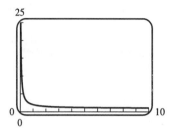

29. $f'(x) = 2\sec x \tan x - \sec^2 x = (2\sin x - 1)/\cos^2 x$, $f'(x) = 0$ for x in $(0, \pi/4)$ when $x = \pi/6$; $f(0) = 2$, $f(\pi/6) = \sqrt{3}$, $f(\pi/4) = 2\sqrt{2} - 1$ so the maximum value is 2 at $x = 0$ and the minimum value is $\sqrt{3}$ at $x = \pi/6$.

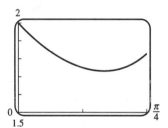

31. $f'(x) = x^2(2x - 3)e^{-2x}$, $f'(x) = 0$ for x in $[1, 4]$ when $x = 3/2$; if $x = 1, 3/2, 4$, then $f(x) = e^{-2}, \dfrac{27}{8}e^{-3}, 64e^{-8}$; critical point at $x = 3/2$; absolute maximum of $\dfrac{27}{8}e^{-3}$ at $x = 3/2$, absolute minimum of $64e^{-8}$ at $x = 4$

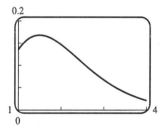

33. $f'(x) = -[\cos(\cos x)]\sin x$; $f'(x) = 0$ if $\sin x = 0$ or if $\cos(\cos x) = 0$. If $\sin x = 0$, then $x = \pi$ is the critical point in $(0, 2\pi)$; $\cos(\cos x) = 0$ has no solutions because $-1 \leq \cos x \leq 1$. Thus $f(0) = \sin(1)$, $f(\pi) = \sin(-1) = -\sin(1)$, and $f(2\pi) = \sin(1)$ so the maximum value is $\sin(1) \approx 0.84147$ and the minimum value is $-\sin(1) \approx -0.84147$.

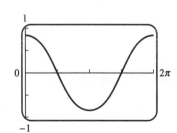

35. $f'(x) = \begin{cases} 4, & x < 1 \\ 2x - 5, & x > 1 \end{cases}$ so $f'(x) = 0$ when $x = 5/2$, and $f'(x)$ does not exist when $x = 1$ because $\lim\limits_{x \to 1^-} f'(x) \neq \lim\limits_{x \to 1^+} f'(x)$ (see Theorem preceding Exercise 75, Section 3.3); $f(1/2) = 0$, $f(1) = 2$, $f(5/2) = -1/4$, $f(7/2) = 3/4$ so the maximum value is 2 and the minimum value is $-1/4$.

37. $\sin 2x$ has a period of π, and $\sin 4x$ a period of $\pi/2$ so $f(x)$ is periodic with period π. Consider the interval $[0, \pi]$. $f'(x) = 4\cos 2x + 4\cos 4x$, $f'(x) = 0$ when $\cos 2x + \cos 4x = 0$, but $\cos 4x = 2\cos^2 2x - 1$ (trig identity) so

$$2\cos^2 2x + \cos 2x - 1 = 0$$
$$(2\cos 2x - 1)(\cos 2x + 1) = 0$$
$$\cos 2x = 1/2 \quad \text{or} \quad \cos 2x = -1.$$

From $\cos 2x = 1/2$, $2x = \pi/3$ or $5\pi/3$ so $x = \pi/6$ or $5\pi/6$. From $\cos 2x = -1$, $2x = \pi$ so $x = \pi/2$. $f(0) = 0$, $f(\pi/6) = 3\sqrt{3}/2$, $f(\pi/2) = 0$, $f(5\pi/6) = -3\sqrt{3}/2$, $f(\pi) = 0$. The maximum value is $3\sqrt{3}/2$ at $x = \pi/6 + n\pi$ and the minimum value is $-3\sqrt{3}/2$ at $x = 5\pi/6 + n\pi$, $n = 0, \pm1, \pm2, \cdots$.

39. Let $f(x) = x - \sin x$, then $f'(x) = 1 - \cos x$ and so $f'(x) = 0$ when $\cos x = 1$ which has no solution for $0 < x < 2\pi$ thus the minimum value of f must occur at 0 or 2π. $f(0) = 0$, $f(2\pi) = 2\pi$ so 0 is the minimum value on $[0, 2\pi]$ thus $x - \sin x \geq 0$, $\sin x \leq x$ for all x in $[0, 2\pi]$.

41. Let $m = $ slope at x, then $m = f'(x) = 3x^2 - 6x + 5$, $dm/dx = 6x - 6$; critical point for m is $x = 1$, minimum value of m is $f'(1) = 2$

43. $f'(x) = \dfrac{2x(x^3 - 24x^2 + 192x - 640)}{(x-8)^3}$; real root of $x^3 - 24x^2 + 192x - 640$ at $x = 4(2 + \sqrt[3]{2})$. Since $\lim\limits_{x \to 8^+} f(x) = \lim\limits_{x \to +\infty} f(x) = +\infty$ and there is only one relative extremum, it must be a minimum.

45. The slope of the line is -1, and the slope of the tangent to $y = -x^2$ is $-2x$ so $-2x = -1$, $x = 1/2$. The line lies above the curve so the vertical distance is given by $F(x) = 2 - x + x^2$; $F(-1) = 4$, $F(1/2) = 7/4$, $F(3/2) = 11/4$. The point $(1/2, -1/4)$ is closest, the point $(-1, -1)$ farthest.

47. The absolute extrema of $y(t)$ can occur at the endpoints $t = 0, 12$ or when $dy/dt = 2\sin t = 0$, i.e. $t = 0, 12, k\pi$, $k = 1, 2, 3$; the absolute maximum is $y = 4$ at $t = \pi, 3\pi$; the absolute minimum is $y = 0$ at $t = 0, 2\pi$.

49. $f'(x) = 2ax + b$; critical point is $x = -\dfrac{b}{2a}$

$f''(x) = 2a > 0$ so $f\left(-\dfrac{b}{2a}\right)$ is the minimum value of f, but

$f\left(-\dfrac{b}{2a}\right) = a\left(-\dfrac{b}{2a}\right)^2 + b\left(-\dfrac{b}{2a}\right) + c = \dfrac{-b^2 + 4ac}{4a}$ thus $f(x) \geq 0$ if and only if

$f\left(-\dfrac{b}{2a}\right) \geq 0$, $\dfrac{-b^2 + 4ac}{4a} \geq 0$, $-b^2 + 4ac \geq 0$, $b^2 - 4ac \leq 0$

EXERCISE SET 6.2

1. Let $x = $ one number, $y = $ the other number, and $P = xy$ where $x + y = 10$. Thus $y = 10 - x$ so $P = x(10 - x) = 10x - x^2$ for x in $[0, 10]$. $dP/dx = 10 - 2x$, $dP/dx = 0$ when $x = 5$. If $x = 0, 5, 10$ then $P = 0, 25, 0$ so P is maximum when $x = 5$ and, from $y = 10 - x$, when $y = 5$.

3. If $y = x + 1/x$ for $1/2 \leq x \leq 3/2$ then $dy/dx = 1 - 1/x^2 = (x^2 - 1)/x^2$, $dy/dx = 0$ when $x = 1$. If $x = 1/2, 1, 3/2$ then $y = 5/2, 2, 13/6$ so

(a) y is as small as possible when $x = 1$. **(b)** y is as large as possible when $x = 1/2$.

5. Let x and y be the dimensions shown in the figure and A the area, then $A = xy$ subject to the cost condition $3(2x) + 2(2y) = 6000$, or $y = 1500 - 3x/2$. Thus $A = x(1500 - 3x/2) = 1500x - 3x^2/2$ for x in $[0, 1000]$. $dA/dx = 1500 - 3x$, $dA/dx = 0$ when $x = 500$. If $x = 0$ or 1000 then $A = 0$, if $x = 500$ then $A = 375,000$ so the area is greatest when $x = 500$ ft and (from $y = 1500 - 3x/2$) when $y = 750$ ft.

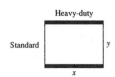
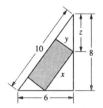

7. Let x, y, and z be as shown in the figure and A the area of the rectangle, then $A = xy$ and, by similar triangles, $z/10 = y/6$, $z = 5y/3$; also $x/10 = (8 - z)/8 = (8 - 5y/3)/8$ thus $y = 24/5 - 12x/25$ so $A = x(24/5 - 12x/25) = 24x/5 - 12x^2/25$ for x in $[0, 10]$. $dA/dx = 24/5 - 24x/25$, $dA/dx = 0$ when $x = 5$. If $x = 0, 5, 10$ then $A = 0, 12, 0$ so the area is greatest when $x = 5$ in. and $y = 12/5$ in.

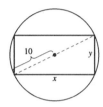

9. $A = xy$ where $x^2 + y^2 = 20^2 = 400$ so $y = \sqrt{400 - x^2}$ and $A = x\sqrt{400 - x^2}$ for $0 \le x \le 20$; $dA/dx = 2(200 - x^2)/\sqrt{400 - x^2}$, $dA/dx = 0$ when $x = \sqrt{200} = 10\sqrt{2}$. If $x = 0, 10\sqrt{2}, 20$ then $A = 0, 200, 0$ so the area is maximum when $x = 10\sqrt{2}$ and $y = \sqrt{400 - 200} = 10\sqrt{2}$.

11. Let $x = $ length of each side that uses the \$1 per foot fencing, $y = $ length of each side that uses the \$2 per foot fencing.

The cost is $C = (1)(2x) + (2)(2y) = 2x + 4y$, but $A = xy = 3200$ thus $y = 3200/x$ so
$$C = 2x + 12800/x \text{ for } x > 0,$$
$$dC/dx = 2 - 12800/x^2, \ dC/dx = 0 \text{ when } x = 80, \ d^2C/dx^2 > 0 \text{ so}$$

C is least when $x = 80$, $y = 40$.

13. Let x and y be the dimensions of a rectangle; the perimeter is $p = 2x + 2y$. But $A = xy$ thus $y = A/x$ so $p = 2x + 2A/x$ for $x > 0$, $dp/dx = 2 - 2A/x^2 = 2(x^2 - A)/x^2$, $dp/dx = 0$ when $x = \sqrt{A}$, $d^2p/dx^2 = 4A/x^3 > 0$ if $x > 0$ so p is a minimum when $x = \sqrt{A}$ and $y = \sqrt{A}$ and thus the rectangle is a square.

15. **(a)** $\dfrac{dN}{dt} = 250(20 - t)e^{-t/20} = 0$ at $t = 20$, $N(0) = 125000$, $N(20) \approx 161788$, and $N(100) \approx 128,369$; the absolute maximum is $N = 161788$ at $t = 20$, the absolute minimum is $N = 125000$ at $t = 0$.

(b) The absolute minimum of $\dfrac{dN}{dt}$ occurs when $\dfrac{d^2N}{dt^2} = 12.5(t - 40)e^{-t/20} = 0$, $t = 40$.

17. $V = x(12 - 2x)^2$ for $0 \le x \le 6$; $dV/dx = 12(x - 2)(x - 6)$, $dV/dx = 0$ when $x = 2$ for $0 < x < 6$. If $x = 0, 2, 6$ then $V = 0, 128, 0$ so the volume is largest when $x = 2$ in.

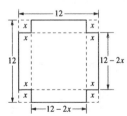

19. Let x be the length of each side of a square, then $V = x(3 - 2x)(8 - 2x) = 4x^3 - 22x^2 + 24x$ for $0 \le x \le 3/2$; $dV/dx = 12x^2 - 44x + 24 = 4(3x - 2)(x - 3)$, $dV/dx = 0$ when $x = 2/3$ for $0 < x < 3/2$. If $x = 0, 2/3, 3/2$ then $V = 0, 200/27, 0$ so the maximum volume is $200/27$ ft^3.

21. Let x = length of each edge of base, y = height, k = \$/cm^2 for the sides. The cost is
$C = (2k)(2x^2) + (k)(4xy) = 4k(x^2 + xy)$, but $V = x^2 y = 2000$ thus $y = 2000/x^2$ so
$C = 4k(x^2 + 2000/x)$ for $x > 0$ $dC/dx = 4k(2x - 2000/x^2)$, $dC/dx = 0$ when
$x = \sqrt[3]{1000} = 10$, $d^2C/dx^2 > 0$ so C is least when $x = 10$, $y = 20$.

23. Let x = height and width, y = length. The surface area is $S = 2x^2 + 3xy$ where $x^2 y = V$, so $y = V/x^2$
and $S = 2x^2 + 3V/x$ for $x > 0$; $dS/dx = 4x - 3V/x^2$, $dS/dx = 0$ when $x = \sqrt[3]{3V/4}$, $d^2S/dx^2 > 0$ so S
is minimum when $x = \sqrt[3]{\dfrac{3V}{4}}$, $y = \dfrac{4}{3}\sqrt[3]{\dfrac{3V}{4}}$.

25. Let r and h be the dimensions shown in the figure, then the surface
area is $S = 2\pi rh + 2\pi r^2$.

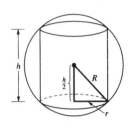

But $r^2 + \left(\dfrac{h}{2}\right)^2 = R^2$ thus $h = 2\sqrt{R^2 - r^2}$ so
$S = 4\pi r\sqrt{R^2 - r^2} + 2\pi r^2$ for $0 \le r \le R$,
$\dfrac{dS}{dr} = \dfrac{4\pi(R^2 - 2r^2)}{\sqrt{R^2 - r^2}} + 4\pi r$; $\dfrac{dS}{dr} = 0$ when

$$\dfrac{R^2 - 2r^2}{\sqrt{R^2 - r^2}} = -r \qquad\qquad \text{(i)}$$
$$R^2 - 2r^2 = -r\sqrt{R^2 - r^2}$$
$$R^4 - 4R^2 r^2 + 4r^4 = r^2(R^2 - r^2)$$
$$5r^4 - 5R^2 r^2 + R^4 = 0$$

and using the quadratic formula $r^2 = \dfrac{5R^2 \pm \sqrt{25R^4 - 20R^4}}{10} = \dfrac{5 \pm \sqrt{5}}{10}R^2$, $r = \sqrt{\dfrac{5 \pm \sqrt{5}}{10}}R$, of which

only $r = \sqrt{\dfrac{5 + \sqrt{5}}{10}}R$ satisfies (i). If $r = 0$, $\sqrt{\dfrac{5 + \sqrt{5}}{10}}R, 0$ then $S = 0, (5 + \sqrt{5})\pi R^2, 2\pi R^2$ so the surface

area is greatest when $r = \sqrt{\dfrac{5 + \sqrt{5}}{10}}R$ and, from $h = 2\sqrt{R^2 - r^2}$, $h = 2\sqrt{\dfrac{5 - \sqrt{5}}{10}}R$.

27. From (13), $S = 2\pi r^2 + 2\pi rh$. But $V = \pi r^2 h$ thus $h = V/(\pi r^2)$ and so $S = 2\pi r^2 + 2V/r$ for $r > 0$.
$dS/dr = 4\pi r - 2V/r^2$, $dS/dr = 0$ if $r = \sqrt[3]{V/(2\pi)}$. Since $d^2S/dr^2 = 4\pi + 4V/r^3 > 0$, the minimum
surface area is achieved when $r = \sqrt[3]{V/2\pi}$ and so $h = V/(\pi r^2) = [V/(\pi r^3)]r = 2r$.

29. The surface area is $S = \pi r^2 + 2\pi rh$ where $V = \pi r^2 h = 500$ so
$h = 500/(\pi r^2)$ and $S = \pi r^2 + 1000/r$ for $r > 0$;
$dS/dr = 2\pi r - 1000/r^2 = (2\pi r^3 - 1000)/r^2$, $dS/dr = 0$ when
$r = \sqrt[3]{500/\pi}$, $d^2S/dr^2 > 0$ for $r > 0$ so S is minimum when
$r = \sqrt[3]{500/\pi}$ and $h = \dfrac{500}{\pi r^2} = \dfrac{500}{\pi r^3} r = \dfrac{500}{\pi(500/\pi)}\sqrt[3]{500/\pi}$
$\qquad\qquad = \sqrt[3]{500/\pi}$.

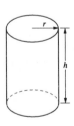

31. Let x be the length of each side of the squares and y the height of the frame, then the volume is $V = x^2 y$.
The total length of the wire is L thus $8x + 4y = L$, $y = (L - 8x)/4$ so $V = x^2(L - 8x)/4 = (Lx^2 - 8x^3)/4$
for $0 \le x \le L/8$. $dV/dx = (2Lx - 24x^2)/4$, $dV/dx = 0$ for $0 < x < L/8$ when $x = L/12$. If
$x = 0, L/12, L/8$ then $V = 0, L^3/1728, 0$ so the volume is greatest when $x = L/12$ and $y = L/12$.

33. Let h and r be the dimensions shown in the figure, then the volume is $V = \frac{1}{3}\pi r^2 h$. But $r^2 + h^2 = L^2$ thus $r^2 = L^2 - h^2$ so

$V = \frac{1}{3}\pi(L^2 - h^2)h = \frac{1}{3}\pi(L^2 h - h^3)$ for $0 \le h \le L$.

$\frac{dV}{dh} = \frac{1}{3}\pi(L^2 - 3h^2)$. $\frac{dV}{dh} = 0$ when $h = L/\sqrt{3}$. If $h = 0, L/\sqrt{3}, 0$

then $V = 0, \frac{2\pi}{9\sqrt{3}}L^3, 0$ so the volume is as large as possible when

$h = L/\sqrt{3}$ and $r = \sqrt{2/3}L$.

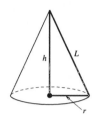

35. The area of the paper is $A = \pi r L = \pi r\sqrt{r^2 + h^2}$, but

$V = \frac{1}{3}\pi r^2 h = 10$ thus $h = 30/(\pi r^2)$ so $A = \pi r\sqrt{r^2 + 900/(\pi^2 r^4)}$.

To simplify the computations let $S = A^2$,

$S = \pi^2 r^2 \left(r^2 + \frac{900}{\pi^2 r^4}\right) = \pi^2 r^4 + \frac{900}{r^2}$ for $r > 0$,

$\frac{dS}{dr} = 4\pi^2 r^3 - \frac{1800}{r^3} = \frac{4(\pi^2 r^6 - 450)}{r^3}$, $dS/dr = 0$ when

$r = \sqrt[6]{450/\pi^2}$, $d^2 S/dr^2 > 0$, so S and hence A is least when

$r = \sqrt[6]{450/\pi^2}$, $h = \frac{30}{\pi}\sqrt[3]{\pi^2/450}$.

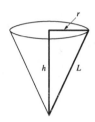

37. The volume of the cone is $V = \frac{1}{3}\pi r^2 h$. By similar triangles (see

figure) $\frac{r}{h} = \frac{R}{\sqrt{h^2 - 2Rh}}$, $r = \frac{Rh}{\sqrt{h^2 - 2Rh}}$ so

$V = \frac{1}{3}\pi R^2 \frac{h^3}{h^2 - 2Rh} = \frac{1}{3}\pi R^2 \frac{h^2}{h - 2R}$ for $h > 2R$,

$\frac{dV}{dh} = \frac{1}{3}\pi R^2 \frac{h(h - 4R)}{(h - 2R)^2}$, $\frac{dV}{dh} = 0$ for $h > 2R$ when $h = 4R$, by the

first derivative test V is minimum when $h = 4R$. If $h = 4R$ then

$r = \sqrt{2}R$.

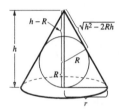

39. Let b and h be the dimensions shown in the figure, then the

cross-sectional area is $A = \frac{1}{2}h(5 + b)$. But $h = 5\sin\theta$ and

$b = 5 + 2(5\cos\theta) = 5 + 10\cos\theta$ so $A = \frac{5}{2}\sin\theta(10 + 10\cos\theta)$

$= 25\sin\theta(1 + \cos\theta)$ for $0 \le \theta \le \pi/2$.

$dA/d\theta = -25\sin^2\theta + 25\cos\theta(1 + \cos\theta)$

$= 25(-\sin^2\theta + \cos\theta + \cos^2\theta)$

$= 25(-1 + \cos^2\theta + \cos\theta + \cos^2\theta)$

$= 25(2\cos^2\theta + \cos\theta - 1) = 25(2\cos\theta - 1)(\cos\theta + 1)$.

$dA/d\theta = 0$ for $0 < \theta < \pi/2$ when $\cos\theta = 1/2$, $\theta = \pi/3$. If

$\theta = 0, \pi/3, \pi/2$ then $A = 0, 75\sqrt{3}/4, 25$ so the cross-sectional area is

greatest when $\theta = \pi/3$.

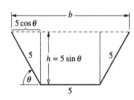

41. Let L, L_1, and L_2 be as shown in the figure, then
$L = L_1 + L_2 = 8\csc\theta + \sec\theta$,
$\dfrac{dL}{d\theta} = -8\csc\theta\cot\theta + \sec\theta\tan\theta$, $0 < \theta < \pi/2$

$= -\dfrac{8\cos\theta}{\sin^2\theta} + \dfrac{\sin\theta}{\cos^2\theta} = \dfrac{-8\cos^3\theta + \sin^3\theta}{\sin^2\theta\cos^2\theta}$;

$\dfrac{dL}{d\theta} = 0$ if $\sin^3\theta = 8\cos^3\theta$, $\tan^3\theta = 8$, $\tan\theta = 2$ which gives the
absolute minimum for L because $\lim\limits_{\theta\to 0^+} L = \lim\limits_{\theta\to\pi/2^-} L = +\infty$. If
$\tan\theta = 2$, then $\csc\theta = \sqrt{5}/2$ and $\sec\theta = \sqrt{5}$ so
$L = 8(\sqrt{5}/2) + \sqrt{5} = 5\sqrt{5}$ ft.

43. **(a)** The daily profit is

$P = $ (revenue) $-$ (production cost) $= 100x - (100,000 + 50x + 0.0025x^2)$
$= -100,000 + 50x - 0.0025x^2$

for $0 \le x \le 7000$, so $dP/dx = 50 - 0.005x$ and $dP/dx = 0$ when $x = 10,000$. Because 10,000 is not in the interval $[0, 7000]$, the maximum profit must occur at an endpoint. When $x = 0$, $P = -100,000$; when $x = 7000$, $P = 127,500$ so 7000 units should be manufactured and sold daily.

(b) Yes, because $dP/dx > 0$ when $x = 7000$ so profit is increasing at this production level.

45. The profit is

$P = $ (profit on nondefective) $-$ (loss on defective) $= 100(x - y) - 20y = 100x - 120y$

but $y = 0.01x + 0.00003x^2$ so $P = 100x - 120(0.01x + 0.00003x^2) = 98.8x - 0.0036x^2$ for $x > 0$, $dP/dx = 98.8 - 0.0072x$, $dP/dx = 0$ when $x = 98.8/0.0072 \approx 13,722$, $d^2P/dx^2 < 0$ so the profit is maximum at a production level of about 13,722 pounds.

47. The distance between the particles is $D = \sqrt{(1 - t - t)^2 + (t - 2t)^2} = \sqrt{5t^2 - 4t + 1}$ for $t \ge 0$. For convenience, we minimize D^2 instead, so $D^2 = 5t^2 - 4t + 1$, $dD^2/dt = 10t - 4$, which is 0 when $t = 2/5$. $d^2D^2/dt^2 > 0$ so D^2 and hence D is minimum when $t = 2/5$. The minimum distance is $D = 1/\sqrt{5}$.

49. Let $P(x, y)$ be a point on the curve $x^2 + y^2 = 1$. The distance between $P(x, y)$ and $P_0(2, 0)$ is $D = \sqrt{(x - 2)^2 + y^2}$, but $y^2 = 1 - x^2$ so $D = \sqrt{(x - 2)^2 + 1 - x^2} = \sqrt{5 - 4x}$ for $-1 \le x \le 1$, $\dfrac{dD}{dx} = -\dfrac{2}{\sqrt{5 - 4x}}$ which has no critical points for $-1 < x < 1$. If $x = -1, 1$ then $D = 3, 1$ so the closest point occurs when $x = 1$ and $y = 0$.

51. Let (x, y) be a point on the curve, then the square of the distance between (x, y) and $(0, 2)$ is $S = x^2 + (y - 2)^2$ where $x^2 - y^2 = 1$, $x^2 = y^2 + 1$ so
$S = (y^2 + 1) + (y - 2)^2 = 2y^2 - 4y + 5$ for any y, $dS/dy = 4y - 4$, $dS/dy = 0$ when $y = 1$,
$d^2S/dy^2 > 0$ so S is least when $y = 1$ and $x = \pm\sqrt{2}$.

53. If $P(x_0, y_0)$ is on the curve $y = 1/x^2$, then $y_0 = 1/x_0^2$. At P the slope of the tangent line is $-2/x_0^3$ so its equation is $y - \dfrac{1}{x_0^2} = -\dfrac{2}{x_0^3}(x - x_0)$, or $y = -\dfrac{2}{x_0^3}x + \dfrac{3}{x_0^2}$. The tangent line crosses the y-axis at $\dfrac{3}{x_0^2}$, and

the x-axis at $\dfrac{3}{2}x_0$. The length of the segment then is $L = \sqrt{\dfrac{9}{x_0^4} + \dfrac{9}{4}x_0^2}$ for $x_0 > 0$. For convenience,

we minimize L^2 instead, so $L^2 = \dfrac{9}{x_0^4} + \dfrac{9}{4}x_0^2$, $\dfrac{dL^2}{dx_0} = -\dfrac{36}{x_0^5} + \dfrac{9}{2}x_0 = \dfrac{9(x_0^6 - 8)}{2x_0^5}$, which is 0 when $x_0^6 = 8$,

$x_0 = \sqrt{2}$. $\dfrac{d^2L^2}{dx_0^2} > 0$ so L^2 and hence L is minimum when $x_0 = \sqrt{2}$, $y_0 = 1/2$.

55. At each point (x, y) on the curve the slope of the tangent line is $m = \dfrac{dy}{dx} = -\dfrac{2x}{(1+x^2)^2}$ for any x,

$\dfrac{dm}{dx} = \dfrac{2(3x^2 - 1)}{(1+x^2)^3}$, $\dfrac{dm}{dx} = 0$ when $x = \pm 1/\sqrt{3}$, by the first derivative test the only relative maximum

occurs at $x = -1/\sqrt{3}$, which is the absolute maximum because $\lim\limits_{x \to \pm\infty} m = 0$. The tangent line has

greatest slope at the point $(-1/\sqrt{3}, 3/4)$.

57. With x and y as shown in the figure, the maximum length of pipe
will be the smallest value of $L = x + y$. By similar triangles
$\dfrac{y}{8} = \dfrac{x}{\sqrt{x^2 - 16}}$, $y = \dfrac{8x}{\sqrt{x^2 - 16}}$ so

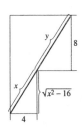

$L = x + \dfrac{8x}{\sqrt{x^2 - 16}}$ for $x > 4$, $\dfrac{dL}{dx} = 1 - \dfrac{128}{(x^2 - 16)^{3/2}}$, $\dfrac{dL}{dx} = 0$ when

$(x^2 - 16)^{3/2} = 128$
$\qquad x^2 - 16 = 128^{2/3} = 16(2^{2/3})$
$\qquad\qquad x^2 = 16(1 + 2^{2/3})$
$\qquad\qquad\ x = 4(1 + 2^{2/3})^{1/2}$,

$d^2L/dx^2 = 384x/(x^2 - 16)^{5/2} > 0$ if $x > 4$ so L is smallest when $x = 4(1 + 2^{2/3})^{1/2}$.
For this value of x, $L = 4(1 + 2^{2/3})^{3/2}$ ft.

59. Let $x =$ distance from the weaker light source, $I =$ the intensity at that point, and k the constant of
proportionality. Then

$I = \dfrac{kS}{x^2} + \dfrac{8kS}{(90 - x)^2}$ if $0 < x < 90$;

$\dfrac{dI}{dx} = -\dfrac{2kS}{x^3} + \dfrac{16kS}{(90 - x)^3} = \dfrac{2kS[8x^3 - (90 - x)^3]}{x^3(90 - x)^3} = 18\dfrac{kS(x - 30)(x^2 + 2700)}{x^3(x - 90)^3}$,

which is 0 when $x = 30$; $\dfrac{dI}{dx} < 0$ if $x < 30$, and $\dfrac{dI}{dx} > 0$ if $x > 30$, so the intensity is minimum at a

distance of 30 cm from the weaker source.

61. Let $v =$ speed of light in the medium. The total time required for the light to travel from A to P to
B is

$t = (\text{total distance from } A \text{ to } P \text{ to } B)/v = \dfrac{1}{v}(\sqrt{(c - x)^2 + a^2} + \sqrt{x^2 + b^2})$,

$\dfrac{dt}{dx} = \dfrac{1}{v}\left[-\dfrac{c - x}{\sqrt{(c - x)^2 + a^2}} + \dfrac{x}{\sqrt{x^2 + b^2}} \right]$

and $\dfrac{dt}{dx} = 0$ when $\dfrac{x}{\sqrt{x^2 + b^2}} = \dfrac{c - x}{\sqrt{(c - x)^2 + a^2}}$. But $x/\sqrt{x^2 + b^2} = \sin\theta_2$ and

$(c - x)/\sqrt{(c - x)^2 + a^2} = \sin\theta_1$ thus $dt/dx = 0$ when $\sin\theta_2 = \sin\theta_1$ so $\theta_2 = \theta_1$.

63. **(a)** The rate at which the farmer walks is analogous to the speed of light in Fermat's principle.

    (b) the best path occurs when $\theta_1 = \theta_2$ **(c)** by similar triangles,
        (see figure). $x/(1/4) = (1 - x)/(3/4)$
                                                                 $3x = 1 - x$
                                                                        $4x = 1$
                                                                      $x = 1/4$ mi.

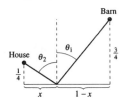

EXERCISE SET 6.3

1. **(a)** positive, negative, slowing down   **(b)** positive, positive, speeding up
   (c) negative, positive, slowing down

3. **(a)** left because $v = ds/dt < 0$ at t_0

   (b) negative because $a = d^2s/dt^2$ and the curve is concave down at $t_0 (d^2s/dt^2 < 0)$

   (c) speeding up because v and a have the same sign

   (d) $v < 0$ and $a > 0$ at t_1 so the particle is slowing down because v and a have opposite signs.

5.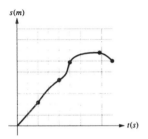

7.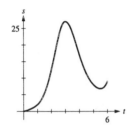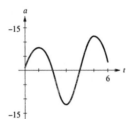

9. **(a)** At 60 mi/h the slope of the estimated tangent line is about 4.6 mi/h/s. Use 1 mi $= 5,280$ ft and 1 h $= 3600$ s to get $a = dv/dt \approx 4.6(5{,}280)/(3600) \approx 6.7$ ft/s^2.

   (b) The slope of the tangent to the curve is maximum at $t = 0$ s.

11. **(a)** $v(t) = 3t^2 - 12t$, $a(t) = 6t - 12$

    (b) $s(1) = -5$ ft, $v(1) = -9$ ft/s, speed $= 9$ ft/s, $a(1) = -6$ ft/s^2

    (c) $v = 0$ at $t = 0, 4$

    (d) for $t \geq 0$, $v(t)$ changes sign at $t = 4$, and $a(t)$ changes sign at $t = 2$; so the particle is speeding up for $0 < t < 2$ and $4 < t$ and is slowing down for $2 < t < 4$

    (e) total distance $= |s(4) - s(0)| + |s(5) - s(4)| = |-32 - 0| + |-25 - (-32)| = 39$ ft

13. **(a)** $v(t) = -(3\pi/2)\sin(\pi t/2)$, $a(t) = -(3\pi^2/4)\cos(\pi t/2)$

    (b) $s(1) = 0$ ft, $v(1) = -3\pi/2$ ft/s, speed $= 3\pi/2$ ft/s, $a(1) = 0$ ft/s^2

    (c) $v = 0$ at $t = 0, 2, 4$

    (d) v changes sign at $t = 0, 2, 4$ and a changes sign at $t = 1, 3, 5$, so the particle is speeding up for $0 < t < 1$, $2 < t < 3$ and $4 < t < 5$, and it is slowing down for $1 < t < 2$ and $3 < t < 4$

    (e) total distance $= |s(2) - s(0)| + |s(4) - s(2)| + |s(5) - s(4)|$
    $$= |-3 - 3| + |3 - (-3)| + |0 - 3| = 15 \text{ ft}$$

15. $v(t) = \dfrac{5 - t^2}{(t^2 + 5)^2}$, $a(t) = \dfrac{2t(t^2 - 15)}{(t^2 + 5)^3}$

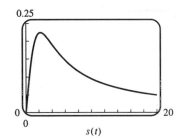

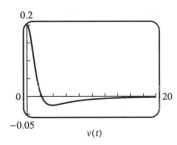

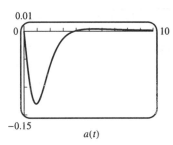

$s(t)$ $v(t)$ $a(t)$

(a) $v = 0$ at $t = \sqrt{5}$ **(b)** $s = \sqrt{5}/10$ at $t = \sqrt{5}$

(c) a changes sign at $t = \sqrt{15}$, so the particle is speeding up for $\sqrt{5} < t < \sqrt{15}$ and slowing down for $0 < t < \sqrt{5}$ and $\sqrt{15} < t$

17. $s = -3t + 2$
$v = -3$
$a = 0$

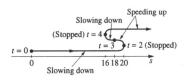

19. $s = t^3 - 9t^2 + 24t$
$v = 3(t - 2)(t - 4)$
$a = 6(t - 3)$

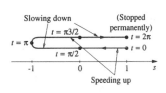

21. $s = \begin{cases} \cos t, & 0 \le t \le 2\pi \\ 1, & t > 2\pi \end{cases}$

$v = \begin{cases} -\sin t, & 0 \le t \le 2\pi \\ 0, & t > 2\pi \end{cases}$

$a = \begin{cases} -\cos t, & 0 \le t < 2\pi \\ 0, & t > 2\pi \end{cases}$

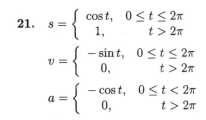

23.   **(a)** $v = 10t - 22$, speed $= |v| = |10t - 22|$. $d|v|/dt$ does not exist at $t = 2.2$ which is the only critical point. If $t = 1, 2.2, 3$ then $|v| = 12, 0, 8$. The maximum speed is 12 ft/s.

     (b)   the distance from the origin is $|s| = |5t^2 - 22t| = |t(5t - 22)|$, but $t(5t - 22) < 0$ for $1 \le t \le 3$ so $|s| = -(5t^2 - 22t) = 22t - 5t^2$, $d|s|/dt = 22 - 10t$, thus the only critical point is $t = 2.2$. $d^2|s|/dt^2 < 0$ so the particle is farthest from the origin when $t = 2.2$. Its position is $s = 5(2.2)^2 - 22(2.2) = -24.2$.

25. $s(t) = s_0 - \frac{1}{2}gt^2 = s_0 - 4.9t^2$ m, $v = -9.8t$ m/s, $a = -9.8$ m/s^2

     (a) $|s(1.5) - s(0)| = 11.025$ m

     (b) $v(1.5) = -14.7$ m/s

     (c) $|v(t)| = 12$ when $t = 12/9.8 = 1.2245$ s

     (d) $s(t) - s_0 = -100$ when $4.9t^2 = 100$, $t = 4.5175$ s

27. $s(t) = s_0 + v_0 t - \frac{1}{2}gt^2 = 60t - 4.9t^2$ m and $v(t) = v_0 - gt = 60 - 9.8t$ m/s

     (a) $v(t) = 0$ when $t = 60/9.8 \approx 6.12$ s

     (b) $s(60/9.8) \approx 183.67$ m

(c) another 6.12 s; solve for t in $s(t) = 0$ to get this result, or use the symmetry of the parabola $s = 60t - 4.9t^2$ about the line $t = 6.12$ in the t-s plane

(d) also 60 m/s, as seen from the symmetry of the parabola (or compute $v(6.12)$)

29. If $g = 32$ ft/s^2, $s_0 = 7$ and v_0 is unknown, then $s(t) = 7 + v_0 t - 16t^2$ and $v(t) = v_0 - 32t$; $s = s_{\max}$ when $v = 0$, or $t = v_0/32$; and $s_{\max} = 208$ yields $208 = s(v_0/32) = 7 + v_0(v_0/32) - 16(v_0/32)^2 = 7 + v_0^2/64$, so $v_0 = 8\sqrt{201} \approx 113.42$ ft/s.

31. $v_0 = 0$ and $g = 9.8$, so $v^2 = -19.6(s - s_0)$; since $v = 24$ when $s = 0$ it follows that $19.6 s_0 = 24^2$ or $s_0 = 29.39$ m.

33. (a) $s = s_{\max}$ when $v = 0$, so $0 = v_0^2 - 2g(s_{\max} - s_0)$, $s_{\max} = v_0^2/2g + s_0$.

    (b) $s_0 = 7$, $s_{\max} = 208$, $g = 32$ and v_0 is unknown, so from part (a) $v_0^2 = 2g(208 - 7) = 64 \cdot 201$, $v_0 = 8\sqrt{201} \approx 113.42$ ft/s.

35. (a)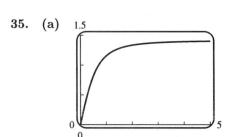

    (b) $v = \dfrac{2t}{\sqrt{2t^2 + 1}}$, $\displaystyle\lim_{t \to +\infty} v = \dfrac{2}{\sqrt{2}} = \sqrt{2}$

37. (a) $s_1 = s_2$ if they collide, so $\dfrac{1}{2}t^2 - t + 3 = -\dfrac{1}{4}t^2 + t + 1$, $\dfrac{3}{4}t^2 - 2t + 2 = 0$ which has no real solution.

    (b) Find the minimum value of $D = |s_1 - s_2| = \left|\frac{3}{4}t^2 - 2t + 2\right|$. From part (a), $\dfrac{3}{4}t^2 - 2t + 2$ is never zero, and for $t = 0$ it is positive, hence it is always positive, so $D = \dfrac{3}{4}t^2 - 2t + 2$.

    $\dfrac{dD}{dt} = \dfrac{3}{2}t - 2 = 0$ when $t = \dfrac{4}{3}$. $\dfrac{d^2D}{dt^2} > 0$ so D is minimum when $t = \dfrac{4}{3}$, $D = \dfrac{2}{3}$.

    (c) $v_1 = t - 1$, $v_2 = -\dfrac{1}{2}t + 1$. $v_1 < 0$ if $0 \le t < 1$, $v_1 > 0$ if $t > 1$; $v_2 < 0$ if $t > 2$, $v_2 > 0$ if $0 \le t < 2$. They are moving in opposite directions during the intervals $0 \le t < 1$ and $t > 2$.

39. (a) From the estimated tangent to the graph at the point where $v = 2000$, $dv/ds \approx -1.25$ ft/s/ft.

    (b) $a = v\,dv/ds \approx (2000)(-1.25) = -2500$ ft/s^2

EXERCISE SET 6.4

1. $f(x) = x^2 - 2$, $f'(x) = 2x$, $x_{n+1} = x_n - \dfrac{x_n^2 - 2}{2x_n}$

   $x_1 = 1$, $x_2 = 1.5$, $x_3 = 1.416666667, \cdots$, $x_5 = x_6 = 1.414213562$

3. $f(x) = x^3 - 6$, $f'(x) = 3x^2$, $x_{n+1} = x_n - \dfrac{x_n^3 - 6}{3x_n^2}$

   $x_1 = 2$, $x_2 = 1.833333333$, $x_3 = 1.817263545, \cdots$, $x_5 = x_6 = 1.817120593$

5. $f(x) = x^3 - x + 3$, $f'(x) = 3x^2 - 1$, $x_{n+1} = x_n - \dfrac{x_n^3 - x_n + 3}{3x_n^2 - 1}$

   $x_1 = -2$, $x_2 = -1.727272727$, $x_3 = -1.673691174, \cdots$, $x_5 = x_6 = -1.671699882$

7. $f(x) = x^5 + x^4 - 5$, $f'(x) = 5x^4 + 4x^3$, $x_{n+1} = x_n - \dfrac{x_n^5 + x_n^4 - 5}{5x_n^4 + 4x_n^3}$

$x_1 = 1$, $x_2 = 1.333333333$, $x_3 = 1.239420573, \cdots, x_6 = x_7 = 1.224439550$

9. $f(x) = x^4 + x - 3$, $f'(x) = 4x^3 + 1$, $x_{n+1} = x_n - \dfrac{x_n^4 + x_n - 3}{4x_n^3 + 1}$

$x_1 = -2$, $x_2 = -1.645161290$,
$x_3 = -1.485723955, \cdots, x_6 = x_7 = -1.452626879$

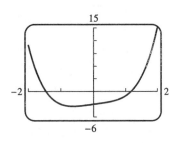

11. $f(x) = 2\sin x - x$, $f'(x) = 2\cos x - 1$, $x_{n+1} = x_n - \dfrac{2\sin x_n - x_n}{2\cos x_n - 1}$

$x_1 = 2$, $x_2 = 1.900995594$, $x_3 = 1.895511645$, $x_4 = x_5 = 1.895494267$

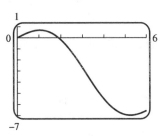

13. $f(x) = x - \tan x$, $f'(x) = 1 - \sec^2 x = -\tan^2 x$,

$x_{n+1} = x_n + \dfrac{x_n - \tan x_n}{\tan^2 x_n}$

$x_1 = 4.5$, $x_2 = 4.493613903$, $x_3 = 4.493409655$,
$x_4 = x_5 = 4.493409458$

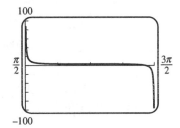

15. At the point of intersection, $x^3 = 0.5x - 1$, $x^3 - 0.5x + 1 = 0$. Let
$f(x) = x^3 - 0.5x + 1$. By graphing $y = x^3$ and $y = 0.5x - 1$ it is
evident that there is only one point of intersection and it occurs in
the interval $[-2, -1]$; note that $f(-2) < 0$ and $f(-1) > 0$.
$f'(x) = 3x^2 - 0.5$ so

$x_{n+1} = x_n - \dfrac{x_n^3 - 0.5x_n + 1}{3x_n^2 - 0.5}$; $x_1 = -1$, $x_2 = -1.2$,

$x_3 = -1.166492147, \cdots$,
$x_5 = x_6 = -1.165373043$

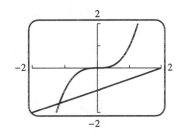

17. The graphs of $y = x^2$ and $y = \sqrt{2x + 1}$ intersect at points near
$x = -0.5$ and $x = 1$; $x^2 = \sqrt{2x + 1}$, $x^4 - 2x - 1 = 0$. Let
$f(x) = x^4 - 2x - 1$, then $f'(x) = 4x^3 - 2$ so

$x_{n+1} = x_n - \dfrac{x_n^4 - 2x_n - 1}{4x_n^3 - 2}$.

If $x_1 = -0.5$, then $x_2 = -0.475$, $x_3 = -0.474626695$,
$x_4 = x_5 = -0.474626618$; if $x_1 = 1$, then $x_2 = 2$,
$x_3 = 1.633333333, \cdots, x_8 = x_9 = 1.395336994$.

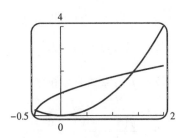

19. **(a)** $f(x) = x^2 - a$, $f'(x) = 2x$, $x_{n+1} = x_n - \dfrac{x_n^2 - a}{2x_n} = \dfrac{1}{2}\left(x_n + \dfrac{a}{x_n}\right)$

(b) $a = 10$; $x_1 = 3$, $x_2 = 3.166666667$, $x_3 = 3.162280702$, $x_4 = x_5 = 3.162277660$

21. $f'(x) = x^3 + 2x + 5$; solve $f'(x) = 0$ to find the critical points. Graph $y = x^3$ and $y = -2x - 5$ to see that they intersect at a point near $x = -1$; $f''(x) = 3x^2 + 2$ so $x_{n+1} = x_n - \dfrac{x_n^3 + 2x_n + 5}{3x_n^2 + 2}$.

$x_1 = -1$, $x_2 = -1.4$, $x_3 = -1.330964467, \cdots, x_5 = x_6 = -1.328268856$ so the minimum value of $f(x)$ occurs at $x \approx -1.328268856$ because $f''(x) > 0$; its value is approximately -4.098859132.

23. Let $f(x)$ be the square of the distance between $(1, 0)$ and any point (x, x^2) on the parabola, then $f(x) = (x-1)^2 + (x^2 - 0)^2 = x^4 + x^2 - 2x + 1$ and $f'(x) = 4x^3 + 2x - 2$. Solve $f'(x) = 0$ to find the critical points; $f''(x) = 12x^2 + 2$ so $x_{n+1} = x_n - \dfrac{4x_n^3 + 2x_n - 2}{12x_n^2 + 2} = x_n - \dfrac{2x_n^3 + x_n - 1}{6x_n^2 + 1}$. $x_1 = 1$, $x_2 = 0.714285714$, $x_3 = 0.605168701, \cdots, x_6 = x_7 = 0.589754512$; the coordinates are approximately $(0.589754512, 0.347810385)$.

25. **(a)** Let s be the arc length, and L the length of the chord, then $s = 1.5L$. But $s = r\theta$ and $L = 2r\sin(\theta/2)$ so $r\theta = 3r\sin(\theta/2)$, $\theta - 3\sin(\theta/2) = 0$.

(b) Let $f(\theta) = \theta - 3\sin(\theta/2)$, then $f'(\theta) = 1 - 1.5\cos(\theta/2)$ so $\theta_{n+1} = \theta_n - \dfrac{\theta_n - 3\sin(\theta_n/2)}{1 - 1.5\cos(\theta_n/2)}$.

$\theta_1 = 3$, $\theta_2 = 2.991592920$, $\theta_3 = 2.991563137$, $\theta_4 = \theta_5 = 2.991563136$ rad so $\theta \approx 171°$.

27. If $x = 1$, then $y^4 + y = 1$, $y^4 + y - 1 = 0$. Graph $z = y^4$ and $z = 1 - y$ to see that they intersect near $y = -1$ and $y = 1$. Let $f(y) = y^4 + y - 1$, then $f'(y) = 4y^3 + 1$ so $y_{n+1} = y_n - \dfrac{y_n^4 + y_n - 1}{4y_n^3 + 1}$.

If $y_1 = -1$, then $y_2 = -1.333333333$, $y_3 = -1.235807860, \cdots, y_6 = y_7 = -1.220744085$;

if $y_1 = 1$, then $y_2 = 0.8$, $y_3 = 0.731233596, \cdots, y_6 = y_7 = 0.724491959$.

29. $S(25) = 250000 = \dfrac{5000}{i}\left[(1+i)^{25} - 1\right]$; set $f(i) = 50i - (1+i)^{25} + 1$, $f'(i) = 50 - 25(1+i)^{24}$; solve $f(i) = 0$. Set $i_0 = .06$ and $i_{k+1} = i_k - \left[50i - (1+i)^{25} + 1\right] / \left[50 - 25(1+i)^{24}\right]$. Then $i_1 = 0.05430$, $i_2 = 0.05338$, $i_3 = 0.05336, \cdots, i = 0.053362$.

(b) $x_1 = 0.5$, $x_2 = -0.3333$, $x_3 = 0.0833$, $x_4 = -0.0012$, $x_5 = 0.0000$ (and $x_n = 0$ for $n \geq 6$)

31. **(a)**

x_1	x_2	x_3	x_4	x_5	x_6	x_7	x_8	x_9	x_{10}
0.5000	−0.7500	0.2917	−1.5685	−0.4654	0.8415	−0.1734	2.7970	1.2197	0.1999

(b) The sequence x_n must diverge, since if it did converge then $f(x) = x^2 + 1 = 0$ would have a solution. It seems the x_n are oscillating back and forth in a quasi-cyclical fashion.

EXERCISE SET 6.5

1. $f(0) = f(4) = 0$; $f'(3) = 0$; $[0, 4]$, $c = 3$

3. $f(2) = f(4) = 0$, $f'(x) = 2x - 6$, $2c - 6 = 0$, $c = 3$

5. $f(\pi/2) = f(3\pi/2) = 0$, $f'(x) = -\sin x$, $-\sin c = 0$, $c = \pi$

7. $f(0) = f(4) = 0$, $f'(x) = \dfrac{1}{2} - \dfrac{1}{2\sqrt{x}}$, $\dfrac{1}{2} - \dfrac{1}{2\sqrt{c}} = 0$, $c = 1$

9. $\dfrac{f(8) - f(0)}{8 - 0} = \dfrac{6}{8} = \dfrac{3}{4} = f'(1.54)$; $c = 1.54$

11. $f(-4) = 12$, $f(6) = 42$, $f'(x) = 2x + 1$, $2c + 1 = \dfrac{42 - 12}{6 - (-4)} = 3$, $c = 1$

13. $f(0) = 1$, $f(3) = 2$, $f'(x) = \dfrac{1}{2\sqrt{x+1}}$, $\dfrac{1}{2\sqrt{c+1}} = \dfrac{2-1}{3-0} = \dfrac{1}{3}$, $\sqrt{c+1} = 3/2$, $c+1 = 9/4$, $c = 5/4$

15. $f(-5) = 0$, $f(3) = 4$, $f'(x) = -\dfrac{x}{\sqrt{25-x^2}}$, $-\dfrac{c}{\sqrt{25-c^2}} = \dfrac{4-0}{3-(-5)} = \dfrac{1}{2}$, $-2c = \sqrt{25-c^2}$,

$4c^2 = 25 - c^2$, $c^2 = 5$, $c = -\sqrt{5}$

(we reject $c = \sqrt{5}$ because it does not satisfy the equation $-2c = \sqrt{25-c^2}$)

17. **(a)** $f(-2) = f(1) = 0$ **(b)** $c = -1.29$

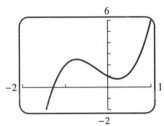

      (c) $x_0 = -1$, $x_1 = -1.5$, $x_2 = -1.32$, $x_3 = -1.290$, $x_4 = -1.2885843$

19. **(a)** $f'(x) = \sec^2 x$, $\sec^2 c = 0$ has no solution   **(b)** $\tan x$ is not continuous on $[0, \pi]$

21. **(a)** Two x-intercepts of f determine two solutions a and b of $f(x) = 0$; by Rolle's Theorem there exists a point c between a and b such that $f'(c) = 0$, i.e. c is an x-intercept for f'.

      (b) $f(x) = \sin x = 0$ at $x = n\pi$, and $f'(x) = \cos x = 0$ at $x = n\pi + \pi/2$, which lies between $n\pi$ and $(n+1)\pi$, $(n = 0, \pm 1, \pm 2, \ldots)$

23. Let $s(t)$ be the position function of the automobile for $0 \leq t \leq 5$, then by the Mean-Value Theorem there is at least one point c in $(0, 5)$ where

$$s'(c) = v(c) = [s(5) - s(0)]/(5-0) = 4/5 = 0.8 \text{ mi/min} = 48 \text{ mi/h}.$$

25. Let $f(t)$ and $g(t)$ denote the distances from the first and second runners to the starting point, and let $h(t) = f(t) - g(t)$. Since they start (at $t = 0$) and finish (at $t = t_1$) at the same time, $h(0) = h(t_1) = 0$, so by Rolle's Theorem there is a time t_2 for which $h'(t_2) = 0$, i.e. $f'(t_2) = g'(t_2)$; so they have the same velocity at time t_2.

27. **(a)** By the Constant Difference Theorem $f(x) - g(x) = k$ for some k; since $f(x_0) = g(x_0)$, $k = 0$, so $f(x) = g(x)$ for all x.

      (b) Set $f(x) = \sin^2 x + \cos^2 x$, $g(x) = 1$; then $f'(x) = 2\sin x \cos x - 2\cos x \sin x = 0 = g'(x)$. Since $f(0) = 1 = g(0)$, $f(x) = g(x)$ for all x.

29. **(a)** If x, y belong to I and $x < y$ then for some c in I, $\dfrac{f(y) - f(x)}{y - x} = f'(c)$,

      so $|f(x) - f(y)| = |f'(c)||x - y| \leq M|x - y|$; if $x > y$ exchange x and y; if $x = y$ the inequality also holds.

      (b) $f(x) = \sin x$, $f'(x) = \cos x$, $|f'(x)| \leq 1 = M$, so $|f(x) - f(y)| \leq |x - y|$ or $|\sin x - \sin y| \leq |x - y|$.

31. **(a)** Let $f(x) = \sqrt{x}$. By the Mean-Value Theorem there is a number c between x and y such that

$$\frac{\sqrt{y} - \sqrt{x}}{y - x} = \frac{1}{2\sqrt{c}} < \frac{1}{2\sqrt{x}} \text{ for } c \text{ in } (x, y), \text{ thus } \sqrt{y} - \sqrt{x} < \frac{y - x}{2\sqrt{x}}$$

      (b) multiply through and rearrange to get $\sqrt{xy} < \dfrac{1}{2}(x + y)$.

33. **(a)** If $f(x) = x^3 + 4x - 1$ then $f'(x) = 3x^2 + 4$ is never zero, so by Exercise 32 f has at most one real root; since f is a cubic polynomial it has at least one real root, so it has exactly one real root.

(b) Let $f(x) = ax^3 + bx^2 + cx + d$. If $f(x) = 0$ has at least two distinct real solutions r_1 and r_2, then $f(r_1) = f(r_2) = 0$ and by Rolle's Theorem there is at least one number between r_1 and r_2 where $f'(x) = 0$. But $f'(x) = 3ax^2 + 2bx + c = 0$ for

$x = (-2b \pm \sqrt{4b^2 - 12ac})/(6a) = (-b \pm \sqrt{b^2 - 3ac})/(3a)$, which are not real if $b^2 - 3ac < 0$

so $f(x) = 0$ must have fewer than two distinct real solutions.

35. **(a)** $\dfrac{d}{dx}[f^2(x) + g^2(x)] = 2f(x)f'(x) + 2g(x)g'(x) = 2f(x)g(x) + 2g(x)[-f(x)] = 0$,

so $f^2(x) + g^2(x)$ is constant.

(b) $f(x) = \sin x$ and $g(x) = \cos x$

37. If $f'(x) = g'(x)$, then $f(x) = g(x) + k$. Let $x = 1$,

$f(1) = g(1) + k = (1)^3 - 4(1) + 6 + k = 3 + k = 2$, so $k = -1$. $f(x) = x^3 - 4x + 5$.

39.

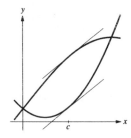

41. similar to the proof of part (a) with $f'(c) < 0$

CHAPTER 6 SUPPLEMENTARY EXERCISES

3. **(a)** If f has an absolute extremum at a point of (a, b) then it must, by Theorem 6.1.4, be at a critical point of f; since f is differentiable on (a, b) the critical point is a stationary point.

(b) It could occur at a critical point which is not a stationary point: for example, $f(x) = |x|$ on $[-1, 1]$ has an absolute minimum at $x = 0$ but is not differentiable there.

5. Yes; by the Mean Value Theorem there is a point c in (a, b) such that $f'(c) = \dfrac{f(b) - f(a)}{b - a} = 0$.

7. **(a)** $f'(x) = -1/x^2 \neq 0$, no critical points; by inspection $M = -1/2$ at $x = -2$; $m = -1$ at $x = -1$

(b) $f'(x) = 3x^2 - 4x^3 = 0$ at $x = 0, 3/4$; $f(-1) = -2, f(0) = 0, f(3/4) = 27/256, f(3/2) = -27/16$, so $m = -2$ at $x = -1$, $M = 27/256$ at $x = 3/4$

(c) $f'(x) = \dfrac{x(7x - 12)}{3(x - 2)^{2/3}}$, critical points at $x = 12/7, 2$; $m = f(12/7) = \dfrac{144}{49}\left(-\dfrac{2}{7}\right)^{1/3} \approx -1.9356$ at $x = 12/7$, $M = 9$ at $x = 3$

(d) $\lim\limits_{x \to 0^+} f(x) = \lim\limits_{x \to +\infty} f(x) = +\infty$ and $f'(x) = \dfrac{e^x(x - 2)}{x^3}$, stationary point at $x = 2$; by Theorem 6.1.5 $f(x)$ has an absolute minimum at $x = 2$, and $m = e^2/4$.

9. $x = 2.3561945$

11. **(a)** yes; $f'(0) = 0$ **(b)** no, f is not differentiable on $(-1, 1)$

(c) yes, $f'(\sqrt{\pi/2}) = 0$

13. Let k be the amount of light admitted per unit area of clear glass. The total amount of light admitted by the entire window is

$$T = k \cdot \text{(area of clear glass)} + \frac{1}{2}k \cdot \text{(area of blue glass)} = 2krh + \frac{1}{4}\pi kr^2.$$

But $P = 2h + 2r + \pi r$ which gives $2h = P - 2r - \pi r$ so

$$T = kr(P - 2r - \pi r) + \frac{1}{4}\pi kr^2 = k\left[Pr - \left(2 + \pi - \frac{\pi}{4}\right)r^2\right]$$

$$= k\left[Pr - \frac{8 + 3\pi}{4}r^2\right] \text{ for } 0 < r < \frac{P}{2 + \pi},$$

$$\frac{dT}{dr} = k\left(P - \frac{8 + 3\pi}{2}r\right), \frac{dT}{dr} = 0 \text{ when } r = \frac{2P}{8 + 3\pi}.$$

This is the only critical point and $d^2T/dr^2 < 0$ there so the most light is admitted when $r = 2P/(8 + 3\pi)$ ft.

15. **(a)** If $a = k$, a constant, then $v = kt + b$ where b is constant; so the velocity changes sign at $t = -b/k$.

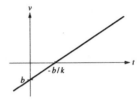

(b) Consider the equation $s = 5 - t^3/6$, $v = -t^2/2$, $a = -t$. Then for $t > 0$, a is decreasing and $av > 0$, so the particle is speeding up.

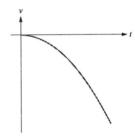

17. **(a)** $s(t) = s_0 + v_0t - \frac{1}{2}gt^2 = v_0t - 4.9t^2$, $v(t) = v_0 - 9.8t$; s_{max} occurs when $v = 0$, i.e. $t = v_0/9.8$, and then $0.76 = s_{max} = v_0(v_0/9.8) - 4.9(v_0/9.8)^2 = v_0^2/19.6$, so $v_0 = \sqrt{0.76 \cdot 19.6} = 3.86$ m/s and $s(t) = 3.86t - 4.9t^2$. Then $s(t) = 0$ when $t = 0, 0.7878$, $s(t) = 0.15$ when $t = 0.0410, 0.7468$, and $s(t) = 0.76 - 0.15 = 0.61$ when $t = 0.2188, 0.5689$, so the player spends $0.5689 - 0.2188 = 0.3501$ s in the top 15.0 cm of the jump and $0.0410 + (0.7878 - 0.7468) = 0.0820$ s in the bottom 15.0 cm.

(b) The height vs time plot is a parabola that opens down, and the slope is smallest near the top of the parabola, so a given change Δh in height corresponds to a large time change Δt near the top of the parabola and a narrower time change at points farther away from the top.

19. **(a)**

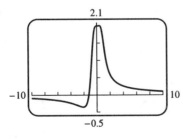

(b) minimum: $(-2.111985, -0.355116)$
maximum: $(0.372591, 2.012931)$

21. **(a)** $v = -2\dfrac{t(t^4 + 2t^2 - 1)}{(t^4 + 1)^2}$, $a = 2\dfrac{3t^8 + 10t^6 - 12t^4 - 6t^2 + 1}{(t^4 + 1)^3}$

(b)

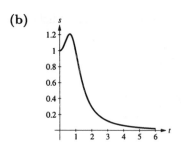 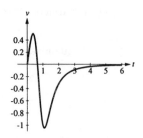 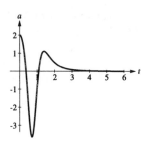

(c) It is farthest from the origin at approximately $t = 0.64$ (when $v = 0$) and $s = 1.2$

(d) Find t so that the velocity $v = ds/dt > 0$. The particle is moving in the positive direction for $0 \le t \le 0.64$ s.

(e) It is speeding up when $a, v > 0$ or $a, v < 0$, so for $0 \le t < 0.36$ and $0.64 < t < 1.1$, otherwise it is slowing down.

(f) Find the maximum value of $|v|$ to obtain: maximum speed $= 1.05$ m/s when $t = 1.10$ s.

23. Solve $\phi - 0.0167 \sin \phi = 2\pi(90)/365$ to get $\phi = 1.565978$ so
$r = 150 \times 10^6(1 - 0.0167 \cos \phi) = 149.988 \times 10^6$ km.

CHAPTER 7
Integration

EXERCISE SET 7.1

1. $A = 1(1)/2 = 1/2$; $\Delta x = (b-a)/n = 1/n$, $x_k^* = k/n$, $f(x_k^*) = k/n$, $A_n = \left[\dfrac{1}{n} + \dfrac{2}{n} + \cdots + \dfrac{n}{n}\right]\dfrac{1}{n}$

n	1	2	3	4	5	6	7	8	9	10
A_n	1.0000	0.7500	0.6666	0.6250	0.6000	0.5833	0.5714	0.5625	0.5556	0.5500

3. $A = 2(2 + 14)/2 = 16$; $\Delta x = (b-a)/n = 2/n$, $x_k^* = 2k/n$, $f(x_k^*) = 2 + 12k/n = 2(1 + 6k/n)$,

$A_n = 2\left[\left(1 + \dfrac{6}{n}\right) + \left(1 + \dfrac{12}{n}\right) + \cdots + \left(1 + \dfrac{6n}{n}\right)\right]\dfrac{2}{n}$

n	1	2	3	4	5	6	7	8	9	10
A_n	28.0000	22.0000	20.0000	19.0000	18.4000	18.0000	17.7143	17.5000	17.3333	17.2000

5. $A(1) - A(0) = 1/2$

7. $A(2) - A(0) = 16$

9. $A(x) = e^x$, area $= A(1) - A(0) = e - 1$

EXERCISE SET 7.2

1. (a) $\displaystyle\int \frac{x}{\sqrt{1+x^2}}dx = \sqrt{1+x^2} + C$

   (b) $\displaystyle\int (x+1)e^x dx = xe^x + C$

3. $\dfrac{d}{dx}\left[\sqrt{x^3+5}\right] = \dfrac{3x^2}{2\sqrt{x^3+5}}$ so $\displaystyle\int \frac{3x^2}{2\sqrt{x^3+5}}dx = \sqrt{x^3+5} + C$

5. $\dfrac{d}{dx}\left[\sin\left(2\sqrt{x}\right)\right] = \dfrac{\cos\left(2\sqrt{x}\right)}{\sqrt{x}}$ so $\displaystyle\int \frac{\cos\left(2\sqrt{x}\right)}{\sqrt{x}}dx = \sin\left(2\sqrt{x}\right) + C$

7. (a) $x^9/9 + C$

   (b) $\dfrac{7}{12}x^{12/7} + C$

   (c) $\dfrac{2}{9}x^{9/2} + C$

9. (a) $\dfrac{1}{2}\displaystyle\int x^{-3}dx = -\dfrac{1}{4}x^{-2} + C$

   (b) $u^4/4 - u^2 + 7u + C$

11. $\displaystyle\int (x^{-3} + x^{1/2} - 3x^{1/4} + x^2)dx = -\dfrac{1}{2}x^{-2} + \dfrac{2}{3}x^{3/2} - \dfrac{12}{5}x^{5/4} + \dfrac{1}{3}x^3 + C$

13. $\displaystyle\int (x + x^4)dx = x^2/2 + x^5/5 + C$

15. $\displaystyle\int x^{1/3}(4 - 4x + x^2)dx = \int (4x^{1/3} - 4x^{4/3} + x^{7/3})dx = 3x^{4/3} - \dfrac{12}{7}x^{7/3} + \dfrac{3}{10}x^{10/3} + C$

17. $\displaystyle\int (x + 2x^{-2} - x^{-4})dx = x^2/2 - 2/x + 1/(3x^3) + C$

19. $2\ln x + 3e^x + C$

21. $-4\cos x + 2\sin x + C$

23. $\displaystyle\int (\sec^2 x + \sec x \tan x)dx = \tan x + \sec x + C$

25. $\ln \theta - 2e^{\theta} + \cot \theta + C$

27. $\int \sec x \tan x \, dx = \sec x + C$ **29.** $\int (1 + \sin \theta) d\theta = \theta - \cos \theta + C$

31. $\int \dfrac{1 - \sin x}{1 - \sin^2 x} dx = \int \dfrac{1 - \sin x}{\cos^2 x} = \int \left(\sec^2 x - \sec x \tan x \right) dx = \tan x - \sec x + C$

33. **(a)**   **(b)** $f(x) = x^2/2 + 5$

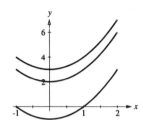

35.

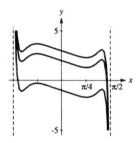

37. $f'(x) = m = -\sin x$ so $f(x) = \int (-\sin x) dx = \cos x + C$; $f(0) = 2 = 1 + C$ so $C = 1$, $f(x) = \cos x + 1$

39. **(a)** $y(x) = \int x^{1/3} dx = \dfrac{3}{4} x^{4/3} + C$, $y(1) = \dfrac{3}{4} + C = 2$, $C = 5/4$; $y(x) = \dfrac{3}{4} x^{4/3} + \dfrac{5}{4}$

(b) $y(t) = \int t^{-1} dt = \ln|t| + C$, $y(-1) = C = 5$, $C = 5$; $y(t) = \ln|t| + 5$

(c) $y(x) = \int (x^{1/2} + x^{-1/2}) dx = \dfrac{2}{3} x^{3/2} + 2x^{1/2} + C$, $y(1) = 0 = \dfrac{8}{3} + C$, $C = -\dfrac{8}{3}$,

$y(x) = \dfrac{2}{3} x^{3/2} + 2x^{1/2} - \dfrac{8}{3}$

41. $f'(x) = \dfrac{2}{3} x^{3/2} + C_1$; $f(x) = \dfrac{4}{15} x^{5/2} + C_1 x + C_2$

43. $dy/dx = 2x + 1, y = \int (2x + 1) dx = x^2 + x + C$; $y = 0$ when $x = -3$

so $(-3)^2 + (-3) + C = 0, C = -6$ thus $y = x^2 + x - 6$

45. $dy/dx = \int 6x \, dx = 3x^2 + C_1$. The slope of the tangent line is -3 so $dy/dx = -3$ when $x = 1$. Thus

$3(1)^2 + C_1 = -3$, $C_1 = -6$ so $dy/dx = 3x^2 - 6$, $y = \int (3x^2 - 6) dx = x^3 - 6x + C_2$; If $x = 1$, then

$y = 5 - 3(1) = 2$ so $(1)^2 - 6(1) + C_2 = 2, C_2 = 7$ thus $y = x^3 - 6x + 7$.

47. **(a)** $F'(x) = G'(x) = 3x + 4$
(b) $F(0) = 16/6 = 8/3$, $G(0) = 0$, so $F(0) - G(0) = 8/3$
(c) $F(x) = (9x^2 + 24x + 16)/6 = 3x^2/2 + 4x + 8/3 = G(x) + 8/3$

49. $\displaystyle\int(\sec^2 x - 1)dx = \tan x - x + C$

51. **(a)** $\displaystyle\frac{1}{2}\int(1 - \cos x)dx = \frac{1}{2}(x - \sin x) + C$ **(b)** $\displaystyle\frac{1}{2}\int(1 + \cos x)\,dx = \frac{1}{2}(x + \sin x) + C$

53. $v = \dfrac{1087}{2\sqrt{273}}\displaystyle\int T^{-1/2}\,dT = \dfrac{1087}{\sqrt{273}}T^{1/2} + C,\ v(273) = 1087 = 1087 + C$ so $C = 0,\ v = \dfrac{1087}{\sqrt{273}}T^{1/2}$ ft/s

EXERCISE SET 7.3

1. **(a)** $\displaystyle\int u^{23}du = u^{24}/24 + C = (x^2 + 1)^{24}/24 + C$

     (b) $\displaystyle-\int u^3 du = -u^4/4 + C = -(\cos^4 x)/4 + C$

     (c) $\displaystyle 2\int \sin u\,du = -2\cos u + C = -2\cos\sqrt{x} + C$

     (d) $\displaystyle\frac{3}{8}\int u^{-1/2}du = \frac{3}{4}u^{1/2} + C = \frac{3}{4}\sqrt{4x^2 + 5} + C$

     (e) $\displaystyle\frac{1}{3}\int u^{-1}\,du = \frac{1}{3}\ln u + C = \frac{1}{3}\ln(x^3 - 4) + C$

3. **(a)** $\displaystyle-\int u\,du = -\frac{1}{2}u^2 + C = -\frac{1}{2}\cot^2 x + C$

     (b) $\displaystyle\int u^9 du = \frac{1}{10}u^{10} + C = \frac{1}{10}(1 + \sin t)^{10} + C$

     (c) $\displaystyle\int\frac{1}{u}du = \ln|u| + C = \ln|\ln x| + C$

     (d) $\displaystyle-\frac{1}{5}\int e^u\,du = -\frac{1}{5}e^u + C = -\frac{1}{5}e^{-5x} + C$

     (e) $\displaystyle-\frac{1}{3}\int\frac{1}{u}du = -\frac{1}{3}\ln|u| + C = -\frac{1}{3}\ln|(1 + \cos 3\theta)| + C$

5. $u = 2x,\ du = 2dx;\ \dfrac{1}{2}\displaystyle\int e^u\,du = \frac{1}{2}e^u + C = \frac{1}{2}e^{2x} + C$

7. $u = 2 - x^2,\ du = -2x\,dx;\ -\dfrac{1}{2}\displaystyle\int u^3 du = -u^4/8 + C = -(2 - x^2)^4/8 + C$

9. $u = 8x,\ du = 8dx;\ \dfrac{1}{8}\displaystyle\int \cos u\,du = \frac{1}{8}\sin u + C = \frac{1}{8}\sin 8x + C$

11. $u = 4x,\ du = 4dx;\ \dfrac{1}{4}\displaystyle\int \sec u\tan u\,du = \frac{1}{4}\sec u + C = \frac{1}{4}\sec 4x + C$

13. $u = 7t^2 + 12,\ du = 14t\,dt;\ \dfrac{1}{14}\displaystyle\int u^{1/2}du = \frac{1}{21}u^{3/2} + C = \frac{1}{21}(7t^2 + 12)^{3/2} + C$

15. $u = x^3 + 1,\ du = 3x^2 dx;\ \dfrac{1}{3}\displaystyle\int u^{-1/2}du = \frac{2}{3}u^{1/2} + C = \frac{2}{3}\sqrt{x^3 + 1} + C$

17. $u = 4x^2 + 1,\ du = 8x\,dx;\ \dfrac{1}{8}\displaystyle\int u^{-3}du = -\frac{1}{16}u^{-2} + C = -\frac{1}{16}(4x^2 + 1)^{-2} + C$

19. $u = \sin x$, $du = \cos x\, dx$; $\displaystyle\int e^u\, du = e^u + C = e^{\sin x} + C$

21. $u = -2x^3$, $du = -6x^2$, $-\dfrac{1}{6}\displaystyle\int e^u du = -\dfrac{1}{6}e^u + C = -\dfrac{1}{6}e^{-2x^3} + C$

23. $u = 5/x$, $du = -(5/x^2)dx$; $-\dfrac{1}{5}\displaystyle\int \sin u\, du = \dfrac{1}{5}\cos u + C = \dfrac{1}{5}\cos(5/x) + C$

25. $u = x^3$, $du = 3x^2 dx$; $\dfrac{1}{3}\displaystyle\int \sec^2 u\, du = \dfrac{1}{3}\tan u + C = \dfrac{1}{3}\tan(x^3) + C$

27. $\displaystyle\int e^{-x}dx$; $u = -x$, $du = -dx$; $-\displaystyle\int e^u du = -e^u + C = -e^{-x} + C$

29. $u = \sin 3t$, $du = 3\cos 3t\, dt$; $\dfrac{1}{3}\displaystyle\int u^5 du = \dfrac{1}{18}u^6 + C = \dfrac{1}{18}\sin^6 3t + C$

31. $u = 2 - \sin 4\theta$, $du = -4\cos 4\theta\, d\theta$; $-\dfrac{1}{4}\displaystyle\int u^{1/2}du = -\dfrac{1}{6}u^{3/2} + C = -\dfrac{1}{6}(2 - \sin 4\theta)^{3/2} + C$

33. $u = \sec 2x$, $du = 2\sec 2x \tan 2x\, dx$; $\dfrac{1}{2}\displaystyle\int u^2 du = \dfrac{1}{6}u^3 + C = \dfrac{1}{6}\sec^3 2x + C$

35. $u = \sqrt{y}$, $du = \dfrac{1}{2\sqrt{y}}dy$, $2\displaystyle\int e^u du = 2e^u + C = 2e^{\sqrt{y}} + C$

39. $u = \sin(a + bx)$, $du = b\cos(a + bx)dx$

$\dfrac{1}{b}\displaystyle\int u^n du = \dfrac{1}{b(n + 1)}u^{n+1} + C = \dfrac{1}{b(n + 1)}\sin^{n+1}(a + bx) + C$

41. $u = x - 3$, $x = u + 3$, $dx = du$

$\displaystyle\int (u + 3)u^{1/2}du = \int (u^{3/2} + 3u^{1/2})du = \dfrac{2}{5}u^{5/2} + 2u^{3/2} + C = \dfrac{2}{5}(x - 3)^{5/2} + 2(x - 3)^{3/2} + C$

43. $u = 3\theta$, $du = 3\, d\theta$

$\dfrac{1}{3}\displaystyle\int \tan^2 u\, du = \dfrac{1}{3}\int (\sec^2 u - 1)du = \dfrac{1}{3}(\tan u - u) + C = \dfrac{1}{3}(\tan 3\theta - 3\theta) + C$

45. $\displaystyle\int \left(1 + \dfrac{1}{t}\right)dt = t + \ln|t| + C$

47. $\ln(e^x) + \ln(e^{-x}) = \ln(e^x e^{-x}) = \ln 1 = 0$ so $\displaystyle\int [\ln(e^x) + \ln(e^{-x})]dx = C$

49. **(a)** with $u = \sin x$, $du = \cos x\, dx$; $\displaystyle\int u\, du = \dfrac{1}{2}u^2 + C_1 = \dfrac{1}{2}\sin^2 x + C_1$;

with $u = \cos x$, $du = -\sin x\, dx$; $-\displaystyle\int u\, du = -\dfrac{1}{2}u^2 + C_2 = -\dfrac{1}{2}\cos^2 x + C_2$

(b) because they differ by a constant:

$\left(\dfrac{1}{2}\sin^2 x + C_1\right) - \left(-\dfrac{1}{2}\cos^2 x + C_2\right) = \dfrac{1}{2}(\sin^2 x + \cos^2 x) + C_1 - C_2 = 1/2 + C_1 - C_2$

51. $y(x) = \displaystyle\int \sqrt{3x + 1}dx = \dfrac{2}{9}(3x + 1)^{3/2} + C$,

$y(1) = \dfrac{16}{9} + C = 5$, $C = \dfrac{29}{9}$ so $y(x) = \dfrac{2}{9}(3x + 1)^{3/2} + \dfrac{29}{9}$

53. $f'(x) = m = \sqrt{3x+1}$, $f(x) = \int (3x+1)^{1/2}dx = \frac{2}{9}(3x+1)^{3/2} + C$; $f(0) = 1 = \frac{2}{9} + C$, $C = \frac{7}{9}$, so

$f(x) = \frac{2}{9}(3x+1)^{3/2} + \frac{7}{9}$

55. $p(t) = \int (4 + 0.15t)^{3/2}dt = \frac{8}{3}(4 + 0.15t)^{5/2} + C$; $p(0) = 100,000 = \frac{8}{3}4^{5/2} + C = \frac{256}{3} + C$,

$C = 100,000 - \frac{256}{3} \approx 99,915$, $p(t) = \frac{8}{3}(4 + 0.15t)^{5/2} + 99,915$, $p(5) = \frac{8}{3}(4.75)^{5/2} + 99,915 \approx 100,416$

EXERCISE SET 7.4

1. **(a)** $1 + 8 + 27 = 36$ **(b)** $5 + 8 + 11 + 14 + 17 = 55$
     (c) $20 + 12 + 6 + 2 + 0 + 0 = 40$ **(d)** $1 + 1 + 1 + 1 + 1 + 1 = 6$
     (e) $1 - 2 + 4 - 8 + 16 = 11$ **(f)** $0 + 0 + 0 + 0 + 0 + 0 = 0$

3. $\displaystyle\sum_{k=1}^{10} k$ **5.** $\displaystyle\sum_{k=1}^{49} k(k+1)$ **7.** $\displaystyle\sum_{k=1}^{10} 2k$

9. $\displaystyle\sum_{k=1}^{6} (-1)^{k+1}(2k-1)$ **11.** $\displaystyle\sum_{k=1}^{5} (-1)^{k}\frac{1}{k}$

13. **(a)** $\displaystyle\sum_{1}^{50} 2k$ **(b)** $\displaystyle\sum_{1}^{50} (2k-1)$

15. $\frac{1}{2}(100)(100+1) = 5050$

17. $\frac{1}{6}(20)(21)(41) = 2,870$

19. $\displaystyle 4\sum_{k=1}^{6} k^3 - 2\sum_{k=1}^{6} k + \sum_{k=1}^{6} 1 = 4\left[\frac{1}{4}(6)^2(7)^2\right] - 2\left[\frac{1}{2}(6)(7)\right] + 6 = 1728$

21. $\displaystyle \sum_{k=1}^{30} k(k^2 - 4) = \sum_{k=1}^{30}(k^3 - 4k) = \sum_{k=1}^{30} k^3 - 4\sum_{k=1}^{30} k = \frac{1}{4}(30)^2(31)^2 - 4 \cdot \frac{1}{2}(30)(31) = 214,365$

23. $\displaystyle \sum_{k=1}^{n}(4k-3) = 4\sum_{k=1}^{n} k - \sum_{k=1}^{n} 3 = 4 \cdot \frac{1}{2}n(n+1) - 3n = 2n^2 - n$

25. $\displaystyle \sum_{k=1}^{n} \frac{3k}{n} = \frac{3}{n}\sum_{k=1}^{n} k = \frac{3}{n} \cdot \frac{1}{2}n(n+1) = \frac{3}{2}(n+1)$

27. $\displaystyle \sum_{k=1}^{n-1} \frac{k^3}{n^2} = \frac{1}{n^2}\sum_{k=1}^{n-1} k^3 = \frac{1}{n^2} \cdot \frac{1}{4}(n-1)^2 n^2 = \frac{1}{4}(n-1)^2$

31. **(a)** $\displaystyle \sum_{k=0}^{19} 3^{k+1} = \sum_{k=0}^{19} 3(3^k) = \frac{3(1 - 3^{20})}{1 - 3} = \frac{3}{2}(3^{20} - 1)$

(b) $\displaystyle\sum_{k=0}^{25} 2^{k+5} = \sum_{k=0}^{25} 2^5 2^k = \frac{2^5(1-2^{26})}{1-2} = 2^{31} - 2^5$

(c) $\displaystyle\sum_{k=0}^{100}(-1)\left(\frac{-1}{2}\right)^k = \frac{(-1)(1-(-1/2)^{101})}{1-(-1/2)} = -\frac{2}{3}(1+1/2^{101})$

33. $\dfrac{1+2+3+\cdots+n}{n^2} = \displaystyle\sum_{k=1}^{n}\dfrac{k}{n^2} = \dfrac{1}{n^2}\sum_{k=1}^{n}k = \dfrac{1}{n^2}\cdot\dfrac{1}{2}n(n+1) = \dfrac{n+1}{2n}; \lim_{n\to+\infty}\dfrac{n+1}{2n} = \dfrac{1}{2}$

35. $\displaystyle\sum_{k=1}^{n}\dfrac{5k}{n^2} = \dfrac{5}{n^2}\sum_{k=1}^{n}k = \dfrac{5}{n^2}\cdot\dfrac{1}{2}n(n+1) = \dfrac{5(n+1)}{2n}; \lim_{n\to+\infty}\dfrac{5(n+1)}{2n} = \dfrac{5}{2}$

37. **(a)** $\displaystyle\sum_{j=0}^{5} 2^j$ **(b)** $\displaystyle\sum_{j=1}^{6} 2^{j-1}$ **(c)** $\displaystyle\sum_{j=2}^{7} 2^{j-2}$

39. **(a)** $\displaystyle\sum_{k=1}^{18}\sin\left(\frac{\pi}{k}\right)$ **(b)** $\displaystyle\sum_{k=0}^{6} e^k = \dfrac{e^7 - 1}{e - 1}$

41. For $1 \le k \le n$ the k-th L-shaped strip consists of the corner square, a strip above and a strip to the right for a combined area of $1 + (k-1) + (k-1) = 2k-1$, so the total area is $\displaystyle\sum_{k=1}^{n}(2k-1) = n^2$.

43. $(3^5 - 3^4) + (3^6 - 3^5) + \cdots + (3^{17} - 3^{16}) = 3^{17} - 3^4$

45. $\left(\dfrac{1}{2^2} - \dfrac{1}{1^2}\right) + \left(\dfrac{1}{3^2} - \dfrac{1}{2^2}\right) + \cdots + \left(\dfrac{1}{20^2} - \dfrac{1}{19^2}\right) = \dfrac{1}{20^2} - 1 = -\dfrac{399}{400}$

47. **(a)** $\displaystyle\sum_{k=1}^{n}\dfrac{1}{(2k-1)(2k+1)} = \dfrac{1}{2}\sum_{k=1}^{n}\left(\dfrac{1}{2k-1} - \dfrac{1}{2k+1}\right)$

$= \dfrac{1}{2}\left[\left(1-\dfrac{1}{3}\right) + \left(\dfrac{1}{3}-\dfrac{1}{5}\right) + \left(\dfrac{1}{5}-\dfrac{1}{7}\right) + \cdots + \left(\dfrac{1}{2n-1} - \dfrac{1}{2n+1}\right)\right]$

$= \dfrac{1}{2}\left[1 - \dfrac{1}{2n+1}\right] = \dfrac{n}{2n+1}$

(b) $\displaystyle\lim_{n\to+\infty}\dfrac{n}{2n+1} = \dfrac{1}{2}$

49. both are valid

51. $\displaystyle\sum_{i=1}^{n}(x_i - \bar{x}) = \sum_{i=1}^{n}x_i - \sum_{i=1}^{n}\bar{x} = \sum_{i=1}^{n}x_i - n\bar{x}$ but $\bar{x} = \dfrac{1}{n}\sum_{i=1}^{n}x_i$ thus

$\displaystyle\sum_{i=1}^{n}x_i = n\bar{x}$ so $\displaystyle\sum_{i=1}^{n}(x_i - \bar{x}) = n\bar{x} - n\bar{x} = 0$

53. $\displaystyle\sum_{k=1}^{n}\left[(k+1)^4 - k^4\right] = (n+1)^4 - 1$ (telescoping sum), expand the

quantity in brackets to get $\displaystyle\sum_{k=1}^{n}(4k^3 + 6k^2 + 4k + 1) = (n+1)^4 - 1$,

$$4\sum_{k=1}^{n}k^3 + 6\sum_{k=1}^{n}k^2 + 4\sum_{k=1}^{n}k + \sum_{k=1}^{n}1 = (n+1)^4 - 1$$

$$\sum_{k=1}^{n}k^3 = \frac{1}{4}\left[(n+1)^4 - 1 - 6\sum_{k=1}^{n}k^2 - 4\sum_{k=1}^{n}k - \sum_{k=1}^{n}1\right]$$

$$= \frac{1}{4}[(n+1)^4 - 1 - n(n+1)(2n+1) - 2n(n+1) - n]$$

$$= \frac{1}{4}(n+1)[(n+1)^3 - n(2n+1) - 2n - 1]$$

$$= \frac{1}{4}(n+1)(n^3 + n^2) = \frac{1}{4}n^2(n+1)^2$$

55. $50\cdot 30 + 49\cdot 29 + \cdots + 22\cdot 2 + 21\cdot 1 = \displaystyle\sum_{k=1}^{30}k(k+20) = \sum_{k=1}^{30}k^2 + 20\sum_{k=1}^{30}k = \frac{30\cdot 31\cdot 61}{6} + 20\frac{30\cdot 31}{2} = 18{,}755$

EXERCISE SET 7.5

1. **(a)** $\dfrac{1}{2}bh = \dfrac{1}{2}\cdot 4\cdot 4 = 8$

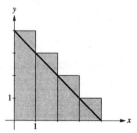

(b) The approximation is greater than A, as the rectangles extend beyond the area.

$$\sum_{k=1}^{4}f(x_k^*)\Delta x = (4 + 3 + 2 + 1)(1) = 10$$

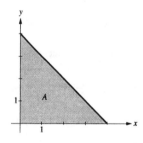

(c) The approximation is less than A, as the rectangles lie inside the area.

$$\sum_{k=1}^{4}f(x_k^*)\Delta x = (3 + 2 + 1 + 0)(1) = 6$$

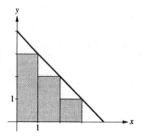

(d) The approximation is equal to A,
as can be seen by measuring congruent triangles.

$$\sum_{k=1}^{4} f(x_k^*)\Delta x = (3.5 + 2.5 + 1.5 + 0.5)(1) = 8$$

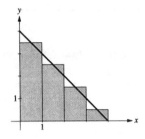

3. (a) $x_k^* = 0, 1, 2, 3, 4$

$$\sum_{k=1}^{5} f(x_k^*)\Delta x = (1 + 2 + 5 + 10 + 17)(1) = 35$$

(b) $x_k^* = 1, 2, 3, 4, 5$

$$\sum_{k=1}^{5} f(x_k^*)\Delta x = (2 + 5 + 10 + 17 + 26)(1) = 60$$

(c) $x_k^* = 1/2, 3/2, 5/2, 7/2, 9/2$

$$\sum_{k=1}^{5} f(x_k^*)\Delta x = (5/4 + 13/4 + 29/4 + 53/4 + 85/4)(1) = 185/4 = 46.25$$

5. (a) $x_k^* = -\pi/2, -\pi/4, 0, \pi/4$

$$\sum_{k=1}^{4} f(x_k^*)\Delta x = (0 + 1/\sqrt{2} + 1 + 1/\sqrt{2})(\pi/4) = (1 + \sqrt{2})\pi/4 \approx 1.896$$

(b) $x_k^* = -\pi/4, 0, \pi/4, \pi/2$

$$\sum_{k=1}^{4} f(x_k^*)\Delta x = (1/\sqrt{2} + 1 + 1/\sqrt{2} + 0)(\pi/4) = (1 + \sqrt{2})\pi/4 \approx 1.896$$

(c) $x_k^* = -3\pi/8, -\pi/8, \pi/8, 3\pi/8$

$$\sum_{k=1}^{4} f(x_k^*)\Delta x = \left[\cos\frac{3\pi}{8} + \cos\frac{\pi}{8} + \cos\frac{\pi}{8} + \cos\frac{3\pi}{8}\right]\frac{\pi}{4} = \pi\cos\frac{\pi}{4}\cos\frac{\pi}{8} = \left(\pi\sqrt{2}\cos\frac{\pi}{8}\right)/2 \approx 2.052$$

7. left endpoints: $x_k^* = 1, 2, 3, 4$; $\displaystyle\sum_{k=1}^{4} f(x_k^*)\Delta x = (2 + 3 + 2 + 1)(1) = 8$

right endpoints: $x_k^* = 2, 3, 4, 5$; $\displaystyle\sum_{k=1}^{4} f(x_k^*)\Delta x = (3 + 2 + 1 + 2)(1) = 8$

9. 0.718771403, 0.668771403, 0.692835360   **11.** 0.919403170, 1.07648280, 1.001028825

13. 0.351220577, 0.420535296, 0.386502483

15.

	n	$1/x$	$1/x^2$	$\sin x$	$\sqrt{x}$	$\ln x$	e^x
(a)	25	0.693097198	0.666154270	1.000164512	5.336963538	0.386327689	1.718167282
(b)	50	0.693134682	0.666538346	1.000041125	5.334644416	0.386302694	1.718253191
(c)	100	0.693144056	0.666634573	1.000010281	5.333803776	0.3862964444	1.718274669

17. **(a)** $A = \frac{1}{2}(3)(3) = 9/2$ **(b)** $-A = -\frac{1}{2}(1)(1+2) = -3/2$

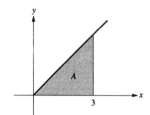
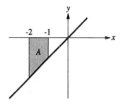

(c) $-A_1 + A_2 = -\frac{1}{2} + 8 = 15/2$ **(d)** $-A_1 + A_2 = 0$

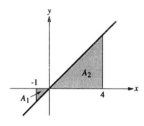
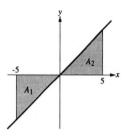

19. **(a)** $A = 2(5) = 10$ **(b)** $0; A_1 = A_2$ by symmetry

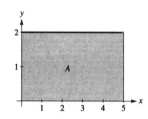
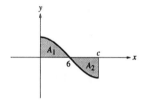

(c) $A_1 + A_2 = \frac{1}{2}(5)(5/2) + \frac{1}{2}(1)(1/2)$ **(d)** $\frac{1}{2}[\pi(1)^2] = \pi/2$

$= 13/2$

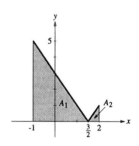
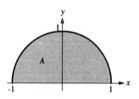

21. **(a)** 0.8 **(b)** -2.6 **(c)** -1.8 **(d)** -0.3

23. $\int_{-1}^{2} f(x)dx + 2\int_{-1}^{2} g(x)dx = 5 + 2(-3) = -1$

25. $\int_{1}^{5} f(x)dx = \int_{0}^{5} f(x)dx - \int_{0}^{1} f(x)dx = 1 - (-2) = 3$

27. **(a)** $\int_0^1 x\,dx + 2\int_0^1 \sqrt{1-x^2}\,dx = 1/2 + 2(\pi/4) = (1+\pi)/2$

(b) $4\int_{-1}^3 dx - 5\int_{-1}^3 x\,dx = 4\cdot 4 - 5(-1/2 + (3\cdot 3)/2) = -4$

29. **(a)** $\sqrt{x} > 0$, $1 - x < 0$ on $[2,3]$ so the integral is negative

(b) $x^2 > 0$, $3 - \cos x > 0$ for all x so the integral is positive

31. $\int_0^{10} \sqrt{25 - (x-5)^2}\,dx = \pi(5)^2/2 = 25\pi/2$

33. **(a)** $\int_{-3}^3 4x(1-3x)\,dx$ **(b)** $\int_0^1 e^x\,dx$

35. $\int_0^1 (3x+1)\,dx = 5/2$

37. **(a)** $\displaystyle\lim_{\max \Delta x_k \to 0} \sum_{k=1}^n 2x_k^* \Delta x_k$; $a = 1$, $b = 2$ **(b)** $\displaystyle\lim_{\max \Delta x_k \to 0} \sum_{k=1}^n \frac{x_k^*}{x_k^* + 1}\Delta x_k$; $a = 0$, $b = 1$

39. **(a)** $x_{k+1}^* = x_k^* + \dfrac{1}{n}$ and $x_1^* = 1 + \dfrac{1}{n}$, so $x_2^* = x_1^* + \dfrac{1}{n} = 1 + \dfrac{2}{n}$, $x_{k+1}^* = x_k^* + \dfrac{1}{n} = 1 + \dfrac{k+1}{n}$ for $k = 2, 3, \cdots, n-1$

(b) $f(x_k^*) = 1 + \dfrac{k}{n}$ and $\Delta x = \dfrac{1}{n}$

(c) $\dfrac{1}{n}\displaystyle\sum_{k=1}^n 1 + \dfrac{1}{n^2}\sum_{k=1}^n k = \dfrac{1}{n}n + \dfrac{1}{n^2}\dfrac{n(n+1)}{2} = \dfrac{3}{2} + \dfrac{1}{2n}$

(d) $\displaystyle\lim_{n \to +\infty}\left(\dfrac{3}{2} + \dfrac{1}{2n}\right) = \dfrac{3}{2}$ which is the area of the trapezoid with base 1 and sides 1 and 2

41. **(a)** (right) $\Delta x = \dfrac{b-a}{n} = \dfrac{1}{n}$, $x_k^* = \dfrac{k}{n}$,

$\displaystyle\sum_{k=1}^n f(x_k^*)\Delta x = \sum_{k=1}^n \left(\dfrac{k}{n}\right)^2 \dfrac{1}{n} = \dfrac{1}{n^3}\sum_{k=1}^n k^2 = \dfrac{1}{n^3}\dfrac{n(n+1)(2n+1)}{6}$; $\displaystyle\lim_{n \to +\infty}\sum_{k=1}^n f(x_k^*)\Delta x = \dfrac{2}{6} = \dfrac{1}{3}$

(b) (left) $\Delta x = \dfrac{b-a}{n} = \dfrac{1}{n}$, $x_k^* = \dfrac{k-1}{n}$,

$\displaystyle\sum_{k=1}^n f(x_k^*)\Delta x = \sum_{k=1}^n \left(\dfrac{k-1}{n}\right)^2 \dfrac{1}{n} = \dfrac{1}{n^3}\sum_{k=1}^n (k-1)^2 = \dfrac{1}{n^3}\dfrac{(n-1)n(2n-1)}{6}$;

$\displaystyle\lim_{n \to +\infty}\sum_{k=1}^n f(x_k^*)\Delta x = \dfrac{2}{6} = \dfrac{1}{3}$

43. **(a)** (right) $\Delta x = \dfrac{b-a}{n} = \dfrac{4}{n}$, $x_k^* = 2 + \dfrac{4k}{n}$,

$\displaystyle\sum_{k=1}^n f(x_k^*)\Delta x = \sum_{k=1}^n \left(2 + \dfrac{4k}{n}\right)^3 \dfrac{4}{n} = 32 + \dfrac{192}{n^2}\dfrac{n(n+1)}{2} + \dfrac{384}{n^3}\dfrac{n(n+1)(2n+1)}{6} + \dfrac{256}{n^4}\left(\dfrac{n(n+1)}{2}\right)^2$;

$\displaystyle\lim_{n \to +\infty}\sum_{k=1}^n f(x_k^*)\Delta x = 32 + \dfrac{192}{2} + \dfrac{384(2)}{6} + \dfrac{256}{4} = 320$

(b) (left) $\Delta x = \dfrac{b-a}{n} = \dfrac{4}{n}$, $x_k^* = 2 + \dfrac{4(k-1)}{n}$,

$$\sum_{k=1}^{n} f(x_k^*)\Delta x = \sum_{k=1}^{n}\left(2 + \frac{4(k-1)}{n}\right)^3 \frac{4}{n} = 32 + \frac{192}{n^2}\frac{(n-1)n}{2} + \frac{384}{n^3}\frac{(n-1)n(2n-1)}{6} + \frac{256}{n^4}\left(\frac{(n-1)n}{2}\right)^2;$$

$$\lim_{n\to+\infty}\sum_{k=1}^{n} f(x_k^*)\Delta x = 32 + \frac{192}{2} + \frac{384(2)}{6} + \frac{256}{4} = 320$$

45. (a) f is continuous on $[-1,1]$ so f is integrable there by part (a) of Theorem 7.5.8

(b) $|f(x)| \leq 1$ so f is bounded on $[-1,1]$, and f has one point of discontinuity, so by part (b) of Theorem 7.5.8 f is integrable on $[-1,1]$

(c) f is not bounded on [-1,1] because $\lim\limits_{x\to 0} f(x) = +\infty$, so f is not integrable on [0,1]

(d) $f(x)$ is discontinuous at the point $x = 0$ because $\lim\limits_{x\to 0}\sin\dfrac{1}{x}$ does not exist. f is continuous elsewhere. $-1 \leq f(x) \leq 1$ for x in $[-1,1]$ so f is bounded there. By part (b), Theorem 7.5.8, f is integrable on $[-1,1]$.

47. (a) Let $S_n = \sum\limits_{k=1}^{n} f(x_k^*)\Delta x_k$ and $S = \int_a^b f(x)dx$ then $\sum\limits_{k=1}^{n} cf(x_k^*)\Delta x_k = cS_n$ and we want to prove that $\lim\limits_{\max \Delta x_k \to 0} cS_n = cS$. If $c = 0$ the result follows immediately, so suppose that $c \neq 0$ then for any $\epsilon > 0$, $|cS_n - cS| = |c||S_n - S| < \epsilon$ if $|S_n - S| < \epsilon/|c|$. But because f is integrable on $[a,b]$, there is a number $\delta > 0$ such that $|S_n - S| < \epsilon/|c|$ whenever $\max \Delta x_k < \delta$ so $|cS_n - cS| < \epsilon$ and hence $\lim\limits_{\max \Delta x_k \to 0} cS_n = cS$.

(b) Let $R_n = \sum\limits_{k=1}^{n} f(x_k^*)\Delta x_k$, $S_n = \sum\limits_{k=1}^{n} g(x_k^*)\Delta x_k$, $T_n = \sum\limits_{k=1}^{n}[f(x_k^*) + g(x_k^*)]\Delta x_k$, $R = \int_a^b f(x)dx$, and $S = \int_a^b g(x)dx$ then $T_n = R_n + S_n$ and we want to prove that $\lim\limits_{\max \Delta x_k \to 0} T_n = R + S$.
$|T_n - (R+S)| = |(R_n - R) + (S_n - S)| \leq |R_n - R| + |S_n - S|$
so for any $\epsilon > 0$ $|T_n - (R+S)| < \epsilon$ if $|R_n - R| + |S_n - S| < \epsilon$.
Because f and g are integrable on $[a,b]$, there are numbers δ_1 and δ_2 such that $|R_n - R| < \epsilon/2$ for $\max \Delta x_k < \delta_1$ and $|S_n - S| < \epsilon/2$ for $\max \Delta x_k < \delta_2$.
If $\delta = \min(\delta_1, \delta_2)$ then $|R_n - R| < \epsilon/2$ and $|S_n - S| < \epsilon/2$ for $\max \Delta x_k < \delta$ thus $|R_n - R| + |S_n - S| < \epsilon$ and so $|T_n - (R+S)| < \epsilon$ for $\max \Delta x_k < \delta$ which shows that $\lim\limits_{\max \Delta x_k \to 0} T_n = R + S$.

EXERCISE SET 7.6

1. (a) $\displaystyle\int_0^2 (2-x)dx = (2x - x^2/2)\Big]_0^2 = 4 - 4/2 = 2$

(b) $\displaystyle\int_{-1}^1 2dx = 2x\Big]_{-1}^1 = 2(1) - 2(-1) = 4$

(c) $\displaystyle\int_1^3 (x+1)dx = (x^2/2 + x)\Big]_1^3 = 9/2 + 3 - (1/2 + 1) = 6$

3. $\displaystyle\int_2^3 x^3 dx = x^4/4\Big]_2^3 = 81/4 - 16/4 = 65/4$

5. $\displaystyle\int_1^9 \sqrt{x}\,dx = \frac{2}{3}x^{3/2}\Big]_1^9 = \frac{2}{3}(27 - 1) = 52/3$

7. $\displaystyle\int_1^3 e^x dx = e^x\Big]_1^3 = e^3 - e$

9. $\left(\dfrac{1}{3}x^3 - 2x^2 + 7x\right)\Big]_{-3}^0 = 48$

11. $\displaystyle\int_1^3 x^{-2}dx = -\frac{1}{x}\Big]_1^3 = 2/3$

13. $\displaystyle\frac{4}{5}x^{5/2}\Big]_4^9 = 844/5$

15. $-\cos\theta\Big]_{-\pi/2}^{\pi/2} = 0$

17. $\sin x\Big]_{-\pi/4}^{\pi/4} = \sqrt{2}$

19. $5e^x\Big]_{\ln 2}^3 = 5e^3 - 5(2) = 5e^3 - 10$

21. $\left(6\sqrt{t} - \frac{10}{3}t^{3/2} + \frac{2}{\sqrt{t}}\right)\Big]_1^4 = -55/3$

23. $\left(\frac{1}{2}x^2 - 2\cot x\right)\Big]_{\pi/6}^{\pi/2} = \pi^2/9 + 2\sqrt{3}$

27. (a) $\displaystyle\int_0^{3/2}(3-2x)dx + \int_{3/2}^2 (2x-3)dx = (3x-x^2)\Big]_0^{3/2} + (x^2-3x)\Big]_{3/2}^2 = 9/4 + 1/4 = 5/2$

 (b) $\displaystyle\int_0^{\pi/2}\cos x\,dx + \int_{\pi/2}^{3\pi/4}(-\cos x)dx = \sin x\Big]_0^{\pi/2} - \sin x\Big]_{\pi/2}^{3\pi/4} = 2 - \sqrt{2}/2$

29. $\displaystyle\int_{-2}^0 x^2 dx + \int_0^3 (-x)dx = \frac{1}{3}x^3\Big]_{-2}^0 - \frac{1}{2}x^2\Big]_0^3 = -11/6$

31. 0.665867079; $\displaystyle\int_1^3 \frac{1}{x^2}dx = -\frac{1}{x}\Big]_1^3 = 2/3$

33. 1.098242635; $\displaystyle\int_1^3 \frac{1}{x}dx = \ln x\Big]_1^3 = \ln 3 \approx 1.098612289$

35. $A = \displaystyle\int_0^3 (x^2+1)dx = \left(\frac{1}{3}x^3 + x\right)\Big]_0^3 = 12$

37. $A = \displaystyle\int_0^{2\pi/3} 3\sin x\,dx = -3\cos x\Big]_0^{2\pi/3} = 9/2$

39. $A_1 = \displaystyle\int_{-3}^{-2}(x^2-3x-10)dx = \left(\frac{1}{3}x^3 - \frac{3}{2}x^2 - 10x\right)\Big]_{-3}^{-2} = 23/6,$

 $A_2 = -\displaystyle\int_{-2}^5 (x^2-3x-10)dx = 343/6,$

 $A_3 = \displaystyle\int_5^8 (x^2-3x-10)dx = 243/6, \quad A = A_1 + A_2 + A_3 = 203/2$

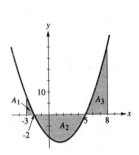

41. (a) the area between the curve and the x-axis breaks into equal parts, one above and one below the x-axis, so the integral is zero

 (b) $\displaystyle\int_{-1}^1 x^3 dx = \frac{1}{4}x^4\Big]_{-1}^1 = \frac{1}{4}(1^4 - (-1)^4) = 0;$

 $\displaystyle\int_{-\pi/2}^{\pi/2} \sin x\,dx = -\cos x\Big]_{-\pi/2}^{\pi/2} = -\cos(\pi/2) + \cos(-\pi/2) = 0 + 0 = 0$

(c) The area on the left side of the y-axis is equal to the area on the right side, so
$$\int_{-a}^{a} f(x)dx = 2\int_{0}^{a} f(x)dx$$

(d) $\int_{-1}^{1} x^2 dx = \dfrac{1}{3}x^3 \Big]_{-1}^{1} = \dfrac{1}{3}(1^3 - (-1)^3) = \dfrac{2}{3} = 2\int_{0}^{1} x^2 dx;$

$\int_{-\pi/2}^{\pi/2} \cos x dx = \sin x \Big]_{-\pi/2}^{\pi/2} = \sin(\pi/2) - \sin(-\pi/2) = 1 + 1 = 2 = 2\int_{0}^{\pi/2} \cos x dx$

43. **(a)** $x^3 + 1$ **(b)** $F(x) = \left(\dfrac{1}{4}t^4 + t\right)\Big]_{1}^{x} = \dfrac{1}{4}x^4 + x - \dfrac{5}{4}; \; F'(x) = x^3 + 1$

45. **(a)** $\sin\sqrt{x}$ **(b)** e^{x^2}

47. $-\dfrac{x}{\cos x}$

49. $F'(x) = \sqrt{3x^2 + 1}, \; F''(x) = \dfrac{3x}{\sqrt{3x^2 + 1}}$

     (a) 0 **(b)** $\sqrt{13}$ **(c)** $6/\sqrt{13}$

51. **(a)** $F'(x) = \dfrac{x - 3}{x^2 + 7} = 0$ when $x = 3$, which is a relative minimum, and hence the absolute minimum, by the first derivative test.

     (b) increasing on $[3, +\infty)$, decreasing on $(-\infty, 3]$

     (c) $F''(x) = \dfrac{7 + 6x - x^2}{(x^2 + 7)^2} = \dfrac{(7 - x)(1 + x)}{(x^2 + 7)^2}$; concave up on $(-1, 7)$, concave down on $(-\infty, -1)$ and on $(7, +\infty)$

53. **(a)** $(0, +\infty)$ because f is continuous there and 1 is in $(0, +\infty)$

     (b) at $x = 1$ because $F(1) = 0$

55. **(a)** $f_{ave} = \dfrac{1}{9}\int_{0}^{9} x^{1/2}dx = 2; \; \sqrt{x^*} = 2, \; x^* = 4$

     (b) $f_{ave} = \dfrac{1}{e-1}\int_{1}^{e} \dfrac{1}{x}dx = \dfrac{1}{e-1}\ln x\Big]_{1}^{e} = \dfrac{1}{e-1}; \; \dfrac{1}{x^*} = \dfrac{1}{e-1}, \; x^* = e - 1$

57. $\sqrt{2} \le \sqrt{x^3 + 2} \le \sqrt{29}$, so $3\sqrt{2} \le \int_{0}^{3} \sqrt{x^3 + 2}dx \le 3\sqrt{29}$

59. $0 \le \ln x \le \ln 5$ for x in $[1, 5]$, so $0 \le \int_{1}^{5} \ln x dx \le 4\ln 5$

EXERCISE SET 7.7

1. **(a)** the increase in height in inches, during the first ten years

     (b) the change in the radius in centimeters, during the time interval $t = 1$ to $t = 2$ seconds

     (c) the change in the speed of sound in ft/s, during an increase in temperature from $t = 32°F$ to $t = 100°F$

     (d) the displacement of the particle in cm, during the time interval $t = t_1$ to $t = t_2$ seconds

3. (a) $\text{displ} = s(3) - s(0)$

$$= \int_0^3 v(t)dt = \int_0^2 (1-t)dt + \int_2^3 (t-3)dt = (t - t^2/2)\Big]_0^2 + (t^2/2 - 3t)\Big]_2^3 = -1/2;$$

$$\text{dist} = \int_0^3 |v(t)|dt = (t - t^2/2)\Big]_0^1 + (t^2/2 - t)\Big]_1^2 + (t^2/2 - 3t)\Big]_2^3 = 1/2$$

(b) $\text{displ} = s(3) - s(0)$

$$= \int_0^3 v(t)dt = \int_0^1 t\,dt + \int_1^2 dt + \int_2^3 (5 - 2t)dt = t^2/2\Big]_0^2 + t\Big]_2^3 + (5t - t^2)\Big]_2^3 = 5;$$

$$\text{dist} = \int_0^1 t\,dt + \int_1^2 dt + \int_2^{5/2} (5 - 2t)dt + \int_{5/2}^3 (2t - 5)dt$$

$$= t^2/2\Big]_0^1 + t\Big]_1^2 + (5t - t^2)\Big]_2^{5/2} + (t^2 - 5t)\Big]_{5/2}^3 = 5/2$$

5. (a) $v(t) = 20 + \int_0^t a(u)du$; add areas of the small blocks to get

$$v(5) \approx 20 + \frac{1}{2}(1.5 + 2.7 + 4.6 + 6.2 + 7.6) = 31.3$$

(b) $v(10) = v(4) + \int_5^{10} a(u)du \approx 31.3 + \frac{1}{2}(8.6 + 9.3 + 9.7 + 10 + 10.1) = 55.15$

7. (a) $s(t) = \int (t^3 - 2t^2 + 1)dt = \frac{1}{4}t^4 - \frac{2}{3}t^3 + t + C,$

$s(0) = \frac{1}{4}(0)^4 - \frac{2}{3}(0)^3 + 0 + C = 1, C = 1, s(t) = \frac{1}{4}t^4 - \frac{2}{3}t^3 + t + 1$

(b) $v(t) = \int 4\cos 2t\,dt = 2\sin 2t + C_1, v(0) = 2\sin 0 + C_1 = -1, C_1 = -1,$

$v(t) = 2\sin 2t - 1, s(t) = \int (2\sin 2t - 1)dt = -\cos 2t - t + C_2,$

$s(0) = -\cos 0 - 0 + C_2 = -3, C_2 = -2, s(t) = -\cos 2t - t - 2$

9. (a) $s(t) = \int (2t - 3)dt = t^2 - 3t + C, s(1) = (1)^2 - 3(1) + C = 5, C = 7, s(t) = t^2 - 3t + 7$

(b) $v(t) = \int \cos t\,dt = \sin t + C_1, v(\pi/2) = 2 = 1 + C_1, C_1 = 1, v(t) = \sin t + 1,$

$s(t) = \int (\sin t + 1)dt = -\cos t + t + C_2, s(\pi/2) = 0 = \pi/2 + C_2, C_2 = -\pi/2, s(t) = -\cos t + t - \pi/2$

11. (a) $\text{displacement} = s(\pi/2) - s(0) = \int_0^{\pi/2} \sin t\,dt = -\cos t\Big]_0^{\pi/2} = 1$

$\text{distance} = \int_0^{\pi/2} |\sin t|dt = 1$

(b) $\text{displacement} = s(2\pi) - s(\pi/2) = \int_{\pi/2}^{2\pi} \cos t\,dt = \sin t\Big]_{\pi/2}^{2\pi} = -1$

$\text{distance} = \int_{\pi/2}^{2\pi} |\cos t|dt = -\int_{\pi/2}^{3\pi/2} \cos t\,dt + \int_{3\pi/2}^{2\pi} \cos t\,dt = 3$

13. (a)
$$v(t) = t^3 - 3t^2 + 2t = t(t-1)(t-2)$$
$$\text{displacement} = \int_0^3 (t^3 - 3t^2 + 2t)dt = 9/4$$
$$\text{distance} = \int_0^3 |v(t)|dt = \int_0^1 v(t)dt + \int_1^2 -v(t)dt + \int_2^3 v(t)dt = 11/4$$

(b) $\text{displacement} = \int_0^3 (e^t - 2)dt = e^3 - 7$
$$\text{distance} = \int_0^3 |v(t)|dt = -\int_0^{\ln 2} v(t)dt + \int_{\ln 2}^3 v(t)dt = e^3 - 9 + 4\ln 2$$

15.
$$v(t) = -2t + 3$$
$$\text{displacement} = \int_1^4 (-2t+3)dt = -6$$
$$\text{distance} = \int_1^4 |-2t+3|dt = \int_1^{3/2} (-2t+3)dt + \int_{3/2}^4 (2t-3)dt = 13/2$$

17.
$$v(t) = \frac{2}{5}\sqrt{5t+1} + \frac{8}{5}$$
$$\text{displacement} = \int_0^3 \left(\frac{2}{5}\sqrt{5t+1} + \frac{8}{5}\right) dt = \frac{4}{75}(5t+1)^{3/2} + \frac{8}{5}t\Big]_0^3 = 204/25$$
$$\text{distance} = \int_0^3 |v(t)|dt = \int_0^3 v(t)dt = 204/25$$

19. (a) $s = \int \sin\frac{1}{2}\pi t\, dt = -\frac{2}{\pi}\cos\frac{1}{2}\pi t + C$

$s = 0$ when $t = 0$ which gives $C = \frac{2}{\pi}$ so $s = -\frac{2}{\pi}\cos\frac{1}{2}\pi t + \frac{2}{\pi}$.

$a = \dfrac{dv}{dt} = \dfrac{\pi}{2}\cos\dfrac{1}{2}\pi t$. When $t = 1$: $s = 2/\pi$, $v = 1$, $|v| = 1$, $a = 0$.

(b) $v = -3\int t\, dt = -\frac{3}{2}t^2 + C_1$, $v = 0$ when $t = 0$ which gives $C_1 = 0$ so $v = -\frac{3}{2}t^2$

$s = -\frac{3}{2}\int t^2 dt = -\frac{1}{2}t^3 + C_2$, $s = 1$ when $t = 0$ which gives $C_2 = 1$ so $s = -\frac{1}{2}t^3 + 1$.
When $t = 1$: $s = 1/2$, $v = -3/2$, $|v| = 3/2$, $a = -3$.

21. $A = A_1 + A_2 = \int_0^1 (1-x^2)dx + \int_1^3 (x^2-1)dx = 2/3 + 20/3 = 22/3$

23. $A = A_1 + A_2 = \int_{-1}^0 (1-e^x)dx + \int_0^1 (e^x-1)dx = 1/e + e - 2$

25. $s(t) = \dfrac{20}{3}t^3 - 50t^2 + 50t + s_0$, $s(0) = 0$ gives $s_0 = 0$, so $s(t) = \dfrac{20}{3}t^3 - 50t^2 + 50t$, $a(t) = 40t - 100$

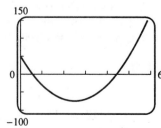
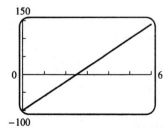
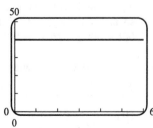

27. **(a)** from the graph the velocity is positive, so the displacement is always increasing and is therefore positive

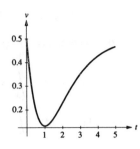

(b) $s(t) = t/2 + (t+1)e^{-t}$

29. **(a)** $a(t) = \begin{cases} 0, & t < 4 \\ -10, & t > 4 \end{cases}$ **(b)** $v(t) = \begin{cases} 25, & t < 4 \\ 65 - 10t, & t > 4 \end{cases}$

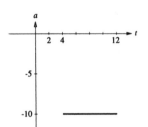   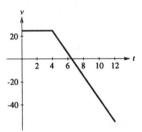

(c) $x(t) = \begin{cases} 25t, & t < 4 \\ 65t - 5t^2 - 80, & t > 4 \end{cases}$, so $x(8) = 120$, $x(12) = -20$

(d) $x(6.5) = 131.25$

31. **(a)** $a = -1$ mi/h/s $= -22/15$ ft/s^2 **(b)** $a = 30$ km/h/min $= 1/7200$ km/s^2

33. $a = a_0$ ft/s^2, $v = a_0 t + v_0 = a_0 t + 132$ ft/s, $s = a_0 t^2/2 + 132t + s_0 = a_0 t^2/2 + 132t$ ft; $s = 200$ ft when $v = 88$ ft/s. Solve $88 = a_0 t + 132$ and $200 = a_0 t^2/2 + 132t$ to get $a_0 = -\dfrac{121}{5}$ when $t = \dfrac{20}{11}$, so $s = -12.1t^2 + 132t$, $v = -\dfrac{121}{5}t + 132$.

(a) $a_0 = -\dfrac{121}{5}$ ft/s^2 **(b)** $v = 55$ mi/h $= \dfrac{242}{3}$ ft/s when $t = \dfrac{70}{33}$ s

(c) $v = 0$ when $t = \dfrac{60}{11}$ s

35. Suppose $s = s_0 = 0$, $v = v_0 = 0$ at $t = t_0 = 0$; $s = s_1 = 120$, $v = v_1$ at $t = t_1$; and $s = s_2$, $v = v_2 = 12$ at $t = t_2$. From Exercise 30(a),

$$2.6 = a = \frac{v_1^2 - v_0^2}{2(s_1 - s_0)}, v_1^2 = 2as_1 = 5.2(120) = 624. \text{ Applying the formula again,}$$

$$-1.5 = a = \frac{v_2^2 - v_1^2}{2(s_2 - s_1)}, v_2^2 = v_1^2 - 3(s_2 - s_1), \text{ so}$$

$$s_2 = s_1 - (v_2^2 - v_1^2)/3 = 120 - (144 - 624)/3 = 280 \text{ m.}$$

37. The truck's velocity is $v_T = 50$ and its position is $s_T = 50t + 5000$. The car's acceleration is $a_C = 2$, so $v_C = 2t$, $s_C = t^2$ (initial position and initial velocity of the car are both zero). $s_T = s_C$ when $50t + 5000 = t^2$, $t^2 - 50t - 5000 = (t + 50)(t - 100) = 0$, $t = 100$ s and $s_C = s_T = t^2 = 10,000$ ft

39. $s = 0$ and $v = 112$ when $t = 0$ so $v(t) = -32t + 112$, $s(t) = -16t^2 + 112t$

(a) $v(3) = 16$ ft/s, $v(5) = -48$ ft/s

(b) $v = 0$ when the projectile is at its maximum height so $-32t + 112 = 0$, $t = 7/2$ s, $s(7/2) = -16(7/2)^2 + 112(7/2) = 196$ ft.

(c) $s = 0$ when it reaches the ground so $-16t^2 + 112t = 0$, $-16t(t - 7) = 0$, $t = 0, 7$ of which $t = 7$ is when it is at ground level on its way down. $v(7) = -112$, $|v| = 112$ ft/s.

41. **(a)** $s(t) = 0$ when it hits the ground, $s(t) = -16t^2 + 16t = -16t(t - 1) = 0$ when $t = 1$ s.

(b) The projectile moves upward until it gets to its highest point where $v(t) = 0$, $v(t) = -32t + 16 = 0$ when $t = 1/2$ s.

43. **(a)** $s(t) = 0$ when the package hits the ground,
$s(t) = -16t^2 + 20t + 200 = 0$ when $t = (5 + 5\sqrt{33})/8$ s

(b) $v(t) = -32t + 20$, $v[(5 + 5\sqrt{33})/8] = -20\sqrt{33}$, the speed at impact is $20\sqrt{33}$ ft/s

45. $s(t) = -4.9t^2 + 49t + 150$ and $v(t) = -9.8t + 49$

(a) the projectile reaches its maximum height when $v(t) = 0$, $-9.8t + 49 = 0$, $t = 5$ s

(b) $s(5) = -4.9(5)^2 + 49(5) + 150 = 272.5$ m

(c) the projectile reaches its starting point when $s(t) = 150$, $-4.9t^2 + 49t + 150 = 150$, $-4.9t(t - 10) = 0$, $t = 10$ s

(d) $v(10) = -9.8(10) + 49 = -49$ m/s

(e) $s(t) = 0$ when the projectile hits the ground, $-4.9t^2 + 49t + 150 = 0$ when (use the quadratic formula) $t \approx 12.46$ s

(f) $v(12.46) = -9.8(12.46) + 49 \approx -73.1$, the speed at impact is about 73.1 m/s

47. $g = 9.8/6 = 4.9/3$ m/s^2, so $v = -(4.9/3)t$, $s = -(4.9/6)t^2 + 5$, $s = 0$ when $t = \sqrt{30/4.9}$ and $v = -(4.9/3)\sqrt{30/4.9} \approx -4.04$, so the speed of the module upon landing is 4.04 m/s

49. $f_{\text{ave}} = \dfrac{1}{3 - 1}\displaystyle\int_1^3 3x\,dx = \dfrac{3}{4}x^2\Big]_1^3 = 6$

51. $f_{\text{ave}} = \dfrac{1}{\pi - 0}\displaystyle\int_0^\pi \sin x\,dx = -\dfrac{1}{\pi}\cos x\Big]_0^\pi = 2/\pi$

53. $f_{\text{ave}} = \dfrac{1}{e - 1} = \displaystyle\int_1^e \dfrac{1}{x}dx = \dfrac{1}{1 - e}(\ln e - \ln 1) = \dfrac{1}{e - 1}$

55. **(a)** $f_{\text{ave}} = \dfrac{1}{2 - 0}\displaystyle\int_0^2 x^2 dx = 4/3$ **(b)** $(x^*)^2 = 4/3$, $x^* = \pm 2/\sqrt{3}$, but only $2/\sqrt{3}$ is in $[0, 2]$

(c)

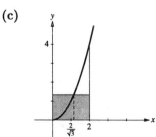

57. **(a)** $v_{\text{ave}} = \dfrac{1}{4 - 1}\displaystyle\int_1^4 (3t^3 + 2)dt = \dfrac{1}{3}\dfrac{789}{4} = \dfrac{263}{4}$

(b) $v_{\text{ave}} = \dfrac{s(4) - s(1)}{4 - 1} = \dfrac{100 - 7}{3} = 31$

59. time to fill tank = (volume of tank)/(rate of filling) = $[\pi(3)^2 5]/(1) = 45\pi$, weight of water in tank at time $t = (62.4)$ (rate of filling)(time) $= 62.4t$,

$$\text{weight}_{\text{ave}} = \frac{1}{45\pi} \int_0^{45\pi} 62.4t \, dt = 1404\pi \text{ lb}$$

61. (a) amount of water = (rate of flow)(time) = $4t$ gal, total amount $= 4(30) = 120$ gal

(b) amount of water $= \int_0^{60} (4 + t/10) dt = 420$ gal

(c) amount of water $= \int_0^{120} (10 + \sqrt{t}) dt = 1200 + 160\sqrt{30} \approx 2076.36$ gal

63. (a) $\int_a^b [f(x) - f_{\text{ave}}] \, dx = \int_a^b f(x) dx - \int_a^b f_{\text{ave}} dx = \int_a^b f(x) dx - f_{\text{ave}}(b - a) = 0$

because $f_{\text{ave}}(b - a) = \int_a^b f(x) dx$

(b) no, because if $\int_a^b [f(x) - c] dx = 0$ then $\int_a^b f(x) dx - c(b - a) = 0$ so

$c = \dfrac{1}{b - a} \int_a^b f(x) dx = f_{\text{ave}}$ is the only value

EXERCISE SET 7.8

1. (a) $\int_1^3 u^7 du$ **(b)** $-\dfrac{1}{2} \int_7^4 u^{1/2} du$ **(c)** $\dfrac{1}{\pi} \int_{-\pi}^{\pi} \sin u \, du$ **(d)** $\int_{-3}^0 (u + 5) u^{20} du$

3. $u = 2x + 1$, $\dfrac{1}{2} \int_1^3 u^4 du = \dfrac{1}{10} u^5 \Big]_1^3 = 121/5$, or $\dfrac{1}{10}(2x + 1)^5 \Big]_0^1 = 121/5$

5. $u = 1 - 2x$, $-\dfrac{1}{2} \int_3^1 u^3 du = -\dfrac{1}{8} u^4 \Big]_3^1 = 10$, or $-\dfrac{1}{8}(1 - 2x)^4 \Big]_{-1}^0 = 10$

7. $u = 1 + x$, $\int_1^9 (u - 1) u^{1/2} du = \int_1^9 (u^{3/2} - u^{1/2}) du = \dfrac{2}{5} u^{5/2} - \dfrac{2}{3} u^{3/2} \Big]_1^9 = 1192/15$,

or $\dfrac{2}{5}(1 + x)^{5/2} - \dfrac{2}{3}(1 + x)^{3/2} \Big]_0^8 = 1192/15$

9. $u = x/2$, $8 \int_0^{\pi/4} \sin u \, du = -8 \cos u \Big]_0^{\pi/4} = 8 - 4\sqrt{2}$, or $-8 \cos(x/2) \Big]_0^{\pi/2} = 8 - 4\sqrt{2}$

11. $u = e^x + 4$, $du = e^x dx$, $u = e^{-\ln 3} + 4 = \dfrac{1}{3} + 4 = \dfrac{13}{3}$ when $x = -\ln 3$,

$u = e^{\ln 3} + 4 = 3 + 4 = 7$ when $x = \ln 3$, $\int_{13/3}^7 \dfrac{1}{u} du = \ln u \Big]_{13/3}^7 = \ln(7) - \ln(13/3) = \ln(21/13)$

13. $\dfrac{1}{3} \int_0^5 \sqrt{25 - u^2} \, du = \dfrac{1}{3} \left[\dfrac{1}{4} \pi (5)^2 \right] = \dfrac{25}{12} \pi$

15. $-\dfrac{1}{2} \int_1^0 \sqrt{1 - u^2} \, du = \dfrac{1}{2} \int_0^1 \sqrt{1 - u^2} \, du = \dfrac{1}{2} \cdot \dfrac{1}{4} [\pi (1)^2] = \pi/8$

17. $\int_0^1 \sin \pi x \, dx = -\frac{1}{\pi} \cos \pi x \Big]_0^1 = -\frac{1}{\pi}(-1-1) = 2/\pi$

19. $\int_3^7 (x+5)^{-2} = -(x+5)^{-1} \Big]_3^7 = -\frac{1}{12} + \frac{1}{8} = \frac{1}{24}$

21. $f_{\text{ave}} = \frac{1}{4-0} \int_0^4 e^{-2x} dx = -\frac{1}{8} e^{-2x} \Big]_0^4 = \frac{1-e^{-8}}{8}$

23. $\frac{2}{3}(3x+1)^{1/2} \Big]_0^1 = 2/3$

25. $\frac{2}{3}(x^3+9)^{1/2} \Big]_{-1}^1 = \frac{2}{3}(\sqrt{10} - 2\sqrt{2})$

27. $u = x^2 + 4x + 7, \; \frac{1}{2} \int_{12}^{28} u^{-1/2} du = u^{1/2} \Big]_{12}^{28} = \sqrt{28} - \sqrt{12} = 2(\sqrt{7} - \sqrt{3})$

29. $\frac{1}{2} \sin^2 x \Big]_{-3\pi/4}^{\pi/4} = 0$

31. $\frac{5}{2} \sin(x^2) \Big]_0^{\sqrt{\pi}} = 0$

33. $u = 3\theta, \; \frac{1}{3} \int_{\pi/4}^{\pi/3} \sec^2 u \, du = \frac{1}{3} \tan u \Big]_{\pi/4}^{\pi/3} = (\sqrt{3} - 1)/3$

35. $u = 4 - 3y, \; y = \frac{1}{3}(4-u), \; dy = -\frac{1}{3} du$

$-\frac{1}{27} \int_4^1 \frac{16 - 8u + u^2}{u^{1/2}} du = \frac{1}{27} \int_1^4 (16u^{-1/2} - 8u^{1/2} + u^{3/2}) du$

$= \frac{1}{27} \left[32u^{1/2} - \frac{16}{3} u^{3/2} + \frac{2}{5} u^{5/2} \right]_1^4 = 106/405$

37. $\ln(x+e) \Big]_0^e = \ln(2e) - \ln e = \ln 2$

41. **(a)** $u = 3x + 1, \frac{1}{3} \int_1^4 f(u) du = 5/3$ **(b)** $u = 3x, \frac{1}{3} \int_0^9 f(u) du = 5/3$

(c) $u = x^2, 1/2 \int_4^0 f(u) du = -1/2 \int_0^4 f(u) du = -1/2$

43. $\sin x = \cos(\pi/2 - x),$

$\int_0^{\pi/2} \sin^n x \, dx = \int_0^{\pi/2} \cos^n(\pi/2 - x) dx = -\int_{\pi/2}^0 \cos^n u \, du \quad (u = \pi/2 - x)$

$= \int_0^{\pi/2} \cos^n u \, du = \int_0^{\pi/2} \cos^n x \, dx \quad \text{(by replacing } u \text{ by } x\text{)}$

45. $y(t) = (802.137) \int e^{1.528t} dt = 524.959 e^{1.528t} + C; \; y(0) = 750 = 524.959 + C, \; C = 225.041, \; y(t) = 524.959 e^{1.528t} + 225.041, \; y(12) = 48,233,525,650$

47. $s(t) = \int (25 + 10e^{-0.05t}) dt = 25t - 200e^{-0.05t} + C$

(a) $s(10) - s(0) = 250 - 200(e^{-0.5} - 1) = 450 - 200/\sqrt{e} \approx 328.69$ ft

(b) yes; without it the distance would have been 250 ft

49. (a) $V_{\text{rms}}^2 = \dfrac{1}{1/f - 0} \displaystyle\int_0^{1/f} V_p^2 \sin^2(2\pi ft)\,dt = \dfrac{1}{2} f V_p^2 \int_0^{1/f} [1 - \cos(4\pi ft)]\,dt$

$\qquad = \dfrac{1}{2} f V_p^2 \left[t - \dfrac{1}{4\pi f} \sin(4\pi ft) \right]_0^{1/f} = \dfrac{1}{2} V_p^2, \text{ so } V_{\text{rms}} = V_p/\sqrt{2}$

(b) $V_p/\sqrt{2} = 120, V_p = 120\sqrt{2} \approx 169.7 \text{ V}$

51. (a) $I = -\displaystyle\int_a^0 \dfrac{f(a-u)}{f(a-u) + f(u)}\,du = \int_0^a \dfrac{f(a-u) + f(u) - f(u)}{f(a-u) + f(u)}\,du$

$\qquad = \displaystyle\int_0^a du - \int_0^a \dfrac{f(u)}{f(a-u) + f(u)}\,du, I = a - I \text{ so } 2I = a, I = a/2$

(b) $3/2$ **(c)** $\pi/4$

53. $\displaystyle\int_0^1 \sin \pi x\,dx = 2/\pi$

55. (a) Let $u = -x$ then

$$\int_{-a}^a f(x)\,dx = -\int_a^{-a} f(-u)\,du = \int_{-a}^a f(-u)\,du = -\int_{-a}^a f(u)\,du$$

so, replacing u by x in the latter integral,

$$\int_{-a}^a f(x)\,dx = -\int_{-a}^a f(x)\,dx, \; 2\int_{-a}^a f(x)\,dx = 0, \int_{-a}^a f(x)\,dx = 0$$

The graph of f is symmetric about the origin so $\displaystyle\int_{-a}^0 f(x)\,dx$ is the negative of $\displaystyle\int_0^a f(x)\,dx$ thus

$$\int_{-a}^a f(x)\,dx = \int_{-a}^0 f(x) + \int_0^a f(x)\,dx = 0$$

(b) $\displaystyle\int_{-a}^a f(x)\,dx = \int_{-a}^0 f(x)\,dx + \int_0^a f(x)\,dx$, let $u = -x$ in $\displaystyle\int_{-a}^0 f(x)\,dx$ to get

$$\int_{-a}^0 f(x)\,dx = -\int_a^0 f(-u)\,du = \int_0^a f(-u)\,du = \int_0^a f(u)\,du = \int_0^a f(x)\,dx$$

so $\displaystyle\int_{-a}^a f(x)\,dx = \int_0^a f(x)\,dx + \int_0^a f(x)\,dx = 2\int_0^a f(x)\,dx$

The graph of $f(x)$ is symmetric about the y-axis so there is as much signed area to the left of the y-axis as there is to the right.

EXERCISE SET 7.9

1. (a)   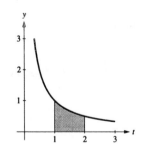 **(b)** 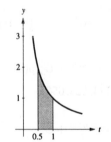 **(c)**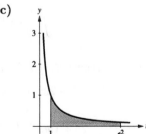

3. (a) $\ln t \Big]_1^{ac} = \ln(ac) = \ln a + \ln c = 7$ (b) $\ln t \Big]_1^{1/c} = \ln(1/c) = -5$

    (c) $\ln t \Big]_1^{a/c} = \ln(a/c) = 2 - 5 = -3$ (d) $\ln t \Big]_1^{a^3} = \ln a^3 = 3 \ln a = 6$

5. $\ln 5 \approx 1.603210678$; $\ln 5 = 1.609437912$; magnitude of error is < 0.0063

7. (a) $x^{-1}, x > 0$ (b) $x^2, x \neq 0$
    (c) $-x^2, -\infty < x < +\infty$ (d) $-x, -\infty < x < +\infty$
    (e) $x^3, x > 0$ (f) $\ln x + x, x > 0$
    (g) $x - \sqrt[3]{x}, -\infty < x < +\infty$ (h) $\dfrac{e^x}{x}, x > 0$

9. (a) $3^\pi = e^{\pi \ln 3}$ (b) $2^{\sqrt{2}} = e^{\sqrt{2} \ln 2}$

11. (a) $\displaystyle\lim_{x \to +\infty} \left[\left(1 + \frac{1}{x}\right)^x\right]^2 = \left[\lim_{x \to +\infty} \left(1 + \frac{1}{x}\right)^x\right]^2 = e^2$

     (b) $y = 2x$, $\displaystyle\lim_{y \to 0}(1 + y)^{2/y} = \lim_{y \to 0}\left[(1 + y)^{1/y}\right]^2 = e^2$

13. $g'(x) = x^2 - x$

15. (a) $\dfrac{1}{x^3}(3x^2) = \dfrac{3}{x}$ (b) $e^{\ln x} \dfrac{1}{x} = 1$

17. $F'(x) = \dfrac{\cos x}{x^2 + 3}$, $F''(x) = \dfrac{-(x^2 + 3)\sin x - 2x \cos x}{(x^2 + 3)^2}$

     (a) 0   (b) 1/3   (c) 0

19. (a) $\dfrac{d}{dx}\displaystyle\int_1^{x^2} t\sqrt{1 + t}\,dt = x^2\sqrt{1 + x^2}(2x) = 2x^3\sqrt{1 + x^2}$

     (b) $\displaystyle\int_1^{x^2} t\sqrt{1 + t}\,dt = -\frac{2}{3}(x^2 + 1)^{3/2} + \frac{2}{5}(x^2 + 1)^{5/2} - \frac{4\sqrt{2}}{15}$

21. (a) $-\sin x^2$ (b) $-\dfrac{\tan^2 x}{1 + \tan^2 x}\sec^2 x = -\tan^2 x$

23. $-3\dfrac{3x - 1}{9x^2 + 1} + 2x\dfrac{x^2 - 1}{x^4 + 1}$

25. (a) $\sin^2(x^3)(3x^2) - \sin^2(x^2)(2x) = 3x^2 \sin^2(x^3) - 2x \sin^2(x^2)$

     (b) $\dfrac{1}{1 + x}(1) - \dfrac{1}{1 - x}(-1) = \dfrac{2}{1 - x^2}$

27. from geometry, $\displaystyle\int_0^3 f(t)dt = 0$, $\displaystyle\int_3^5 f(t)dt = 6$, $\displaystyle\int_5^7 f(t)dt = 0$; and $\displaystyle\int_7^{10} f(t)dt = \int_7^{10}(4t - 37)/3\,dt = -3$

     (a) $F(0) = 0$, $F(3) = 0$, $F(5) = 6$, $F(7) = 6$, $F(10) = 3$

     (b) F is increasing where $F' = f$ is positive, so on $[3/2, 6]$ and $[37/4, 10]$, decreasing on $[0, 3/2]$ and $[6, 37/4]$

     (c) critical points when $F'(x) = f(x) = 0$, so $x = 3/2, 6, 37/4$; maximum 15/2 at $x = 6$, minimum $-9/4$ at $x = 3/2$

(d)

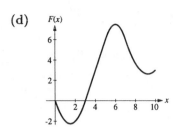

29. $x < 0 : F(x) = \int_{-1}^{x} (-t)dt = -\frac{1}{2}t^2 \Big]_{-1}^{x} = \frac{1}{2}(1 - x^2)$,

$x \geq 0 : F(x) = \int_{-1}^{0} (-t)dt + \int_{0}^{x} t\, dt = \frac{1}{2} + \frac{1}{2}x^2; \; F(x) = \begin{cases} (1 - x^2)/2, & x < 0 \\ (1 + x^2)/2, & x \geq 0 \end{cases}$

31. $y(x) = 2 + \int_{1}^{x} t^{1/3}dt = 2 + \frac{3}{4}t^{4/3} \Big]_{1}^{x} = \frac{5}{4} + \frac{3}{4}x^{4/3}$

33. $y(x) = 1 + \int_{\pi/4}^{x} (\sec^2 t - \sin t)dt = \tan x + \cos x - \sqrt{2}/2$

35. $P(x) = P_0 + \int_{0}^{x} r(t)dt$ individuals

37. II has a minimum at $x = 1$, and I has a zero there, so I could be the derivative of II; on the other hand I has a minimum near $x = 1/3$, but II is not zero there, so II could not be the derivative of I

39. **(a)** where $f(t) = 0$; by the first derivative test, at $t = 3$

(b) where $f(t) = 0$; by the first derivative test, at $t = 1$

(c) at $t = 0, 1$ or 5; from the graph it is evident that it is at $t = 5$

(d) at $t = 0, 3$ or 5; from the graph it is evident that it is at $t = 3$

(e) F is concave up when $F'' = f'$ is positive, i.e. where f is increasing, so on $(0, 1/2)$ and $(2, 4)$; it is concave down on $(1/2, 2)$ and $(4, 5)$

(f)

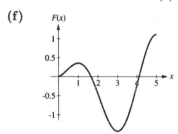

41. $C'(x) = \cos(\pi x^2/2)$, $C''(x) = -\pi x \sin(\pi x^2/2)$

(a) $\cos t$ goes from negative to positive at $2k\pi - \pi/2$, and from positive to negative at $t = 2k\pi + \pi/2$, so $C(x)$ has relative minima when $\pi x^2/2 = 2k\pi - \pi/2$, $x = \pm\sqrt{4k - 1}$, $k = 1, 2, \ldots$, and $C(x)$ has relative maxima when $\pi x^2/2 = (4k + 1)\pi/2$, $x = \pm\sqrt{4k + 1}$, $k = 0, 1, \ldots$.

(b) $\sin t$ changes sign at $t = k\pi$, so $C(x)$ has inflection points at $\pi x^2/2 = k\pi$, $x = \pm\sqrt{2k}$, $k = 1, 2, \ldots$; the case $k = 0$ is distinct due to the factor of x in $C''(x)$, but x changes sign at $x = 0$ and $\sin(\pi x^2/2)$ does not, so there is also a point of inflection at $x = 0$

43. Differentiate: $f(x) = 3e^{3x}$, so $2 + \int_a^x f(t)dt = 2 + \int_a^x 3e^{3t}dt = 2 + e^{3t}\Big]_a^x = 2 + e^{3x} - e^{3a} = e^{3x}$ provided $e^{3a} = 2$, $a = (\ln 2)/3$.

45. From Exercise 44(d) $\left| e - \left(1 + \dfrac{1}{50}\right)^{50} \right| < y(50)$, and from the graph $y(50) < 0.06$

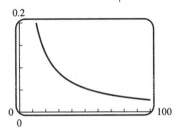

CHAPTER 7 SUPPLEMENTARY EXERCISES

5. If the acceleration $a = $ const, then $v(t) = at + v_0$, $s(t) = \frac{1}{2}at^2 + v_0t + s_0$

7. **(a)** $\dfrac{1}{2} + \dfrac{1}{4} = \dfrac{3}{4}$ **(b)** $-1 - \dfrac{1}{2} = -\dfrac{3}{2}$

    (c) $5\left(-1 - \dfrac{3}{4}\right) = -\dfrac{35}{4}$ **(d)** -2

    (e) not enough information   **(f)** not enough information

9. **(a)** $\displaystyle\int_{-1}^1 dx + \int_{-1}^1 \sqrt{1 - x^2}dx = 2(1) + \pi(1)^2/2 = 2 + \pi/2$

    (b) $\dfrac{1}{3}(x^2 + 1)^{3/2}\Big]_0^3 - \pi(3)^2/4 = \dfrac{1}{3}(10^{3/2} - 1) - 9\pi/4$

    (c) $u = x^2$, $du = 2xdx$; $\dfrac{1}{2}\displaystyle\int_0^1 \sqrt{1 - u^2}du = \dfrac{1}{2}\pi(1)^2/4 = \pi/8$

11. The rectangle with vertices $(0,0)$, $(\pi, 0)$, $(\pi, 1)$ and $(0, 1)$ has area π and is much too large; so is the triangle with vertices $(0,0)$, $(\pi, 0)$ and $(\pi, 1)$ which has area $\pi/2$; $1 - \pi$ is negative; so the answer is $35\pi/128$.

13. Since $y = e^x$ and $y = \ln x$ are inverse functions, their graphs are symmetric with respect to the line $y = x$; consequently the areas A_1 and A_3 are equal (see figure). But $A_1 + A_2 = e$, so

$$\int_1^e \ln xdx + \int_0^1 e^x dx = A_2 + A_3 = A_2 + A_1 = e$$

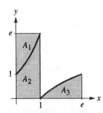

15. Since $f(x) = \dfrac{1}{x}$ is positive and increasing on the interval $[1, 2]$, the left endpoint approximation overestimates the integral of $\dfrac{1}{x}$ and the right endpoint approximation underestimates it.

    (a) For $n = 5$ this becomes

$$0.2\left[\frac{1}{1.2} + \frac{1}{1.4} + \frac{1}{1.6} + \frac{1}{1.8} + \frac{1}{2.0}\right] < \int_1^2 \frac{1}{x}dx < 0.2\left[\frac{1}{1.0} + \frac{1}{1.2} + \frac{1}{1.4} + \frac{1}{1.6} + \frac{1}{1.8}\right]$$

(b) For general n the left endpoint approximation to $\int_1^2 \frac{1}{x} dx = \ln 2$ is

$$\frac{1}{n}\sum_{k=1}^{n}\frac{1}{1+(k-1)/n} = \sum_{k=1}^{n}\frac{1}{n+k-1} = \sum_{k=0}^{n-1}\frac{1}{n+k} \text{ and the right endpoint approximation is}$$

$$\sum_{k=1}^{n}\frac{1}{n+k}. \text{ This yields } \sum_{k=1}^{n}\frac{1}{n+k} < \int_1^2 \frac{1}{x}dx < \sum_{k=0}^{n-1}\frac{1}{n+k} \text{ which is the desired inequality.}$$

(c) By telescoping, the difference is $\frac{1}{n} - \frac{1}{2n} = \frac{1}{2n}$ so $\frac{1}{2n} \leq 0.1$, $n \geq 5$

(d) $n \geq 1{,}000$

17. **(a)** $1\cdot2 + 2\cdot3 + \cdots + n(n+1) = \sum_{k=1}^{n} k(k+1) = \sum_{k=1}^{n} k^2 + \sum_{k=1}^{n} k$

$$= \frac{1}{6}n(n+1)(2n+1) + \frac{1}{2}n(n+1) = \frac{1}{3}n(n+1)(n+2)$$

(b) $\sum_{k=1}^{n-1}\left(\frac{9}{n} - \frac{k}{n^2}\right) = \frac{9}{n}\sum_{k=1}^{n-1}1 - \frac{1}{n^2}\sum_{k=1}^{n-1}k = \frac{9}{n}(n-1) - \frac{1}{n^2}\cdot\frac{1}{2}(n-1)(n) = \frac{17}{2}\left(\frac{n-1}{n}\right)$;

$$\lim_{n\to+\infty}\frac{17}{2}\left(\frac{n-1}{n}\right) = \frac{17}{2}$$

(c) $\sum_{i=1}^{3}\left[\sum_{j=1}^{2} i + \sum_{j=1}^{2} j\right] = \sum_{i=1}^{3}\left[2i + \frac{1}{2}(2)(3)\right] = 2\sum_{i=1}^{3} i + \sum_{i=1}^{3} 3 = 2\cdot\frac{1}{2}(3)(4) + (3)(3) = 21$

19. **(a)** If $u = \sec x$, $du = \sec x \tan x\,dx$, $\int \sec^2 x \tan x\,dx = \int u\,du = u^2/2 + C_1 = (\sec^2 x)/2 + C_1$;

if $u = \tan x$, $du = \sec^2 x\,dx$, $\int \sec^2 x \tan x\,dx = \int u\,du = u^2/2 + C_2 = (\tan^2 x)/2 + C_2$.

(b) They are equal only if $\sec^2 x$ and $\tan^2 x$ differ by a constant, which is true.

21. $\int \sqrt{1 + x^{-2/3}}\,dx = \int x^{-1/3}\sqrt{x^{2/3} + 1}\,dx$; $u = x^{2/3} + 1$, $du = \frac{2}{3}x^{-1/3}dx$

$$\frac{3}{2}\int u^{1/2}du = u^{3/2} + C = (x^{2/3} + 1)^{3/2} + C$$

23. **(a)** $\int_1^x \frac{1}{1+t^2}dt$

(b) $\int_{\tan(\pi/4-2)}^x \frac{1}{1+t^2}dt$

25. $F'(x) = \frac{1}{1+x^2} + \frac{1}{1+(1/x)^2}(-1/x^2) = 0$ so F is constant on $(0, +\infty)$.

27. **(a)** The domain is $(-\infty, +\infty)$; $F(x)$ is 0 if $x = 1$, positive if $x > 1$, and negative if $x < 1$, because the integrand is positive, so the sign of the integral depends on the orientation (forwards or backwards).

(b) The domain is $[-2, 2]$; $F(x)$ is 0 if $x = -1$, positive if $-1 < x \leq 2$, and negative if $-2 \leq x < -1$; same reasons as in part (a).

29. **(a)** $\int_0^{24}\left(2000e^{-t/48} + 500\sin(\pi t/12)\right)dt = 96000(1 - 1/\sqrt{e}) \approx 37{,}773.06$

(b) $\frac{1}{8-0}\int_0^8\left(2000e^{-t/48} + 500\sin(\pi t/12)dt\right) = 1125/\pi + 12000(1 - e^{-1/6}) \approx 2{,}200.32$

(c)

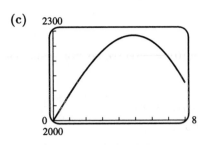

(d) maximum rate is 2285.32 kW/h at $t = 4.8861$

31. **(a)** no, since the velocity curve is not a straight line

    (b) $25 < t < 40$

    (c) 3.54 ft/s

    (d) 141.5 ft

    (e) no since the velocity is positive and the acceleration is never negative

    (f) need the position at any one given time (e.g. s_0)

33. $u = 5 + 2\sin 3x$, $du = 6\cos 3x\,dx$; $\displaystyle\int \frac{1}{6\sqrt{u}}du = \frac{1}{3}u^{1/2} + C = \frac{1}{3}\sqrt{5 + 2\sin 3x} + C$

35. $u = ax^3 + b$, $du = 3ax^2 dx$; $\displaystyle\int \frac{1}{3au^2}du = -\frac{1}{3au} + C = -\frac{1}{3a^2 x^3 + 3ab} + C$

37. $\ln(e^x) + \ln(e^{-x}) = \ln(e^x e^{-x}) = \ln 1 = 0$ so $\displaystyle\int [\ln(e^x) + \ln(e^{-x})]dx = C$

39. $u = \ln x$, $du = (1/x)dx$; $\displaystyle\int_1^2 \frac{1}{u}du = \ln u \Big]_1^2 = \ln 2$

41. $u = e^{-2x}$, $du = -2e^{-2x}dx$; $\displaystyle -\frac{1}{2}\int_1^{1/4}(1 + \cos u)du = \frac{3}{8} + \frac{1}{2}\left(\sin 1 - \sin\frac{1}{4}\right)$

43. With $b = 1.618034$, area $= \displaystyle\int_0^b (x + x^2 - x^3)dx = 1.007514$.

45. **(a)** Solve $\dfrac{1}{4}k^4 - k - k^2 + \dfrac{7}{4} = 0$ to get $k = 2.073948$.

    (b) Solve $-\dfrac{1}{2}\cos 2k + \dfrac{1}{3}k^3 + \dfrac{1}{2} = 3$ to get $k = 1.837992$.

47. **(a)**   **(b)** 0.7651976866   **(c)** $J_0(x) = 0$ if $x = 2.404826$

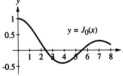

49. $100,000/(\ln 100,000) \approx 8,686$; $\displaystyle\int_2^{100,000} \frac{1}{\ln t}dt \approx 9,629$, so the integral is better

CHAPTER 7 HORIZON MODULE

1. $v_x(0) = 35 \cos\alpha$, so from Equation (1), $x(t) = (35\cos\alpha)t$; $v_y(0) = 35\sin\alpha$, so from Equation (2), $y(t) = (35\sin\alpha)t - 4.9t^2$.

3. $t = x/(35\cos\alpha)$ so $y = (35\sin\alpha)(x/(35\cos\alpha)) - 4.9(x/(35\cos\alpha))^2 = (\tan\alpha)x - \dfrac{0.004}{\cos^2\alpha}x^2$;
   the trajectory is a parabola because y is a quadratic function of x.

5. $y(t) = (35\sin\alpha\ \text{s})t - 4.9t^2 = 0$ when $t = 35\sin\alpha/4.9$, at which time
   $x = (35\cos\alpha)(35\sin\alpha/4.9) = 125\sin 2\alpha$; this is the maximum value of x, so $R = 125\sin 2\alpha$ m.

7. $0.4019 < \alpha < 0.4636$ (radians), or $23.03° < \alpha < 26.57°$

APPENDIX A
Real Numbers, Intervals, and Inequalities

EXERCISE SET A

1. **(a)** rational **(b)** integer, rational **(c)** integer, rational
   (d) rational **(e)** integer, rational **(f)** irrational
   (g) rational **(h)** integer, rational

3. **(a)** $x = 0.123123123\ldots$, $1000x = 123 + x$, $x = 123/999 = 41/333$

   (b) $x = 12.7777\ldots$, $10(x - 12) = 7 + (x - 12)$, $9x = 115$, $x = 115/9$

   (c) $x = 38.07818181\ldots$, $100x = 3807.81818181\ldots$, $99x = 100x - x = 3769.74$,
   $$x = \frac{3769.74}{99} = \frac{376974}{9900} = \frac{20943}{550}$$

   (d) $\dfrac{4296}{10000}$

5. **(a)** If r is the radius, then $D = 2r$ so $\left(\dfrac{8}{9}D\right)^2 = \left(\dfrac{16}{9}r\right)^2 = \dfrac{256}{81}r^2$. The area of a circle of radius r is
   πr^2 so $256/81$ was the approximation used for π.

   (b) $22/7 \approx 3.1429$ is better than $256/81 \approx 3.1605$.

7.

Line	2	3	4	5	6	7
Blocks	3, 4	1, 2	3, 4	2, 4, 5	1, 2	3, 4

9. **(a)** always correct (add -3 to both sides of $a \le b$)

   (b) not always correct (correct only if $a = b$)

   (c) not always correct (correct only if $a = b$)

   (d) always correct (multiply both sides of $a \le b$ by 6)

   (e) not always correct (correct only if $a \ge 0$)

   (f) always correct (multiply both sides of $a \le b$ by the nonnegative quantity a^2)

11. **(a)** all values because $a = a$ is always valid **(b)** none

13. **(a)** yes, because $a \le b$ is true if $a < b$ **(b)** no, because $a < b$ is false if $a = b$ is true

15. **(a)** $\{x : x \text{ is a positive odd integer}\}$ **(b)** $\{x : x \text{ is an even integer}\}$
   (c) $\{x : x \text{ is irrational}\}$ **(d)** $\{x : x \text{ is an integer and } 7 \le x \le 10\}$

17. **(a)** false, there are points inside the triangle that are not inside the circle

   (b) true, all points inside the triangle are also inside the square

   (c) true **(d)** false **(e)** true

   (f) true, a is inside the circle **(g)** true

19. **(a)**

4

(b)

−3

(c)

−1   7

(d)

−3   3

(e)

−3   3

(f)

−3   3

21. **(a)** $[-2, 2]$ **(b)** $(-\infty, -2) \cup (2, +\infty)$

23. $3x < 10$; $(-\infty, 10/3)$ **25.** $2x \leq -11$; $(-\infty, -11/2]$

$\frac{10}{3}$

$-\frac{11}{2}$

27. $2x \leq 1$ and $2x > -3$; $(-3/2, 1/2]$

$-\frac{3}{2}$ $\frac{1}{2}$

29. $\dfrac{x}{x-3} - 4 < 0$, $\dfrac{12-3x}{x-3} < 0$, $\dfrac{4-x}{x-3} < 0$;

$(-\infty, 3) \cup (4, +\infty)$

31. $\dfrac{3x+1}{x-2} - 1 = \dfrac{2x+3}{x-2} < 0$, $\dfrac{x+3/2}{x-2} < 0$;

$\left(-\frac{3}{2}, 2\right)$

33. $\dfrac{4}{2-x} - 1 = \dfrac{x+2}{2-x} \le 0;\ (-\infty, -2] \cup (2, +\infty)$

35. $x^2 - 9 = (x+3)(x-3) > 0;$
$(-\infty, -3) \cup (3, +\infty)$

37. $(x-4)(x+2) > 0;\ (-\infty, -2) \cup (4, +\infty)$

39. $(x-4)(x-5) \le 0;\ [4, 5]$

41. $\dfrac{3}{x-4} - \dfrac{2}{x} = \dfrac{x+8}{x(x-4)} > 0;\ (-8,0) \cup (4,+\infty)$

43. By trial-and-error we find that $x = 2$ is a root of the equation $x^3 - x^2 - x - 2 = 0$ so $x - 2$ is a factor of $x^3 - x^2 - x - 2$. By long division we find that $x^2 + x + 1$ is another factor so $x^3 - x^2 - x - 2 = (x-2)(x^2 + x + 1)$. The linear factors of $x^2 + x + 1$ can be determined by first finding the roots of $x^2 + x + 1 = 0$ by the quadratic formula. These roots are complex numbers so $x^2 + x + 1 \neq 0$ for all real x; thus $x^2 + x + 1$ must be always positive or always negative. Since $x^2 + x + 1$ is positive when $x = 0$, it follows that $x^2 + x + 1 > 0$ for all real x. Hence $x^3 - x^2 - x - 2 > 0$, $(x-2)(x^2 + x + 1) > 0$, $x - 2 > 0$, $x > 2$, so $S = (2,+\infty)$.

45. $\sqrt{x^2 + x - 6}$ is real if $x^2 + x - 6 \geq 0$. Factor to get $(x+3)(x-2) \geq 0$ which has as its solution $x \leq -3$ or $x \geq 2$.

47. $25 \leq \dfrac{5}{9}(F - 32) \leq 40,\ 45 \leq F - 32 \leq 72,\ 77 \leq F \leq 104$

49. **(a)** Assume m and n are rational, then $m = \dfrac{p}{q}$ and $n = \dfrac{r}{s}$ where p, q, r, and s are integers so
$m + n = \dfrac{p}{q} + \dfrac{r}{s} = \dfrac{ps + rq}{qs}$ which is rational because $ps + rq$ and qs are integers.

  (b) (proof by contradiction) Assume m is rational and n is irrational, then $m = \dfrac{p}{q}$ where p and q are integers. Suppose that $m + n$ is rational, then $m + n = \dfrac{r}{s}$ where r and s are integers so
$n = \dfrac{r}{s} - m = \dfrac{r}{s} - \dfrac{p}{q} = \dfrac{rq - ps}{sq}$. But $rq - ps$ and sq are integers, so n is rational which contradicts the assumption that n is irrational.

51. $a = \sqrt{2}, b = \sqrt{3}, c = \sqrt{6}, d = -\sqrt{2}$ are irrational, and $a + d = 0$, a rational; $a + a = 2\sqrt{2}$, an irrational; $ad = -2$, a rational; and $ab = c$, an irrational.

53. The average of a and b is $\frac{1}{2}(a + b)$; if a and b are rational then so is the average, by Exercise 49(a) and Exercise 50(a). On the other hand if $a = b = \sqrt{2}$ then the average of a and b is irrational, but the average of a and $-b$ is rational.

55. $8x^3 - 4x^2 - 2x + 1$ can be factored by grouping terms:
$(8x^3 - 4x^2) - (2x - 1) = 4x^2(2x - 1) - (2x - 1) = (2x - 1)(4x^2 - 1) = (2x - 1)^2(2x + 1)$. The problem, then, is to solve $(2x - 1)^2(2x + 1) < 0$. By inspection, $x = 1/2$ is not a solution. If $x \neq 1/2$, then $(2x - 1)^2 > 0$ and it follows that $2x + 1 < 0$, $2x < -1$, $x < -1/2$, so $S = (-\infty, -1/2)$.

57. If $a < b$, then $ac < bc$ because c is positive; if $c < d$, then $bc < bd$ because b is positive, so $ac < bd$ (Theorem A.1(a)).

APPENDIX B
Absolute Value

EXERCISE SET B

1. **(a)** 7   **(b)** $\sqrt{2}$ **(c)** k^2 **(d)** k^2

3. $|x - 3| = |3 - x| = 3 - x$ if $3 - x \geq 0$, which is true if $x \leq 3$

5. All real values of x because $x^2 + 9 > 0$.

7. $|3x^2 + 2x| = |x(3x + 2)| = |x||3x + 2|$. If $|x||3x + 2| = x|3x + 2|$, then $|x||3x + 2| - x|3x + 2| = 0$, $(|x| - x)|3x + 2| = 0$, so either $|x| - x = 0$ or $|3x + 2| = 0$. If $|x| - x = 0$, then $|x| = x$, which is true for $x \geq 0$. If $|3x + 2| = 0$, then $x = -2/3$. The statement is true for $x \geq 0$ or $x = -2/3$.

9. $\sqrt{(x + 5)^2} = |x + 5| = x + 5$ if $x + 5 \geq 0$, which is true if $x \geq -5$.

13. **(a)** $|7 - 9| = |-2| = 2$ **(b)** $|3 - 2| = |1| = 1$
    (c) $|6 - (-8)| = |14| = 14$ **(d)** $|-3 - \sqrt{2}| = |-(3 + \sqrt{2})| = 3 + \sqrt{2}$
    (e) $|-4 - (-11)| = |7| = 7$ **(f)** $|-5 - 0| = |-5| = 5$

15. **(a)** B is 6 units to the left of A; $b = a - 6 = -3 - 6 = -9$.

    (b) B is 9 units to the right of A; $b = a + 9 = -2 + 9 = 7$.

    (c) B is 7 units from A; either $b = a + 7 = 5 + 7 = 12$ or $b = a - 7 = 5 - 7 = -2$. Since it is given that $b > 0$, it follows that $b = 12$.

17. $|6x - 2| = 7$

Case 1:	Case 2:
$6x - 2 = 7$	$6x - 2 = -7$
$6x = 9$	$6x = -5$
$x = 3/2$	$x = -5/6$

19. $|6x - 7| = |3 + 2x|$

Case 1:	Case 2:
$6x - 7 = 3 + 2x$	$6x - 7 = -(3 + 2x)$
$4x = 10$	$8x = 4$
$x = 5/2$	$x = 1/2$

21. $|9x| - 11 = x$

Case 2:	
$9x - 11 = x$	$-9x - 11 = x$
$8x = 11$	$-10x = 11$
$x = 11/8$	$x = -11/10$

23. $\left|\dfrac{x + 5}{2 - x}\right| = 6$

Case 1:	Case 2:
$\dfrac{x + 5}{2 - x} = 6$	$\dfrac{x + 5}{2 - x} = -6$
$x + 5 = 12 - 6x$	$x + 5 = -12 + 6x$
$7x = 7$	$-5x = -17$
$x = 1$	$x = 17/5$

25. $|x + 6| < 3$
    $-3 < x + 6 < 3$
    $-9 < x < -3$
    $S = (-9, -3)$

27. $|2x - 3| \leq 6$
    $-6 \leq 2x - 3 \leq 6$
    $-3 \leq 2x \leq 9$
    $-3/2 \leq x \leq 9/2$
    $S = [-3/2, 9/2]$

29. $|x + 2| > 1$

Case 1:   Case 2:

$x + 2 > 1$ $x + 2 < -1$

   $x > -1$ $x < -3$

$S = (-\infty, -3) \cup (-1, +\infty)$

31. $|5 - 2x| \geq 4$

Case 1:   Case 2:

$5 - 2x \geq 4$ $5 - 2x \leq -4$

  $-2x \geq -1$ $-2x \leq -9$

    $x \leq 1/2$ $x \geq 9/2$

$S = (-\infty, 1/2] \cup [9/2, +\infty)$

33. $\dfrac{1}{|x - 1|} < 2, x \neq 1$

$|x - 1| > 1/2$

Case 1:   Case 2:

$x - 1 > 1/2$ $x - 1 < -1/2$

  $x > 3/2$ $x < 1/2$

$S = (-\infty, 1/2) \cup (3/2, +\infty)$

35. $\dfrac{3}{|2x - 1|} \geq 4, x \neq 1/2$

$\dfrac{|2x - 1|}{3} \leq \dfrac{1}{4}$

$|2x - 1| \leq 3/4$

$-3/4 \leq 2x - 1 \leq 3/4$

$1/4 \leq 2x \leq 7/4$

$1/8 \leq x \leq 7/8$

$S = [1/8, 1/2) \cup (1/2, 7/8]$

37. $\sqrt{(x^2 - 5x + 6)^2} = x^2 - 5x + 6$ if $x^2 - 5x + 6 \geq 0$ or, equivalently, if $(x - 2)(x - 3) \geq 0$; $x \in (-\infty, 2] \cup [3, +\infty)$.

39. If $u = |x - 3|$ then $u^2 - 4u = 12$, $u^2 - 4u - 12 = 0$, $(u - 6)(u + 2) = 0$, so $u = 6$ or $u = -2$. If $u = 6$ then $|x - 3| = 6$, so $x = 9$ or $x = -3$. If $u = -2$ then $|x - 3| = -2$ which is impossible. The solutions are -3 and 9.

41. $|a - b| = |a + (-b)|$

       $\leq |a| + |-b|$ (triangle inequality)

       $= |a| + |b|$.

43. From Exercise 42

(i) $|a| - |b| \leq |a - b|$; but $|b| - |a| \leq |b - a| = |a - b|$, so (ii) $|a| - |b| \geq -|a - b|$.

Combining (i) and (ii): $-|a - b| \leq |a| - |b| \leq |a - b|$, so $||a| - |b|| \leq |a - b|$.

APPENDIX C
Coordinate Planes and Lines

EXERCISE SET C

1.

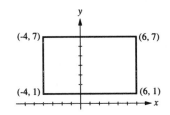

3. **(a)** $x = 2$

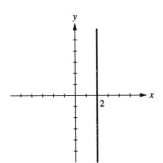

(b) $y = -3$

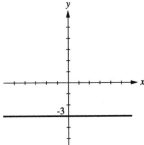

(c) $x \geq 0$

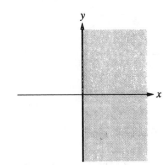

(d) $y = x$

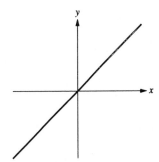

(e) $y \geq x$

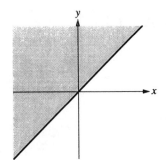

(f) $|x| \geq 1$

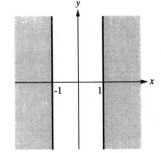

5. $y = 4 - x^2$

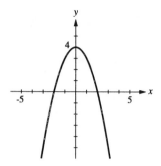

7. $y = \sqrt{x - 4}$

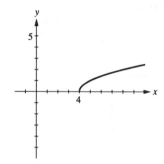

9. $x^2 - x + y = 0$

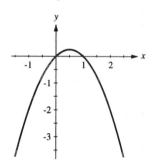

11. $x^2 y = 2$

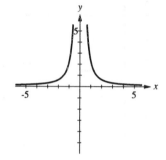

13. **(a)** $m = \dfrac{4 - 2}{3 - (-1)} = \dfrac{1}{2}$

(b) $m = \dfrac{1 - 3}{7 - 5} = -1$

(c) $m = \dfrac{\sqrt{2} - \sqrt{2}}{-3 - 4} = 0$

(d) $m = \dfrac{12 - (-6)}{-2 - (-2)} = \dfrac{18}{0}$, not defined

15. **(a)** The line through $(1, 1)$ and $(-2, -5)$ has slope $m_1 = \dfrac{-5 - 1}{-2 - 1} = 2$, the line through $(1, 1)$ and $(0, -1)$ has slope $m_2 = \dfrac{-1 - 1}{0 - 1} = 2$. The given points lie on a line because $m_1 = m_2$.

(b) The line through $(-2, 4)$ and $(0, 2)$ has slope $m_1 = \dfrac{2 - 4}{0 + 2} = -1$, the line through $(-2, 4)$ and $(1, 5)$ has slope $m_2 = \dfrac{5 - 4}{1 + 2} = \dfrac{1}{3}$. The given points do not lie on a line because $m_1 \neq m_2$.

17.

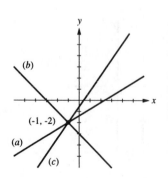

19. III < II < IV < I

21. Use the points $(1, 2)$ and (x, y) to calculate the slope: $(y - 2)/(x - 1) = 3$

    (a) if $x = 5$, then $(y - 2)/(5 - 1) = 3$, $y - 2 = 12$, $y = 14$

    (b) if $y = -2$, then $(-2 - 2)/(x - 1) = 3$, $x - 1 = -4/3$, $x = -1/3$

23. Using $(3, k)$ and $(-2, 4)$ to calculate the slope, we find $\dfrac{k - 4}{3 - (-2)} = 5$, $k - 4 = 25$, $k = 29$.

25. $\dfrac{0 - 2}{x - 1} = -\dfrac{0 - 5}{x - 4}$, $-2x + 8 = 5x - 5$, $7x = 13$, $x = 13/7$

27. Show that opposite sides are parallel by showing that they have the same slope:
using $(3, -1)$ and $(6, 4)$, $m_1 = 5/3$; using $(6, 4)$ and $(-3, 2)$, $m_2 = 2/9$;
using $(-3, 2)$ and $(-6, -3)$, $m_3 = 5/3$; using $(-6, -3)$ and $(3, -1)$, $m_4 = 2/9$.
Opposite sides are parallel because $m_1 = m_3$ and $m_2 = m_4$.

29. **(a)**
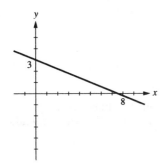

       (b)
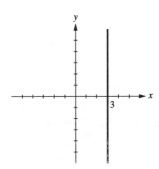

    (c)
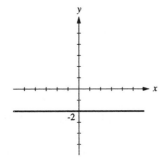

       (c)
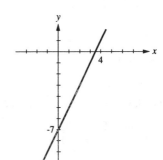

31. **(a)**
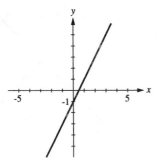
  (b)
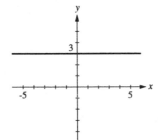
  (c)
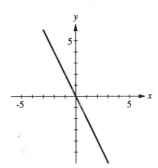

33. **(a)** $m = 3$, $b = 2$ **(b)** $m = -\dfrac{1}{4}$, $b = 3$

    (c) $y = -\dfrac{3}{5}x + \dfrac{8}{5}$ so $m = -\dfrac{3}{5}$, $b = \dfrac{8}{5}$ **(d)** $m = 0$, $b = 1$

    (e) $y = -\dfrac{b}{a}x + b$ so $m = -\dfrac{b}{a}$, y-intercept b

35. **(a)** $m = (0 - (-3))/(2 - 0)) = 3/2$ so $y = 3x/2 - 3$

      (b) $m = (-3 - 0)/(4 - 0) = -3/4$ so $y = -3x/4$

37. $y = -2x + 4$

39. The slope m of the line must equal the slope of $y = 4x - 2$, thus $m = 4$ so the equation is $y = 4x + 7$.

41. The slope m of the line must be the negative reciprocal of the slope of $y = 5x + 9$, thus $m = -1/5$ and the equation is $y = -x/5 + 6$.

43. $y - 4 = \dfrac{-7 - 4}{1 - 2}(x - 2) = 11(x - 2)$, $y = 11x - 18$.

45. The line passes through $(0, 2)$ and $(-4, 0)$, thus $m = \dfrac{0 - 2}{-4 - 0} = \dfrac{1}{2}$ so $y = \dfrac{1}{2}x + 2$.

47. $y = 1$

49. **(a)** $m_1 = 4$, $m_2 = 4$; parallel because $m_1 = m_2$

      (b) $m_1 = 2$, $m_2 = -1/2$; perpendicular because $m_1 m_2 = -1$

      (c) $m_1 = 5/3$, $m_2 = 5/3$; parallel because $m_1 = m_2$

      (d) If $A \neq 0$ and $B \neq 0$, then $m_1 = -A/B$, $m_2 = B/A$ and the lines are perpendicular because $m_1 m_2 = -1$. If either A or B (but not both) is zero, then the lines are perpendicular because one is horizontal and the other is vertical.

      (e) $m_1 = 4$, $m_2 = 1/4$; neither

51. $y = (-3/k)x + 4/k$, $k \neq 0$

      (a) $-3/k = 2$, $k = -3/2$

      (b) $4/k = 5$, $k = 4/5$

      (c) $3(-2) + k(4) = 4$, $k = 5/2$

      (d) The slope of $2x - 5y = 1$ is $2/5$ so $-3/k = 2/5$, $k = -15/2$.

      (e) The slope of $4x + 3y = 2$ is $-4/3$ so the slope of the line perpendicular to it is $3/4$; $-3/k = 3/4$, $k = -4$.

53. $(x - y)(x + y) = 0$: the union of the graphs of $x - y = 0$ and $x + y = 0$

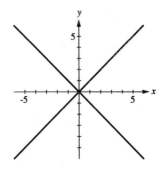

55. $u = 3v^2$

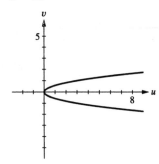

57. Solve $x = 5t + 2$ for t to get $t = \dfrac{1}{5}x - \dfrac{2}{5}$, so $y = \left(\dfrac{1}{5}x - \dfrac{2}{5}\right) - 3 = \dfrac{1}{5}x - \dfrac{17}{5}$, which is a line.

59. An equation of the line through $(1, 4)$ and $(2, 1)$ is $y = -3x + 7$. It crosses the y-axis at $y = 7$, and the x-axis at $x = 7/3$, so the area of the triangle is $\dfrac{1}{2}(7)(7/3) = 49/6$.

61. **(a)** yes   **(b)** yes   **(c)** no   **(d)** yes   **(e)** yes   **(f)** yes   **(g)** no

APPENDIX D
Distance, Circles, Quadratic Equations

EXERCISE SET D

1. in the proof of Theorem D.1

3. (a) $d = \sqrt{(1-7)^2 + (9-1)^2} = \sqrt{36+64} = \sqrt{100} = 10$

    (b) $\left(\dfrac{7+1}{2}, \dfrac{1+9}{2}\right) = (4,5)$

5. (a) $d = \sqrt{[-7-(-2)]^2 + [-4-(-6)]^2} = \sqrt{25+4} = \sqrt{29}$

    (b) $\left(\dfrac{-2+(-7)}{2}, \dfrac{-6+(-4)}{2}\right) = (-9/2, -5)$

7. Let $A(5,-2)$, $B(6,5)$, and $C(2,2)$ be the given vertices and a, b, and c the lengths of the sides opposite these vertices; then
$$a = \sqrt{(2-6)^2 + (2-5)^2} = \sqrt{25} = 5 \text{ and } b = \sqrt{(2-5)^2 + (2+2)^2} = \sqrt{25} = 5.$$
Triangle ABC is isosceles because it has two equal sides ($a = b$).

9. $P_1(0,-2)$, $P_2(-4,8)$, and $P_3(3,1)$ all lie on a circle whose center is $C(-2,3)$ if the points P_1, P_2 and P_3 are equidistant from C. Denoting the distances between P_1, P_2, P_3 and C by d_1, d_2 and d_3 we find that $d_1 = \sqrt{(0+2)^2 + (-2-3)^2} = \sqrt{29}$, $d_2 = \sqrt{(-4+2)^2 + (8-3)^2} = \sqrt{29}$, and $d_3 = \sqrt{(3+2)^2 + (1-3)^2} = \sqrt{29}$, so P_1, P_2 and P_3 lie on a circle whose center is $C(-2,3)$ because $d_1 = d_2 = d_3$.

11. If $(2,k)$ is equidistant from $(3,7)$ and $(9,1)$, then
$$\sqrt{(2-3)^2 + (k-7)^2} = \sqrt{(2-9)^2 + (k-1)^2}, \ 1+(k-7)^2 = 49 + (k-1)^2,$$
$1 + k^2 - 14k + 49 = 49 + k^2 - 2k + 1, \ -12k = 0, \ k = 0.$

13. The slope of the line segment joining $(2,8)$ and $(-4,6)$ is $\dfrac{6-8}{-4-2} = \dfrac{1}{3}$ so the slope of the perpendicular bisector is -3. The midpoint of the line segment is $(-1,7)$ so an equation of the bisector is $y - 7 = -3(x+1); \ y = -3x + 4.$

15. Method (see figure): Find an equation of the perpendicular bisector of the line segment joining $A(3,3)$ and $B(7,-3)$. All points on this perpendicular bisector are equidistant from A and B, thus find where it intersects the given line.

The midpoint of AB is $(5,0)$, the slope of AB is $-3/2$ thus the slope of the perpendicular bisector is $2/3$ so an equation is
$$y - 0 = \frac{2}{3}(x-5)$$
$$3y = 2x - 10$$
$2x - 3y - 10 = 0.$
The solution of the system
$$\begin{cases} 4x - 2y + 3 = 0 \\ 2x - 3y - 10 = 0 \end{cases}$$
gives the point $(-29/8, -23/4)$.

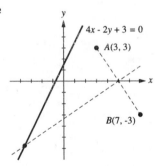

17. Method (see figure): write an equation of the line that goes through the given point and that is perpendicular to the given line; find the point P where this line intersects the given line; find the distance between P and the given point.

The slope of the given line is $4/3$, so the slope of a line perpendicular to it is $-3/4$.

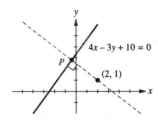

The line through $(2,1)$ having a slope of $-3/4$ is $y-1 = -\dfrac{3}{4}(x-2)$ or, after simplification, $3x+4y = 10$ which when solved simultaneously with $4x-3y+10 = 0$ yields $(-2/5, 14/5)$ as the point of intersection. The distance d between $(-2/5, 14/5)$ and $(2,1)$ is $d = \sqrt{(2+2/5)^2 + (1-14/5)^2} = 3$.

19. If $B = 0$, then the line $Ax + C = 0$ is vertical and $x = -C/A$ for each point on the line. The line through (x_0, y_0) and perpendicular to the given line is horizontal and intersects the given line at the point $(-C/A, y_0)$. The distance d between $(-C/A, y_0)$ and (x_0, y_0) is

$$d = \sqrt{(x_0 + C/A)^2 + (y_0 - y_0)^2} = \sqrt{\frac{(Ax_0 + C)^2}{A^2}} = \frac{|Ax_0 + C|}{\sqrt{A^2}}$$

which is the value of $\dfrac{|Ax_0 + By_0 + C|}{\sqrt{A^2 + B^2}}$ for $B = 0$.

If $B \neq 0$, then the slope of the given line is $-A/B$ and the line through (x_0, y_0) and perpendicular to the given line is

$$y - y_0 = \frac{B}{A}(x - x_0), \ Ay - Ay_0 = Bx - Bx_0, \ Bx - Ay = Bx_0 - Ay_0.$$

The point of intersection of this line and the given line is obtained by solving $Ax + By = -C$ and $Bx - Ay = Bx_0 - Ay_0$.

Multiply the first equation through by A and the second by B and add the results to get

$$(A^2 + B^2)x = B^2 x_0 - ABy_0 - AC \ \text{so} \ x = \frac{B^2 x_0 - ABy_0 - AC}{A^2 + B^2}$$

Similarly, by multiplying by B and $-A$, we get $y = \dfrac{-ABx_0 + A^2 y_0 - BC}{A^2 + B^2}$.

The square of the distance d between (x, y) and (x_0, y_0) is

$$d^2 = \left[x_0 - \frac{B^2 x_0 - ABy_0 - AC}{A^2 + B^2}\right]^2 + \left[y_0 - \frac{-ABx_0 + A^2 y_0 - BC}{A^2 + B^2}\right]^2$$

$$= \frac{(A^2 x_0 + ABy_0 + AC)^2}{(A^2 + B^2)^2} + \frac{(ABx_0 + B^2 y_0 + BC)^2}{(A^2 + B^2)^2}$$

$$= \frac{A^2(Ax_0 + By_0 + C)^2 + B^2(Ax_0 + By_0 + C)^2}{(A^2 + B^2)^2}$$

$$= \frac{(Ax_0 + By_0 + C)^2 (A^2 + B^2)}{(A^2 + B^2)^2} = \frac{(Ax_0 + By_0 + C)^2}{A^2 + B^2}$$

so $d = \dfrac{|Ax_0 + By_0 + C|}{\sqrt{A^2 + B^2}}$.

21. $d = \dfrac{|5(8) + 12(4) - 36|}{\sqrt{5^2 + 12^2}} = \dfrac{|52|}{\sqrt{169}} = \dfrac{52}{13} = 4.$

23. (a) center $(0,0)$, radius 5 (b) center $(1,4)$, radius 4

     (c) center $(-1,-3)$, radius $\sqrt{5}$ (d) center $(0,-2)$, radius 1

25. $(x - 3)^2 + (y - (-2))^2 = 4^2$, $(x - 3)^2 + (y + 2)^2 = 16$

27. $r = 8$ because the circle is tangent to the x-axis, so $(x+4)^2 + (y-8)^2 = 64$.

29. $(0,0)$ is on the circle, so $r = \sqrt{(-3-0)^2 + (-4-0)^2} = 5$; $(x+3)^2 + (y+4)^2 = 25$.

31. The center is the midpoint of the line segment joining $(2,0)$ and $(0,2)$ so the center is at $(1,1)$. The radius is $r = \sqrt{(2-1)^2 + (0-1)^2} = \sqrt{2}$, so $(x-1)^2 + (y-1)^2 = 2$.

33. $(x^2 - 2x) + (y^2 - 4y) = 11$, $(x^2 - 2x + 1) + (y^2 - 4y + 4) = 11 + 1 + 4$, $(x-1)^2 + (y-2)^2 = 16$; center $(1,2)$ and radius 4

35. $2(x^2 + 2x) + 2(y^2 - 2y) = 0$, $2(x^2 + 2x + 1) + 2(y^2 - 2y + 1) = 2 + 2$, $(x+1)^2 + (y-1)^2 = 2$; center $(-1,1)$ and radius $\sqrt{2}$

37. $(x^2 + 2x) + (y^2 + 2y) = -2$, $(x^2 + 2x + 1) + (y^2 + 2y + 1) = -2 + 1 + 1$, $(x+1)^2 + (y+1)^2 = 0$; the point $(-1,-1)$

39. $x^2 + y^2 = 1/9$; center $(0,0)$ and radius $1/3$

41. $x^2 + (y^2 + 10y) = -26$, $x^2 + (y^2 + 10y + 25) = -26 + 25$, $x^2 + (y+5)^2 = -1$; no graph

43. $16\left(x^2 + \dfrac{5}{2}x\right) + 16(y^2 + y) = 7$, $16\left(x^2 + \dfrac{5}{2}x + \dfrac{25}{16}\right) + 16\left(y^2 + y + \dfrac{1}{4}\right) = 7 + 25 + 4$,

$(x + 5/4)^2 + (y + 1/2)^2 = 9/4$; center $(-5/4, -1/2)$ and radius $3/2$

45. **(a)** $y^2 = 16 - x^2$, so $y = \pm\sqrt{16 - x^2}$. The bottom half is $y = -\sqrt{16 - x^2}$.

   (b) Complete the square in y to get $(y-2)^2 = 3 - 2x - x^2$, so $y - 2 = \pm\sqrt{3 - 2x - x^2}$, or $y = 2 \pm \sqrt{3 - 2x - x^2}$. The top half is $y = 2 + \sqrt{3 - 2x - x^2}$.

47. **(a)**

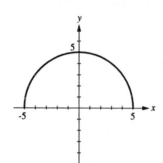

   (b) $y = \sqrt{5 + 4x - x^2}$

   $\quad = \sqrt{5 - (x^2 - 4x)}$

   $\quad = \sqrt{5 + 4 - (x^2 - 4x + 4)}$

   $\quad = \sqrt{9 - (x-2)^2}$

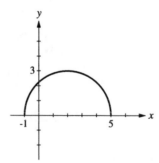

49. The tangent line is perpendicular to the radius at the point. The slope of the radius is $4/3$, so the slope of the perpendicular is $-3/4$. An equation of the tangent line is $y - 4 = -\dfrac{3}{4}(x-3)$, or $y = -\dfrac{3}{4}x + \dfrac{25}{4}$.

51. **(a)** The center of the circle is at $(0,0)$ and its radius is $\sqrt{20} = 2\sqrt{5}$. The distance between P and the center is $\sqrt{(-1)^2 + (2)^2} = \sqrt{5}$ which is less than $2\sqrt{5}$, so P is inside the circle.

(b) Draw the diameter of the circle that passes through P, then the shorter segment of the diameter is the shortest line that can be drawn from P to the circle, and the longer segment is the longest line that can be drawn from P to the circle (can you prove it?). Thus, the smallest distance is $2\sqrt{5} - \sqrt{5} = \sqrt{5}$, and the largest is $2\sqrt{5} + \sqrt{5} = 3\sqrt{5}$.

53. Let (a, b) be the coordinates of T (or T'). The radius from $(0, 0)$ to T (or T') will be perpendicular to L (or L') so, using slopes, $b/a = -(a-3)/b$, $a^2 + b^2 = 3a$. But (a, b) is on the circle so $a^2 + b^2 = 1$, thus $3a = 1$, $a = 1/3$. Let $a = 1/3$ in $a^2 + b^2 = 1$ to get $b^2 = 8/9$, $b = \pm\sqrt{8}/3$. The coordinates of T and T' are $(1/3, \sqrt{8}/3)$ and $(1/3, -\sqrt{8}/3)$.

55. (a) $[(x-4)^2 + (y-1)^2] + [(x-2)^2 + (y+5)^2] = 45$
$x^2 - 8x + 16 + y^2 - 2y + 1 + x^2 - 4x + 4 + y^2 + 10y + 25 = 45$
$2x^2 + 2y^2 - 12x + 8y + 1 = 0$, which is a circle.

(b) $2(x^2 - 6x) + 2(y^2 + 4y) = -1$, $2(x^2 - 6x + 9) + 2(y^2 + 4y + 4) = -1 + 18 + 8$,
$(x-3)^2 + (y+2)^2 = 25/2$; center $(3, -2)$, radius $5/\sqrt{2}$.

57. $y = x^2 + 2$

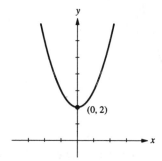

59. $y = x^2 + 2x - 3$

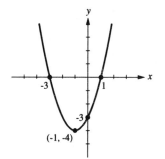

61. $y = -x^2 + 4x + 5$

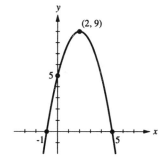

63. $y = (x-2)^2$

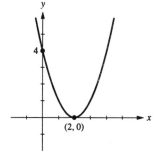

65. $x^2 - 2x + y = 0$

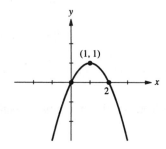

67. $y = 3x^2 - 2x + 1$

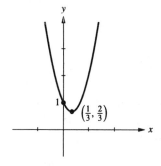

69. $x = -y^2 + 2y + 2$

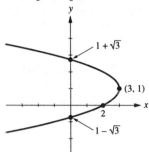

71. (a) $x^2 = 3 - y$, $x = \pm\sqrt{3-y}$. The right half is $x = \sqrt{3-y}$.

     (b)   Complete the square in x to get $(x-1)^2 = y+1$, $x = 1 \pm \sqrt{y+1}$. The left half is $x = 1 - \sqrt{y+1}$.

73. (a)   **(b)**

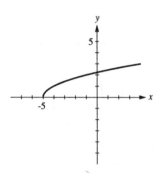 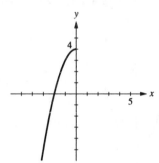

75. (a)   **(b)**   The ball will be at its highest point when $t = 1$ sec; it will rise 16 ft.

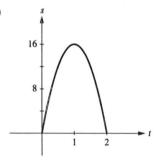

77. (a) $(3)(2x) + (2)(2y) = 600$, $6x + 4y = 600$, $y = 150 - 3x/2$

     (b) $A = xy = x(150 - 3x/2) = 150x - 3x^2/2$

     (c)   The graph of A versus x is a parabola with its vertex (high point) at $x = -b/(2a) = -150/(-3) = 50$, so the maximum value of A is $A = 150(50) - 3(50)^2/2 = 3{,}750 \text{ ft}^2$.

79. (a)   The parabola $y = 2x^2 + 5x - 1$ opens upward and has x-intercepts of $x = (-5 \pm \sqrt{33})/4$, so $2x^2 + 5x - 1 < 0$ if $(-5 - \sqrt{33})/4 < x < (-5 + \sqrt{33})/4$.

     (b)   The parabola $y = x^2 - 2x + 3$ opens upward and has no x-intercepts, so $x^2 - 2x + 3 > 0$ if $-\infty < x < +\infty$.

81. (a)   The t-coordinate of the vertex is $t = -40/[(2)(-16)] = 5/4$, so the maximum height is $s = 5 + 40(5/4) - 16(5/4)^2 = 30$ ft.

     (b) $s = 5 + 40t - 16t^2 = 0$ if $t \approx 2.6$ s

     (c) $s = 5 + 40t - 16t^2 > 12$ if $16t^2 - 40t + 7 < 0$, which is true if $(5 - 3\sqrt{2})/4 < t < (5 + 3\sqrt{2})/4$. The length of this interval is $(5 + 3\sqrt{2})/4 - (5 - 3\sqrt{2})/4 = 3\sqrt{2}/2 \approx 2.1$ s.

APPENDIX E
Trigonometry Review

EXERCISE SET E

1. (a) $5\pi/12$ (b) $13\pi/6$ (c) $\pi/9$ (d) $23\pi/30$

3. (a) $12°$ (b) $(270/\pi)°$ (c) $288°$ (d) $540°$

5.

	$\sin\theta$	$\cos\theta$	$\tan\theta$	$\csc\theta$	$\sec\theta$	$\cot\theta$
(a)	$\sqrt{21}/5$	$2/5$	$\sqrt{21}/2$	$5/\sqrt{21}$	$5/2$	$2/\sqrt{21}$
(b)	$3/4$	$\sqrt{7}/4$	$3/\sqrt{7}$	$4/3$	$4/\sqrt{7}$	$\sqrt{7}/3$
(c)	$3/\sqrt{10}$	$1/\sqrt{10}$	3	$\sqrt{10}/3$	$\sqrt{10}$	$1/3$

7. $\sin\theta = 3/\sqrt{10}$, $\cos\theta = 1/\sqrt{10}$ 9. $\tan\theta = \sqrt{21}/2$, $\csc\theta = 5/\sqrt{21}$

11. Let x be the length of the side adjacent to θ, then $\cos\theta = x/6 = 0.3$, $x = 1.8$.

13.

	θ	$\sin\theta$	$\cos\theta$	$\tan\theta$	$\csc\theta$	$\sec\theta$	$\cot\theta$
(a)	$225°$	$-1/\sqrt{2}$	$-1/\sqrt{2}$	1	$-\sqrt{2}$	$-\sqrt{2}$	1
(b)	$-210°$	$1/2$	$-\sqrt{3}/2$	$-1/\sqrt{3}$	2	$-2/\sqrt{3}$	$-\sqrt{3}$
(c)	$5\pi/3$	$-\sqrt{3}/2$	$1/2$	$-\sqrt{3}$	$-2/\sqrt{3}$	2	$-1/\sqrt{3}$
(d)	$-3\pi/2$	1	0	$-$	1	$-$	0

15.

	$\sin\theta$	$\cos\theta$	$\tan\theta$	$\csc\theta$	$\sec\theta$	$\cot\theta$
(a)	$4/5$	$3/5$	$4/3$	$5/4$	$5/3$	$3/4$
(b)	$-4/5$	$3/5$	$-4/3$	$-5/4$	$5/3$	$-3/4$
(c)	$1/2$	$-\sqrt{3}/2$	$-1/\sqrt{3}$	2	$-2\sqrt{3}$	$-\sqrt{3}$
(d)	$-1/2$	$\sqrt{3}/2$	$-1/\sqrt{3}$	-2	$2/\sqrt{3}$	$-\sqrt{3}$
(e)	$1/\sqrt{2}$	$1/\sqrt{2}$	1	$\sqrt{2}$	$\sqrt{2}$	1
(f)	$1/\sqrt{2}$	$-1/\sqrt{2}$	-1	$\sqrt{2}$	$-\sqrt{2}$	-1

17. (a) $x = 3\sin 25° \approx 1.2679$ (b) $x = 3/\tan(2\pi/9) \approx 3.5753$

19.

	$\sin\theta$	$\cos\theta$	$\tan\theta$	$\csc\theta$	$\sec\theta$	$\cot\theta$
(a)	$a/3$	$\sqrt{9-a^2}/3$	$a/\sqrt{9-a^2}$	$3/a$	$3/\sqrt{9-a^2}$	$\sqrt{9-a^2}/a$
(b)	$a/\sqrt{a^2+25}$	$5/\sqrt{a^2+25}$	$a/5$	$\sqrt{a^2+25}/a$	$\sqrt{a^2+25}/5$	$5/a$
(c)	$\sqrt{a^2-1}/a$	$1/a$	$\sqrt{a^2-1}$	$a/\sqrt{a^2-1}$	a	$1/\sqrt{a^2-1}$

21. (a) $\theta = 3\pi/4 \pm n\pi$, $n = 0, 1, 2, \ldots$

    (b) $\theta = \pi/3 \pm 2n\pi$ and $\theta = 5\pi/3 \pm 2n\pi$, $n = 0, 1, 2, \ldots$

23. (a) $\theta = \pi/6 \pm n\pi$, $n = 0, 1, 2, \ldots$

    (b) $\theta = 4\pi/3 \pm 2n\pi$ and $\theta = 5\pi/3 \pm 2n\pi$, $n = 0, 1, 2, \ldots$

25. **(a)** $\theta = 3\pi/4 \pm n\pi$, $n = 0, 1, 2, \ldots$ **(b)** $\theta = \pi/6 \pm n\pi$, $n = 0, 1, 2, \ldots$

27. **(a)** $\theta = \pi/3 \pm 2n\pi$ and $\theta = 2\pi/3 \pm 2n\pi$, $n = 0, 1, 2, \ldots$

    (b) $\theta = \pi/6 \pm 2n\pi$ and $\theta = 11\pi/6 \pm 2n\pi$, $n = 0, 1, 2, \ldots$

29. $\sin \theta = 2/5$, $\cos \theta = -\sqrt{21}/5$, $\tan \theta = -2/\sqrt{21}$, $\csc \theta = 5/2$, $\sec \theta = -5/\sqrt{21}$, $\cot \theta = -\sqrt{21}/2$

31. **(a)** $\theta = \pm n\pi$, $n = 0, 1, 2, \ldots$ **(b)** $\theta = \pi/2 \pm n\pi$, $n = 0, 1, 2, \ldots$
    (c) $\theta = \pm n\pi$, $n = 0, 1, 2, \ldots$ **(d)** $\theta = \pm n\pi$, $n = 0, 1, 2, \ldots$
    (e) $\theta = \pi/2 \pm n\pi$, $n = 0, 1, 2, \ldots$ **(f)** $\theta = \pm n\pi$, $n = 0, 1, 2, \ldots$

33. **(a)** $s = r\theta = 4(\pi/6) = 2\pi/3$ cm   **(b)** $s = r\theta = 4(5\pi/6) = 10\pi/3$ cm

35. $\theta = s/r = 2/5$

37. **(a)** $2\pi r = R(2\pi - \theta)$, $r = \dfrac{2\pi - \theta}{2\pi} R$

    (b) $h = \sqrt{R^2 - r^2} = \sqrt{R^2 - (2\pi - \theta)^2 R^2/(4\pi^2)} = \dfrac{\sqrt{4\pi\theta - \theta^2}}{2\pi} R$

39. Let h be the altitude as shown in the figure, then

$h = 3 \sin 60° = 3\sqrt{3}/2$ so $A = \dfrac{1}{2}(3\sqrt{3}/2)(7) = 21\sqrt{3}/4$.

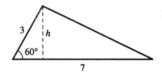

41. Let x be the distance above the ground, then $x = 10 \sin 67° \approx 9.2$ ft.

43. From the figure, $h = x - y$ but $x = d \tan \beta$,
$y = d \tan \alpha$ so $h = d(\tan \beta - \tan \alpha)$.

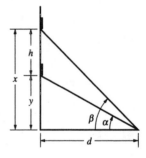

45. **(a)** $\sin 2\theta = 2 \sin \theta \cos \theta = 2(\sqrt{5}/3)(2/3) = 4\sqrt{5}/9$
    (b) $\cos 2\theta = 2 \cos^2 \theta - 1 = 2(2/3)^2 - 1 = -1/9$

47. $\sin 3\theta = \sin(2\theta + \theta) = \sin 2\theta \cos \theta + \cos 2\theta \sin \theta = (2 \sin \theta \cos \theta) \cos \theta + (\cos^2 \theta - \sin^2 \theta) \sin \theta$
$= 2 \sin \theta \cos^2 \theta + \sin \theta \cos^2 \theta - \sin^3 \theta = 3 \sin \theta \cos^2 \theta - \sin^3 \theta$; similarly, $\cos 3\theta = \cos^3 \theta - 3 \sin^2 \theta \cos \theta$

49. $\dfrac{\cos \theta \tan \theta + \sin \theta}{\tan \theta} = \dfrac{\cos \theta(\sin \theta/\cos \theta) + \sin \theta}{\sin \theta/\cos \theta} = 2 \cos \theta$

51. $\tan \theta + \cot \theta = \dfrac{\sin \theta}{\cos \theta} + \dfrac{\cos \theta}{\sin \theta} = \dfrac{\sin^2 \theta + \cos^2 \theta}{\sin \theta \cos \theta} = \dfrac{1}{\sin \theta \cos \theta} = \dfrac{2}{2 \sin \theta \cos \theta} = \dfrac{2}{\sin 2\theta} = 2 \csc 2\theta$

53. $\dfrac{\sin \theta + \cos 2\theta - 1}{\cos \theta - \sin 2\theta} = \dfrac{\sin \theta + (1 - 2 \sin^2 \theta) - 1}{\cos \theta - 2 \sin \theta \cos \theta} = \dfrac{\sin \theta(1 - 2 \sin \theta)}{\cos \theta(1 - 2 \sin \theta)} = \tan \theta$

55. Using (47), $2\cos 2\theta \sin \theta = 2(1/2)[\sin(-\theta) + \sin 3\theta] = \sin 3\theta - \sin \theta$

57. $\tan(\theta/2) = \dfrac{\sin(\theta/2)}{\cos(\theta/2)} = \dfrac{2\sin(\theta/2)\cos(\theta/2)}{2\cos^2(\theta/2)} = \dfrac{\sin \theta}{1 + \cos \theta}$

59. From the figure, area $= \dfrac{1}{2}hc$ but $h = b\sin A$

so area $= \dfrac{1}{2}bc\sin A$. The formulas

area $= \dfrac{1}{2}ac\sin B$ and area $= \dfrac{1}{2}ab\sin C$

follow by drawing altitudes from vertices B and C, respectively.

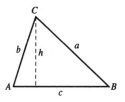

61. **(a)** $\sin(\pi/2 + \theta) = \sin(\pi/2)\cos \theta + \cos(\pi/2)\sin \theta = (1)\cos \theta + (0)\sin \theta = \cos \theta$

　　(b) $\cos(\pi/2 + \theta) = \cos(\pi/2)\cos \theta - \sin(\pi/2)\sin \theta = (0)\cos \theta - (1)\sin \theta = -\sin \theta$

　　(c) $\sin(3\pi/2 - \theta) = \sin(3\pi/2)\cos \theta - \cos(3\pi/2)\sin \theta = (-1)\cos \theta - (0)\sin \theta = -\cos \theta$

　　(d) $\cos(3\pi/2 + \theta) = \cos(3\pi/2)\cos \theta - \sin(3\pi/2)\sin \theta = (0)\cos \theta - (-1)\sin \theta = \sin \theta$

63. **(a)** Add (34) and (36) to get $\sin(\alpha - \beta) + \sin(\alpha + \beta) = 2\sin \alpha \cos \beta$ so
$\sin \alpha \cos \beta = (1/2)[\sin(\alpha - \beta) + \sin(\alpha + \beta)]$.

　　(b) Subtract (35) from (37).

　　(c) Add (35) and (37).

65. $\sin \alpha + \sin(-\beta) = 2\sin \dfrac{\alpha - \beta}{2} \cos \dfrac{\alpha + \beta}{2}$, but $\sin(-\beta) = -\sin \beta$ so

$\sin \alpha - \sin \beta = 2\cos \dfrac{\alpha + \beta}{2} \sin \dfrac{\alpha - \beta}{2}$.

67. Consider the triangle having a, b, and d as sides. The angle formed by sides a and b is $\pi - \theta$ so from the law of cosines, $d^2 = a^2 + b^2 - 2ab\cos(\pi - \theta) = a^2 + b^2 + 2ab\cos \theta$, $d = \sqrt{a^2 + b^2 + 2ab\cos \theta}$.

APPENDIX F
Solving Polynomial Equations

EXERCISE SET F

1. (a) $q(x) = x^2 + 4x + 2, r(x) = -11x + 6$ (b) $q(x) = 2x^2 + 4, r(x) = 9$

   (c) $q(x) = x^3 - x^2 + 2x - 2, r(x) = 2x + 1$

   (c) $q(x) = 5x^3 - 5, r(x) = 4x^2 + 10$

3. (a) $q(x) = 3x^2 + 6x + 8, r(x) = 15$ (b) $q(x) = x^3 - 5x^2 + 20x - 100, r(x) = 504$

   (c) $q(x) = x^4 + x^3 + x^2 + x + 1, r(x) = 0$

   (c) $q(x) = x^6 + x^5 + x^4 + x^3 + x^2 + x + 1, r(x) = 2$

5.

x	0	1	-3	7
$p(x)$	-4	-3	101	5001

7. (a) $q(x) = x^2 + 6x + 13, r = 20$ (b) $q(x) = x^2 + 3x - 2, r = -4$

9. Assume $r = a/b$ a and b integers with $a > 0$:

   (a) b divides 1, $b = \pm 1$; a divides 24, $a = 1, 2, 3, 4, 6, 8, 12, 24$;
the possible candidates are $\{\pm 1, \pm 2, \pm 3, \pm 4, \pm 6, \pm 8, \pm 12, \pm 24\}$

   (b) b divides 3 so $b = \pm 1, \pm 3$; a divides -10 so $a = 1, 2, 5, 10$;
the possible candidates are $\{\pm 1, \pm 2, \pm 5, \pm 10, \pm 1/3, \pm 2/3, \pm 5/3, \pm 10/3\}$

   (c) b divides 1 so $b = \pm 1$; a divides 17 so $a = 1, 17$;
the possible candidates are $\{\pm 1, \pm 17\}$

11. $(x + 1)(x - 1)(x - 2)$ 13. $(x + 3)^3 (x + 1)$

15. $(x + 3)(x + 2)(x + 1)^2 (x - 3)$ 17. -3 is the only real root.

19. $x = -2, -2/3$ are the only real roots.   21. $-2, 2, 3$ are the only real roots.

23. If $x - 1$ is a factor then $p(1) = 0$, so $k^2 - 7k + 10 = 0$, $k^2 - 7k + 10 = (k - 2)(k - 5)$, so $k = 2, 5$.

25. If the side of the cube is x then $x^2(x - 3) = 196$; the only real root of this equation is $x = 7$ cm.

27. Use the Factor Theorem with x as the variable and y as the constant c.
   (a) For any positive integer n the polynomial $x^n - y^n$ has $x = y$ as a root.
   (b) For any positive even integer n the polynomial $x^n - y^n$ has $x = -y$ as a root.
   (c) For any positive odd integer n the polynomial $x^n + y^n$ has $x = -y$ as a root.

APPENDIX G
Selected Proofs

EXERCISE SET G

1. From Theorem G.1.(a), $\lim_{x \to a}(-1) = -1$ so from Theorem G.1.(c),

$$\lim_{x \to a}[(-1)g(x)] = \lim_{x \to a}(-1)\lim_{x \to a}g(x) = (-1)L_2 = -L_2 \text{ thus, using Theorem G.1.(b),}$$

$$\lim_{x \to a}[f(x) - g(x)] = \lim_{x \to a}[f(x) + (-g(x))] = \lim_{x \to a}f(x) + \lim_{x \to a}[-g(x)] = L_1 + (-L_2) = L_1 - L_2$$

3. $|k - k| = |0| = 0 < \epsilon$ when $x > N$ for any $N > 0$.

5. $|[f(x) + g(x)] - [L_1 + L_2]| = |[f(x) - L_1] + [g(x) - L_2]| \leq |f(x) - L_1| + |g(x) - L_2|$.

Given $\epsilon > 0$, there exist negative numbers N_1 and N_2 such that $|f(x) - L_1| < \epsilon/2$ and $|g(x) - L_2| < \epsilon/2$ whenever $x < N_1$ and $x < N_2$, respectively. Let $N = \min(N_1, N_2)$, if $x < N$ then $|f(x) - L_1| + |g(x) - L_2| < \epsilon/2 + \epsilon/2 = \epsilon$ so $|[f(x) + g(x)] - [L_1 + L_2]| < \epsilon$.

7. (a) Given $N > 0$, there exist numbers $\delta_1 > 0$ and $\delta_2 > 0$ such that $f(x) > N/2$ and $g(x) > N/2$ whenever $0 < |x - a| < \delta_1$ and $0 < |x - a| < \delta_2$, respectively. Let $\delta = \min(\delta_1, \delta_2)$ then $f(x) > N/2$ and $g(x) > N/2$ whenever $0 < |x - a| < \delta$ so $f(x) + g(x) > N/2 + N/2 = N$.

(b) No, for example $\lim_{x \to 0}(1/x^4 - 1/x^2) = \lim_{x \to 0}[(1 - x^2)/x^4] = +\infty$

9. If $\lim_{x \to a}f(x) = L$ then given $\epsilon > 0$, there exists a $\delta > 0$ such that $|f(x) - L| < \epsilon$ whenever $0 < |x - a| < \delta$. But $|f(x) - L| = |[f(x) - L] - 0| < \epsilon$ whenever $0 < |x - a| < \delta$ so $\lim_{x \to a}[f(x) - L] = 0$. If $\lim_{x \to a}[f(x) - L] = 0$ then given $\epsilon > 0$, there exists a $\delta > 0$ such that $|[f(x) - L] - 0| < \epsilon$ whenever $0 < |x - a| < \delta$, but $|[f(x) - L] - 0| = |f(x) - L| < \epsilon$ whenever $0 < |x - a| < \delta$ so $\lim_{x \to a}f(x) = L$.

CHAPTER 1
Sample Exams

SECTION 1.1

1. Answer true or false. Given the equation $y = x^2 - 5x + 4$, the values of x for which $y = 0$ are -4 and -1.

2. Answer true or false. Given the equation $y = x^2 - 5x + 6$, $y \geq 0$ for all $x \geq 0$.

3. Answer true or false. Given the equation $y = 1 - \sqrt{x}$, $y = 1$ when $x = 0$.

4. Answer true or false. Given the equation $y = -x^2 + 4$, it can be determined that y has a minimum value.

5. Answer true or false. Referring to the graph of $y = \sqrt[3]{x}$, y can be determined to have a maximum value.

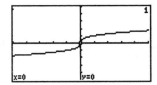

6. Assume the function $y = x^3 - 4x^2$ is used to describe the profit/loss of a company over the first 10 years after having started business. Initially, the company expects to lose money. After how many years will the company start to make a profit?

   A. 1 year   B. 2 years   C. 4 years   D. 8 years

7. Use the equation $y = x^2 - 6x + 8$. For what values of x is $y \geq 0$?

   A. $\{x : 2 \leq x \leq 4\}$ B. $\{x : x \leq 2 \text{ or } x \leq 4\}$

   C. $\{x : -4 \leq x \leq -2\}$ D. $\{x : x \leq -4 \text{ or } x \leq -2\}$

8. From the graph of $y = x^2 - 5x$ determine for which value(s) of x where $y = 0$.

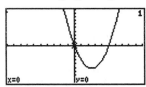

   A. 0   B. 5   C. 0, 5   D. $-5, 0$

9. From the graph of $y = 2x^2 + 4x - 7$ determine the minimum value of y.

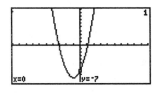

   A. -1   B. 1   C. -9 D. 9

10. From the graph of $y = 2x^2 + 6x - 8$ determine at what x the graph has a minimum.

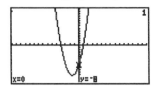

A. $\dfrac{-3}{2}$ B. $\dfrac{3}{2}$ C. 0 D. -1

11. From the graph of $y = x^4 - 3x^2 - 4$ determine for what x values the graph appears to be below the x-axis.

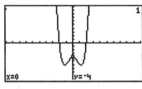

A. $(-2, 2)$ B. $(0, 2)$ C. $(-5, 0)$ D. $(-6, 0)$

12. Assume it is possible to measure the observations given below. Which, if any, would most likely generate a broken graph?

    A. the temperature over a 6 hour period

    B. the number of hamburgers served at a fast food restaurant

    C. the speed of an automobile for the first 10 minutes after leaving a red light

    D. none of the above

13. If a company recorded its profit over a year graphically with time represented on the horizontal axis, the graph would be

    A. continuous (unbroken)

    B. broken because money is earned in lump sums at sales

    C. broken because no graph is continuous (unbroken)

    D. broken because the printer cannot really handle continuous (unbroken) graphs

14. A manufacturer makes boxes taking rectangular sheets of cardboard that initially are twice as long as they are wide by cutting squares from the corners and turning up the sides. A customer requests that the such a box have a minimum volume. Why is this not practical?

    A. If the length of the square that is cut out has half the original width of the cardboard, the volume would be zero, hence there would be no box.

    B. Tools can cut only a certain size square.

    C. The squares cut from the corners would be very small.

    D. The manufacturer would have to cut rectangles, not squares, from the corners.

15. A person makes a cube, then finds the surface area to volume ratio is improved by beating the points down with a hammer. As the object distorts, more and more points form, each of which is beat down with the hammer to further improve the surface area to volume ratio. What three dimensional object would this suggest has the best surface area to volume ratio?

A. multi-sided polygon   B. cone

C. pyramid   D. sphere

SECTION 1.2

1. Answer true or false. If $f(x) = 4x^2 - 1$, then $f(0) = 0$.

2. Answer true or false. If $f(x) = \dfrac{1}{x}$, then $f(0) = 0$.

3. $f(x) = \dfrac{1}{x^2} - 1$. The natural domain of the function is

    A. all real numbers
    B. all real numbers except 1
    C. all real numbers except -1 and 1
    D. all real numbers except -1, 0, and 1

4. Use a graphing utility to determine the natural domain of $h(x) = \dfrac{1}{|x| - 1}$.

    A. all real numbers
    B. all real numbers except 1
    C. all real numbers except -1 and 1
    D. all real numbers except -1, 0, and 1

5. Use a graphing utility to determine the natural domain of $g(x) = \sqrt{9 - x^2}$.
    A. $\{x : -3 \leq x \leq 3\}$ B. $\{x : -9 \leq x \leq 3\}$
    C. $\{x : x \geq -9\}$ D. $\{x : x \geq -3\}$

6. Answer true or false. $f(x) = x - |x + 1|$ can be represented in the piecewise form by
$$f(x) = \begin{cases} 2x + 1, & \text{if } x \leq -1 \\ -1, & \text{if } x > -1 \end{cases}.$$

7. Find the x-coordinate of any hole(s) in the graph of $f(x) = \dfrac{(x^2 - 9)(x + 4)}{(x + 3)(x + 4)}$.

    A. 3   B. -3 and -4 C. 3 and 4   D. -12

8. Answer true or false. $f(x) = \dfrac{x^2 - 4}{x + 2}$ and $g(x) = x - 2$ are identical except $f(x)$ has a hole at $x = -2$.

9. Use a graphing device to plot the function, then find the indicated value from observing the graph.
A flying object attains a height $h(t)$ over time according to the equation $h(t) = 3\sin t - \cos t$. If $t = \dfrac{\pi}{4}$, $h\left(\dfrac{\pi}{4}\right)$ is approximately
    A. 0   B. 0.707   C. 1.414   D. 3

10. A box is made from a piece of sheet metal by cutting a square whose sides measure x from each corner. If the sheet of metal initially measured 20 cm by 10 cm, the volume of the box is given by
    A. $V(x) = (20 - 2x)(10)x$ cm^3 B. $V(x) = (20 - 2x)(10 - x)x$ cm^3
    C. $V(x) = (20 - 2x)(10 - 2x)x$ cm^3 D. $V(x) = (20 - 2x)(10 - 2x)(2x)$ cm^3

11. Answer true or false. At a given location on a certain day the temperature T in °F changed according to the equation $T(t) = t \sin\left(\dfrac{t\pi}{12}\right) + 4$ where t represents time in hours starting at midnight. The temperature at 6 P. M. was approximately 58°F.

12. The speed of a truck in miles/hour for the first 10 seconds after leaving a red light is given by $f(x) = \dfrac{x^2}{2}$. Find the speed of the truck 6 seconds after leaving the red light.

A. 18 miles/hour
C. 3 miles/hour

B. 36 miles/hour
D. 6 miles/hour

13. Find $f(2)$ if $f(x) = \left\{ \dfrac{4}{x}, \text{ if } x < 2 \text{ and } 3x \text{ if } x \geq 2 \right\}$.

A. 2

B. 4

C. 6

D. It cannot be determined.

14. Determine all x-values where there are holes in the graph of $f(x) = \dfrac{x^2 - 4}{(x+2)^2(x-2)}$.

A. $-2, 2$

B. -2

C. 2

D. none

15. Assume the hourly temperature in °F starting at midnight is given by $T(x) = 36 - (x-15)^2 + x$. Find the temperature at 3 P. M.

A. 36°F

B. 51°F

C. 39°F

D. 27°F

SECTION 1.3

1. Answer true or false. $f(x) = x^3 - 2x^2 - x + 5$ has one localized maximum and one localized minimum. The window on a graphing utility with $-10 \leq x \leq 10$ and $-10 \leq y \leq 10$ will show enough detail of the graph of $f(x)$ to include both of these.

2. Answer true or false. $f(x) = x^4 - 8$ has a minimum value. This can be shown on a graphing utility with a window defined by $-5 \leq x \leq 5$ and $-5 \leq y \leq 5$.

3. The smallest domain that is needed to show the entire graph of $f(x) = \sqrt{25 - x^2}$ on a graphing utility is

A. $-10 \leq x \leq 10$

B. $-5 \leq x \leq 5$

C. $0 \leq x \leq 10$

D. $0 \leq x \leq 5$

4. The smallest range that is needed to show the entire graph of $f(x) = \sqrt{36 - x^2}$ on a graphing utility is

A. $0 \leq y \leq 6$

B. $-6 \leq y \leq 6$

C. $0 \leq y \leq 10$

D. $-10 \leq y \leq 10$

5. If xScl is changed from 1 to 2 on a graphing utility which of these statements describes what happens?

A. The domain becomes twice as large as the original domain.

B. The domain becomes half as large as the original domain.

C. The domain becomes four times as large as the original domain.

D. The domain remains the same.

6. Using a graphing utility, the graph of $y = \dfrac{x}{x^2 - 4}$ will generate how many false line segments on a $-10 \leq x \leq 10$ domain?

A. 3

B. 0

C. 1

D. 2

7. How many functions are needed to graph the circle $x^2 + y^2 = 10$ on a graphing utility?

A. 1

B. 2

C. 3

D. 4

8. A student tries to graph the circle $x^2 + y^2 = 9$ on a graphing utility, but the graph appears to be elliptical. To view this as a circle the student could

A. increase the range of x B. increase the range of y
C. increase xScl   D. increase yScl

9. Answer true or false. A student wishes to graph $f(x) = \begin{cases} x^3, & \text{if } x \leq 2 \\ x - 4, & \text{if } 2 < x \leq 4 \\ x^2, & \text{if } x > 4 \end{cases}$. This can be accomplished by graphing three functions, then sketching the graph from the information obtained.

10. The graph of $f(x) = |x - 1| + |x + 2|$ touches the x-axis

A. nowhere   B. at 1 point   C. at 2 points   D. at 4 points

11. Answer true or false. The graph of $y = x \cos x$ has its greatest difference between consecutive localized maxima and minima when x is near 0.

12. If a graphing utility is not generating the complete graph of $f(x) = x^{2/3}$, the graph of what function should remedy this?

A. $g(x) = |x|^{2/3}$

B. $g(x) = \left(\dfrac{|x|}{x}\right)|x|^{2/3}$

C. $g(x) = \dfrac{x}{x^{1/3}}$

D. $g(x) = \begin{cases} -x^{2/3}, & \text{if } x < 0 \\ x^{2/3}, & \text{if } x \geq 0 \end{cases}$

13. Which of these functions generates a graph that goes negative?
A. $f(x) = |\sin x|$ B. $G(x) = |\sin|x||$
C. $h(x) = \sin|x|$ D. $F(x) = |\sin x| + |\cos x|$

14. The window that best shows $f(x) = \sqrt{5x + 10}$ should include what restriction on the x-values?
A. $x \leq 2$ B. $x \leq -2$ C. $x \geq 2$ D. $x \geq -2$

15. The window that best shows $f(x) = \sqrt{5x + 10} - 5$ should include what restriction on the y-values?
A. $y \leq 5$ B. $y \leq -5$ C. $y \geq 5$ D. $y \geq -5$

SECTION 1.4

1.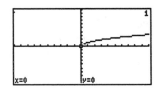

The graph on the left is the graph of $f(x) = \sqrt{x}$. The graph on the right is the graph of
A. $y = \sqrt{f(x + 4)}$ B. $y = \sqrt{f(x - 4)}$ C. $y = f(x) - 4$ D. $y = f(x) + 4$

2. The graph of $y = 1 + (x + 2)^2$ is obtained from the graph of $y = x^2$ by

A. translating horizontally 2 units to the right, then translating vertically 1 unit up
B. translating horizontally 2 units to the left, then translating vertically 1 unit up
C. translating horizontally 2 units to the right, then translating vertically 1 unit down
D. translating horizontally 2 units to the left, then translating vertically 1 unit down

3. The graph of $y = \sqrt{x}$ and $y = \sqrt{-x}$ are related. The graph of $y = \sqrt{-x}$ is obtained by

    A. reflecting the graph of $y = \sqrt{x}$ about the x-axis

    B. reflecting the graph of $y = \sqrt{x}$ about the y-axis

    C. reflecting the graph of $y = \sqrt{x}$ about the origin

    D. The equations are not both defined.

4. The graphs of $y = x^3$ and $y = 4 - 2(x - 1)^3$ are related. Of reflection, stretching, vertical translation, and horizontal translation, which should be done first?

A. reflection   B. stretching

C. vertical translation   D. horizontal translation

5. Answer true or false. $f(x) = x^2$ and $g(x) = x - 2$. Then $(f - g)(x) = x^2 - x - 2$.

6. Answer true or false. $f(x) = x^2 - 9$ and $g(x) = x^3 + 8$. f/g has the same domain as g/f.

7. $f(x) = \sqrt{x^2 + 1}$ and $g(x) = x^2 - 2$. $f \circ g(x) =$

A. $\sqrt{x^4 - 1}$ B. $\sqrt{x^2 - 1}$ C. $\sqrt{x^4 - 4x^2 + 5}$ D. $\sqrt{x^2 + 2x - 1}$

8. $f(x) = |(x + 3)^3|$ is the composition of

A. $f(x) = x + 3$; $g(x) = |x^3|$ B. $f(x) = (x + 3)^3$; $g(x) = |x^3|$

C. $f(x) = \sqrt[3]{x + 3}$; $g(x) = |x^3|$ D. $f(x) = x^3$; $g(x) = |x + 3|$

9. $f(x) = \sqrt[3]{x}$. Find $f(3x)$.

    A. $3\sqrt[3]{x}$ B. $\sqrt[3]{3x}$ C. $\dfrac{\sqrt[3]{x}}{3}$ D. $\sqrt[3]{\dfrac{x}{3}}$

10. $f(x) = x^2 + 1$. Find $f(f(x))$.

    A. $x^4 + 2$ B. $2x^2 + 2$ C. $x^4 + 2x^2 + 2$ D. $x^4 + 2x^2$

11. $f(x) = |x + 2|$ is

A. an even function only   B. an odd function only

C. both an even and an odd function   D. neither an even nor an odd function

12. $f(x) = 0$ is

A. an even function only   B. an odd function only

C. both an even and an odd function   D. neither an even nor an odd function

13.

The function graphed above is

A. an even function only   B. an odd function only

C. both an even and an odd function   D. neither an even nor an odd function

14. Answer true or false. $f(x) = |x| + \cos x$ is an even function.

15. $f(x) = 3|x| + 2\cos x$ is symmetric about

    A. the x-axis   B. the y-axis   C. the origin   D. nothing

16. $f(x) = 5x^3 - 2x$ is symmetric about

    A. the x-axis   B. the y-axis   C. the origin   D. nothing

SECTION 1.5

1. Answer true or false. The points $(1,1)$, $(2,3)$, and $(4,7)$ lie on the same line.

2. A particle, initially at $(4,3)$, moves along a line of slope $m = 3$ to a new position (x, y). Find y if $x = 6$.

    A. 8   B. 9   C. 16   D. 5

3. Find the angle of inclination of the line $3x + 2y = 5$ to the nearest degree.

    A. $56°$ B. $-56°$ C. $21°$ D. $-21°$

4. The slope-intercept form of a line having a slope of 4 and a y-intercept of 5 is

    A. $x = 4y + 5$ B. $y = 4x + 5$ C. $y = -4x - 5$ D. $x = -4y - 5$

5. Answer true or false. The lines $y = 5x + 4$ and $y = -5x + 4$ are parallel.

6. Answer true or false. The lines $y = 2x - 1$ and $x + 2y = 6$ are perpendicular.

7.

    The slope-intercept form of the equation of the graphed line is

    A. $y = 3x - 5$ B. $y = 3x + 5$ C. $y = -3x + 5$ D. $y = -3x - 5$

8. A particle moving along an x-axis with a constant velocity is at the point $x = 3$ when $t = 1$ and $x = 8$ when $t = 2$. The position of the particle if x is in meters and t is in seconds is

    A. 5 m/s   B. $\dfrac{1}{2}$ m/s   C. $\dfrac{8}{3}$ m/s   D. $\dfrac{3}{8}$ m/s

9. Answer true or false. A particle moving along an x-axis with constant acceleration has velocity $v = 5$ m/s at time $t = 1$ s and velocity $v = 9$ m/s at time $t = 2$ s. The acceleration of the particle is 4 m/s^2.

10. A family travels north along a highway at 60 mi/hr, then turns back and travels south at 65 mi/hr until returning to the starting point. Their average velocity is

    A. 62.5 mi/hr   B. 125 mi/hr   C. 5 mi/hr   D. 0 mi/hr

11. Answer true or false. An arrow is shot upward at 100 ft/s. If the effect of gravity is to cause velocity as a function of time to be $v = 100 - 32t$, the arrow will be moving downward when $t = 4$s.

12. A spring with a natural length of 4.00 m is stretched to the length of 4.05 m when an object weighing 5.00 N is suspended from it. If a 50-N object is later suspended from it, it will stretch to

    A. 4.50 m   B. 45.0 m   C. 6.50 m   D. 4.55 m

13. A company makes a certain object for $6 each, and sells each such object for $10. If the company has a monthly overhead expense of $10,000, how many of these objects must the company make and sell each month not to lose money?

    A. 25   B. 25,000   C. 2,500   D. 250

14. Answer true or false. A particle has a velocity with respect to time given by the function $v = t^2 - 3t + 6$. At time $t = 0$ the particle is not moving.

15. A circuit has a 20 volt battery, and a variable resistor. The current I in amperes (A) is given as a function of resistance, R, and is given in ohms (Ω) by $I = \dfrac{20}{R}$. What is the current when $R = 4\Omega$?

A. 5 A

B. 80 A

C. $\dfrac{1}{5}$ A

D. $\dfrac{1}{80}$ A

SECTION 1.6

1. What do all members of the family of lines of the form $y = 5x + b$ have in common?

   A. Their slope is 5.
   B. Their slope is -5.
   C. They go through the origin.
   D. They cross the x-axis at the point $(5,0)$.

2. What points do all graphs of equations of the form $y = x^n$, n is odd, have in common?
   A. (0,0) only
   B. (0,0) and (1,1)
   C. $(-1,-1)$, (0,0), and (1,1)
   D. none

3.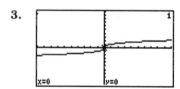

   The equation whose graph is given is

   A. $y = \sqrt{x}$

   B. $y = \sqrt[3]{x}$

   C. $y = \dfrac{1}{x^2}$

   D. $y = \dfrac{1}{x^3}$

4. Answer true or false. The graph of $y = -3(x-4)^3$ can be obtained by making transformations to the graph of $y = x^3$.

5. Answer true or false. The graph of $y = x^2 + 6x + 9$ can be obtained by transforming the graph of $y = x^2$ to the left three units.

6. Answer true or false. There is no difference in the graphs of $y = \sqrt{|x|}$ and $y = |\sqrt{x}|$.

7. Determine the vertical asymptote(s) of $y = \dfrac{x+3}{x^2 + 2x - 8}$.

   A. $x = -4$, $x = 2$
   B. $x = 4$
   C. $x = -2$, $x = 4$
   D. $x = 8$

8. Find the vertical asymptote(s) of $y = \dfrac{x^6}{3x^6 - 3}$.

   A. $x = 0$
   B. $x = -1$, $x = 1$
   C. $x = 3$
   D. $x = \dfrac{1}{3}$

9. For which of the given angles, if any, is all of the trigonometric functions negative?

   A. $\dfrac{\pi}{3}$
   B. $\dfrac{2\pi}{3}$
   C. $\dfrac{4\pi}{3}$
   D. No such angle exists.

10. Use the trigonometric function of a calculating utility set to the radian mode to evaluate $\sin\left(\frac{\pi}{7}\right)$.

    A. 0.0078   B. 0.4339   C. 0.1424   D. 0.1433

11. A rolling wheel of radius 2.00 m turns through an angle of $180°$. How far does the wheel travel as it turns?

    A. 6.28 m   B. 200 m   C. 2.00 m   D. 4.00 m

12. Answer true or false. The amplitude of $5\cos(3x - \pi)$ is 3.

13. Answer true or false. The phase shift of $2\sin\left(3x - \frac{\pi}{3}\right)$ is $\frac{\pi}{3}$.

14. Use a graphing utility to graph $y_1 = \sin\left(x - \frac{\pi}{3}\right)$ and $y_2 = \sin\left(2\left(x - \frac{\pi}{3}\right)\right)$.

    A. y_1 has the greatest phase shift.

    B. y_2 has the greatest phase shift.

    C. y_1 and y_2 have the same phase shift.

    D.   Neither y_1 nor y_2 have a phase shift.

15. Answer true or false. The period of $y = \cos\left(5x - \frac{\pi}{3}\right)$ is 10π.

16. Answer true or false. A force acting on an object, $F = \frac{k}{x^2}$, that is inversely proportional to the square of the distance from the object to the source of the force is found to be 25 N when $x = 1$ m. The force will be 100 N if x becomes 2 m.

SECTION 1.7

1. If $x = 3\cos^2(\pi t)$ and $y = \sin\left(\frac{\pi}{2}t\right)$ $(0 \le t \le 4)$, where t is time in seconds, describe the motion of particle, then the x- and y-coordinates of the position of the particle at time $t = 25$ are

    A. (3,0)   B. (0,1)   C. $(-3,0)$ D. (0,1)

2. Answer true or false. Given the parametric equations $x = 5t$ and $y = t - 2$, eliminating the parameter t gives $x = 5(y + 2)$.

3. Use a graphing utility to graph $x = 4\cos t$ and $y = 2\sin t$ $(0 \le t \le 2\pi)$. The resulting graph is

    A. A circle   B. A hyperbola   C. An ellipse   D. A parabola

4. Identify the equation in rectangular coordinates that is a representation of $x = 2\cos t$, $y = 3\sin t$ $(0 \le t \le 2\pi)$.

    A. $2x^2 + 3y^2 = 1$ B. $4x^2 + 3y^2 = 1$ C. $\frac{x^2}{2} + \frac{y^2}{3} = 1$ D. $\frac{x^2}{4} + \frac{y^2}{9} = 1$

5. Answer true or false. The graph in the rectangular coordinate system of $x = \cot t$, $y = \tan t$ $(0 \le t \le \pi/2)$ is a hyperbola.

6. Answer true or false. The parametric representation of $4x^2 + 4y^2 = 1$ is $x = 2\sin t$, $y = 2\cos t$ $(0 \le t \le 2\pi)$.

7. The circle represented by $x = 2 + 3\cos t$, $y = 4 + 3\sin t$ $(0 \le t \le 2\pi)$ is centered at

    A. (0,0)   B. (2,4)   C. $(-2,-4)$ D. $\left(\frac{2}{3}, \frac{4}{3}\right)$

8. Answer true or false. The trajectory of a particle is given by $x = t^3$, $y = t^2 - 4t + 6$ over the interval $-12 \le t \le 12$. The time at which the particle crosses the y-axis is 6.

9. Answer true or false. $x = t - 4$, $y = t$ $(1 \le t \le 3)$ is the parametric representation of the line segment from P to Q, where P is the point $(-3, 1)$ and Q is the point $(-1, 3)$.

10. $x = a$, $y = t$, where a is a constant, is the parametric representation of a
   A. horizontal line   B. vertical line   C. line with slope $+1$ D. line with slope -1

11. Use a graphing utility to graph $x = 4y^2 - 2y + 6$. The resulting graph is a parabola that opens
   A. upward   B. downward   C. left   D. right

12. Answer true or false. $x = 3 + 2t, y = 3 + 2t$ represents a line passing through the point (3,5).

13. The parametric form of a horizontal line passing through (0,2) is
   A. $x = 2$, $y = t$ B. $x = t$, $y = 2$ C. $x = -2$, $y = t$ D. $x = t$, $y = -2$

14. Answer true or false. The curve represented by the piecewise parametric equation $x = 3t$, $y = t$ $(0 \le 2)$; $x = \dfrac{3t^2}{4}$, $y = t^2$ $(2 < t \le 4)$ can be graphed as a continuous curve over the interval $(0 \le t \le 4)$.

15. Answer true or false. A ball is thrown at an angle of $30°$ above the horizontal with an initial speed $v_0 = 10$ m/s. The ball will rise 1.28 m (rounded to the nearest hundredth of a meter) in the absence of air resistance.

CHAPTER 1 TEST

1. Answer true or false. For the equation $y = x^2 + 10x + 21$, the values of x that cause y to be zero are 3 and 7.

2. Answer true or false. The graph of $y = x^2 - 4x + 9$ has a minimum value.

3. A company has a profit/loss given by $P(x) = 0.1x^2 - 2x - 10,000$, where x is time in years, good for the first 20 years. After how many years will the graph of the profit/loss equation first begin to rise?
   A. 5 years   B. 10 years   C. 15 years   D. 0 years

4. Use a graphing utility to determine the natural domain of $g(x) = \dfrac{1}{|x - 2|}$.

   A. all real numbers   B. all real numbers except 2
   C. all real numbers except -2 D. all real numbers except -2 and 2

5. Answer true or false. If $f(x) = \dfrac{2x}{x^2 + 1}$, then $f(1) = 1$.

6. Find the hole(s) in the graph of $f(x) = \dfrac{x - 4}{x^2 - 5x + 4}$.
   A. $x = 4$ B. $x = 1$ C. $x = 1, 4$ D. $x = -4$

7. The cumulative number of electrons passing through an experiment over time, given in seconds, is given by $n(t) = t^2 + 4t + 6$. How many electrons pass through the experiment in the first 5 seconds?
   A. 13   B. 39   C. 15   D. 51

8. Use a graphing utility to determine the entire domain of $f(x) = \sqrt{49 - x^2}$.
   A. all real numbers   B. $0 \le x \le 7$ C. $-7 \le x \le 7$ D. $0 \le x \le 49$

9. Answer true or false. The graph of $f(x) = |x + 5|$ touches the x-axis.

10. Answer true or false. The graph of $y = \dfrac{x^2 - 8}{x - 9}$ would produce a false line segment on a graphing utility on the domain of $-10 \leq x \leq 10$.

11. The graph of $y = (x - 2)^3$ is obtained from the graph of $y = x^3$ by

   A. translating vertically 2 units upward
   B. translating vertically 2 units downward
   C. translating horizontally 2 units to the left
   D. translating horizontally 2 units to the right

12. If $f(x) = x^3 + 2$ and $g(x) = x^2$, then $g \circ f(x) =$
   A. $x^5 + 2$
   B. $(x^3 + 2)^2$
   C. $x^3 + x^2 + 2$
   D. $x^6 + 2$

13. Answer true or false. $f(x) = |x| + \sin x$ is an odd function.

14. A particle initially at (1,3) moves along a line of slope $m = 4$ to a new position (x, y). Find y if $x = 4$.
   A. 12
   B. 15
   C. 16
   D. 19

15. The slope-intercept form of a line having a slope of 5 and a y-intercept of 3 is
   A. $x = 5y + 3$
   B. $x = 5y - 3$
   C. $y = 5x + 3$
   D. $y = 5x - 3$

16. A spring is initially 3 m long. When 2 kg are suspended from the spring it stretches 4 cm. How long will the spring be if 10 kg are suspended from it?
   A. 3.20 m
   B. 3.02 m
   C. 3.40 m
   D. 3.04 m

17. The equation whose graph is given is

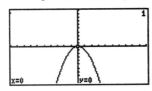

   A. $y = x^2$
   B. $y = (-x)^2$
   C. $y = -x^2$
   D. $y = x^{-2}$

18. Answer true or false. The only asymptote of $y = \dfrac{x + 5}{x^2 + 6x + 5}$ is $y = -1$.

19. A rolling wheel of radius 2 cm turns through an angle of 330°. How far does the wheel travel while rolling through this angle? (Round to the nearest hundredth of a centimeter.)
   A. 5.76 cm
   B. 5.75 cm
   C. 5.74 cm
   D. 5.73 cm

20. If $x = 4\cos(\pi t)$ and $y = \sin(2\pi t)$ $(0 \leq t \leq 2)$, where t is time in seconds, describe the motion of a particle, the x- and y-coordinates of the position of the particle at $t = 0.5$ s are
   A. (0,0)
   B. (−1,1)
   C. (0,1)
   D. (1,1)

21. The ellipse represented by $x = 6\cos t$, $y = 2\sin t$ $(0 \leq t \leq 2\pi)$ is centered at
   A. (6,2)
   B. (−6,−2)
   C. $(\sqrt{6}, \sqrt{2})$
   D. (0,0)

22. The graph of $x = 5 + 2\cos t$, $y = 1 + 2\sin t$ $(0 \leq t \leq 2\pi)$ is
   A. a circle
   B. a hyperbola
   C. an ellipse
   D. a parabola

ANSWERS TO SAMPLE TESTS

SECTION 1.1:

1. F 2. F 3. T 4. T 5. F 6. C 7. B 8. C 9. C 10. A 11. A 12. B 13. B 14. A 15. D

SECTION 1.2:

1. F 2. F 3. C 4. C 5. A 6. T 7. B 8. T 9. C 10. C 11. F 12. A 13. C 14. C 15. B

SECTION 1.3:

1. T 2. F 3. B 4. A 5. D 6. D 7. B 8. A 9. T 10. A 11. F 12. A 13. C 14. D 15. D

SECTION 1.4:

1. B 2. B 3. B 4. D 5. F 6. F 7. C 8. D 9. B 10. C 11. D 12. C 13. B 14. T 15. B 16. C

SECTION 1.5:

1. T 2. B 3. B 4. B 5. F 6. T 7. A 8. A 9. T 10. D 11. T 12. A 13. C 14. F 15. A

SECTION 1.6:

1. A 2. C 3. B 4. T 5. T 6. F 7. A 8. B 9. D 10. B 11. A 12. F 13. T 14. B 15. F 16. F

SECTION 1.7:

1. B 2. T 3. C 4. D 5. T 6. F 7. B 8. F 9. T 10. B 11. D 12. F 13. B 14. F 15. T

CHAPTER 1 TEST:

1. F 2. T 3. B 4. B 5. T 6. A 7. D 8. C 9. T 10. T 11. D 12. B 13. F 14. B 15. C 16. A 17. C 18. F 19. A 20. A 21. D 22. A

Sample Exams

SECTION 2.1

1.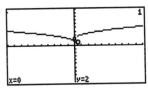

   The function $f(x)$ is graphed. $\lim\limits_{x \to 0^-} f(x) =$

   A. 1   B. 2   C. $\dfrac{3}{2}$ D. undefined

2.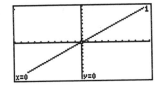

   Answer true or false. For the function graphed $\lim\limits_{x \to 2} f(x)$ is undefined.

3. Approximate the $\lim\limits_{x \to 2} \dfrac{x^2 - 4}{x - 2}$ by evaluating $f(x) = \dfrac{x^2 - 4}{x - 2}$ at $x = 3$, 2.5, 2.1, 2.01, 2.001, 1, 1.5, 1.9, 1.99, and 1.999.

   A. 2   B. -2 C. 0   D. 4

4. Answer true or false. If $\lim\limits_{x \to 0^+} f(x) = 4$ and $\lim\limits_{x \to 0^-} f(x) = 4$, then $\lim\limits_{x \to 0} f(x) = 4$

5. Approximate the $\lim\limits_{x \to 2^-} \dfrac{x}{x - 2}$ by evaluating $f(x) = \dfrac{x}{x - 2}$ at appropriate values of x.

   A. 1   B. 0   C. ∞ D. $-\infty$

6. Approximate the limit by evaluating $f(x) = \dfrac{\sin x}{5x}$ at appropriate values of x. $\lim\limits_{x \to 0^-} \dfrac{\sin x}{5x} =$

   A. 1   B. 5   C. $\dfrac{1}{5}$ D. ∞

7. Approximate the limit by evaluating $f(x) = \dfrac{x}{\sin x}$ at appropriate values of x. $\lim\limits_{x \to 0} \dfrac{x}{\sin x} =$

   A. 1   B. -1 C. 0   D. ∞

8. Approximate the limit by evaluating $f(x) = \dfrac{\sqrt{x + 4} - 2}{x}$ at appropriate values of x. $\lim\limits_{x \to 0^-} \dfrac{\sqrt{x + 4} - 2}{x} =$

   A. $\dfrac{1}{4}$ B. 0   C. ∞ D. $-\infty$

9. Use a graphing utility to approximate the y-coordinates of any horizontal asymptote of $y = f(x) = \dfrac{4x - 9}{x + 3}$.

   A. 4   B. 1   C. None exist.   D. -3

10. Use a graphing utility to approximate the y-coordinate of any horizontal asymptote of
    $y = f(x) = \dfrac{\cos x}{x}$.

    A. 0   B. 1   C. -1 and 1   D. -1

11. Use a graphing utility to approximate the y-coordinate of any horizontal asymptote of
    $y = f(x) = \dfrac{x^2 + 4}{x - 2}$.

    A. 0   B. None exist.   C. 1   D. -1 and 1

12. Answer true or false. A graphing utility can be used to show $f(x) = \left(1 + \dfrac{2}{x}\right)^x$ has a horizontal asymptote.

13. Answer true or false. A graphing utility can be used to show $f(x) = \left(6 + \dfrac{1}{x}\right)^x$ has a horizontal asymptote.

14. Answer true or false. $\displaystyle\lim_{x \to +\infty} \dfrac{2 + x}{1 - x}$ is equivalent to $\displaystyle\lim_{x \to 0^+} \left(\dfrac{\frac{2}{x} + 1}{\frac{1}{x} - 1}\right)$.

15. Answer true or false. $\displaystyle\lim_{x \to +\infty} \dfrac{\sin(2\pi x)}{x - 2}$ is equivalent to $\displaystyle\lim_{x \to 0^+} \sin(2\pi x)$.

16. Answer true or false. $f(x) = \dfrac{x}{x^2 - 4}$ has no horizontal asymptote.

SECTION 2.2

1. Given that $\displaystyle\lim_{x \to a} f(x) = 3$ and $\displaystyle\lim_{x \to a} g(x) = 5$, find, if it exists, $\displaystyle\lim_{x \to a}[f(x) - g(x)]^2$.

   A. -4 B. 4   C. 22   D. It does not exist.

2. $\displaystyle\lim_{x \to 3} 4 =$

   A. 4   B. 3   C. 7   D. 12

3. Answer true or false. $\displaystyle\lim_{x \to 2} 4x = 8$.

4. $\displaystyle\lim_{x \to -3} \dfrac{x^2 - 9}{x + 3} =$

   A. $-\infty$ B. -6 C. 6   D. 1

5. $\displaystyle\lim_{x \to 5} \dfrac{4}{x - 5} =$

   A. $+\infty$ B. $-\infty$ C. 0   D. It does not exist.

6. $\displaystyle\lim_{x \to +\infty} \dfrac{10x}{x^2 - 5x + 3} =$

   A. 0   B. 2   C. 5   D. It does not exist.

7. $\displaystyle\lim_{x \to -\infty} \dfrac{2x^2 - x}{x^2} =$

   A. 2   B. $-\infty$ C. ∞ D. It does not exist.

8. $\lim\limits_{x \to 1} \dfrac{4x}{x^2 - 6x + 5} =$

   A. $+\infty$ B. $-\infty$ C. 0   D. It does not exist.

9. $\lim\limits_{x \to 1} \dfrac{x - 4}{\sqrt{x} - 1} =$

   A. $+\infty$ B. $-\infty$ C. 1   D. It does not exist.

10. $\lim\limits_{x \to -\infty} \sqrt[4]{\dfrac{32x^8 - 6x^5 + 2}{2x^8 - 3x^3 + 1}} =$

    A. $+\infty$ B. $-\infty$ C. 2   D. It does not exist.

11. $\lim\limits_{x \to +\infty} (x^4 - 500x^3)$

    A. $+\infty$ B. $-\infty$ C. -500 D. It does not exist.

12. Let $f(x) = \begin{cases} x + 4, & x \le 2 \\ x^2, & x > 2 \end{cases}$. $\lim\limits_{x \to 2^-} f(x) =$

    A. 6   B. 4   C. 3   D. It does not exist.

13. Let $g(x) = \begin{cases} x^2 + 4, & x \le 1 \\ x^3, & x > 1 \end{cases}$. $\lim\limits_{x \to 1} g(x) =$

    A. 5   B. 1   C. 3   D. It does not exist.

14. Answer true or false. $\lim\limits_{x \to +\infty} \dfrac{\sqrt{x^2 + 9} - 3}{x}$ does not exist.

15. Answer true or false. $\lim\limits_{x \to 0} \dfrac{\sqrt{x^2 + 25} - 5}{x} = \dfrac{1}{10}$.

SECTION 2.3

1. Find a least number δ such that $|f(x) - L| < \epsilon$ if $0 < |x - a| < \delta$. $\lim\limits_{x \to 5} 4x = 20$; $\epsilon = 0.1$

   A. 0.1   B. 0.25   C. 0.5   D. 0.025

2. Find a least number δ such that $|f(x) - L| < \epsilon$ if $0 < |x - a| < \delta$. $\lim\limits_{x \to 2} 3x - 4 = 2$; $\epsilon = 0.1$

   A. 0.033   B. 0.33   C. 3.0   D. 0.3

3. Answer true or false. A least number δ such that $|f(x) - L| < \epsilon$ if $0 < |x - a| < \delta$. $\lim\limits_{x \to 3} x^3 = 27$; $\epsilon = 0.05$ is $\delta = \sqrt[3]{27.05} - 3$.

4. Find a least number δ such that $|f(x) - L| < \epsilon$ if $0 < |x - a| < \delta$. $\lim\limits_{x \to 5} \dfrac{x^2 - 25}{x - 5} = 10$; $\epsilon = 0.001$

   A. 0.001   B. 0.000001   C. 0.005   D. 0.025

5. Find a least positive integer N such that $|f(x) - L| < \epsilon$ if $x > N$. $\lim\limits_{x \to +\infty} \dfrac{12}{x^3} = 0$; $\epsilon = 0.1$

   A. $N = 100$ B. $N = 1,000$ C. $N = 4$ D. $N = 5$

6. Find a greatest negative integer N such that $|f(x) - L| < \epsilon$ if $x < N$. $\lim\limits_{x \to -\infty} \dfrac{1}{x^5} = 0$; $\epsilon = 0.1$

    A. $N = -100,000$ B. $N = -10,000$ C. $N = -1$ D. $N = -2$

7. Answer true or false. It is possible to prove that $\lim\limits_{x \to +\infty} \dfrac{1}{x^2 + 1} = 0$.

8. Answer true or false. It is possible to prove that $\lim\limits_{x \to -\infty} \dfrac{1}{x + 6} = 0$.

9. Answer true or false. It is possible to prove that $\lim\limits_{x \to +\infty} \dfrac{x}{x - 5} = 0$.

10. Answer true or false. It is possible to prove that $\lim\limits_{x \to 5} \dfrac{1}{x - 5} = +\infty$.

11. To prove that $\lim\limits_{x \to 5}(x + 2) = 7$ a reasonable relationship between δ and ϵ would be

    A. $\delta = 5\epsilon$ B. $\delta = \epsilon$ C. $\delta = \sqrt{\epsilon}$ D. $\delta = \dfrac{1}{\epsilon}$

12. Answer true or false. To use a δ-ϵ approach to show that $\lim\limits_{x \to 0^+} \dfrac{1}{x^3} = +\infty$, a reasonable first step would be to change the limit to $\lim\limits_{x \to +\infty} x^3 = 0$.

13. Answer true or false. It is possible to show that $\lim\limits_{x \to 4^-} \dfrac{1}{x - 4} = -\infty$.

14. To prove that $\lim\limits_{x \to 3} f(x) = 6$ where $f(x) = \begin{cases} 2x, & x < 3 \\ x + 3, & x \geq 3 \end{cases}$ a reasonable relationship between δ and ϵ would be

    A. $\delta = 2\epsilon$ B. $\delta = \epsilon$ C. $\delta = \epsilon + 3$ D. $\delta = 2\epsilon + 3$

15. Answer true or false. It is possible to show that $\lim\limits_{x \to +\infty} \dfrac{x}{5} = 5$.

SECTION 2.4

1.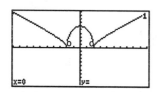

    On the interval of $[-10, 10]$, where is f not continuous?
    A. $-2, 2$ B. 2 C. -2 D. nowhere

2.
    On the interval of $[-10, 10]$, where is f not continuous?
    A. 3 B. $0, 3$ C. 0 D. nowhere

3. Answer true or false. $f(x) = x^6 - 4x^4 + 2x^2 - 8$ has no point of discontinuity.

4. Answer true or false. $f(x) = |x + 4|$ has a point of discontinuity at $x = -4$.

5. Find the x-coordinates for all points of discontinuity for $f(x) = \dfrac{x + 6}{x^2 + 8x + 12}$.

    A. $-6, -2$ B. -2 C. $2, 6$ D. 2

6. Find the x-coordinates for all points of discontinuity for $f(x) = \dfrac{|x + 5|}{x^2 + 5x}$.

    A. 0 B. -5 C. $-5, 0$ D. $-5, 0, 5$

7. Find the x-coordinates for all points of discontinuity for $f(x) = \begin{cases} x^2 - 5, & x \le 1 \\ -4, & x > 1 \end{cases}$.

    A. 1 B. $-\sqrt{5}, \sqrt{5}$ C. $-4, -\sqrt{5}, \sqrt{5}$ D. None exists.

8. Find the value of k, if possible, that will make the function continuous. $f(x) = \begin{cases} x - 2, & x \le 1 \\ kx^3, & x > 1 \end{cases}$

    A. 1 B. -1 C. 2 D. None exists.

9. Answer true or false. The function $f(x) = \dfrac{x^3 - 1}{x - 1}$ has a removable discontinuity at $x = 1$.

10. Answer true or false. The function $f(x) = \begin{cases} x^2, & x \le 2 \\ x - 4, & x > 2 \end{cases}$ is continuous everywhere.

11. Answer true or false. If f and g are each continuous at c, $f + g$ may be discontinuous at c.

12. Answer true or false. The Intermediate-Value Theorem can be used to approximate the locations of all discontinuities for $f(x) = \dfrac{x}{x^3 - 5x + 13}$.

13. Answer true or false. $f(x) = x^5 - 6x^2 + 2 = 0$ has at least one solution on the interval $[-1, 0]$.

14. Answer true or false. $f(x) = x^3 + 2x + 9 = 0$ has at least one solution on the interval $[0, 1]$.

15. Use the fact that $\sqrt{8}$ is a solution of $x^2 - 8 = 0$ to approximate $\sqrt{8}$ with an error of at most 0.005.

    A. 2.82 B. 2.81 C. 2.83 D. 2.84

SECTION 2.5

1. Answer true or false. $f(x) = \cos(x^2 + 5)$ has no point of discontinuity.

2. A point of discontinuity of $f(x) = \dfrac{1}{|-1 + 2\cos x|}$ is at

    A. $\dfrac{\pi}{2}$ B. $\dfrac{\pi}{3}$ C. $\dfrac{\pi}{4}$ D. $\dfrac{\pi}{6}$

3. Find the limit. $\lim\limits_{x \to +\infty} \cos\left(\dfrac{4}{x}\right) =$

    A. 0 B. 1 C. -1 D. $+\infty$

4. Find the limit. $\lim\limits_{x \to 0^-} \dfrac{\sin x}{x^3} =$

   A. $+\infty$ B. 0   C. 1   D. $-\infty$

5. Find the limit. $\lim\limits_{x \to 0} \dfrac{\sin(3x)}{\sin(8x)} =$

   A. $+\infty$ B. 0   C. $\dfrac{3}{8}$ D. 1

6. Find the limit. $\lim\limits_{x \to 0} \dfrac{4}{1 - \sin x} =$

   A. 1   B. -1 C. 4   D. 0

7. Find the limit. $\lim\limits_{x \to 0} \dfrac{1 + \cos x}{1 - \cos x} =$

   A. 0   B. $+\infty$ C. $-\infty$ D. 2

8. Find the limit. $\lim\limits_{x \to 0} \dfrac{\tan x}{\cos x} =$

   A. 0   B. 1   C. $+\infty$ D. $-\infty$

9. Find the limit. $\lim\limits_{x \to 0^-} \cos \dfrac{1}{x} =$

   A. 1   B. -1 C. $-\infty$ D. does not exist

10. Find the limit. $\lim\limits_{x \to 0^+} \dfrac{-1.3x + \cos x}{x} =$

    A. 0   B. 1   C. -1 D. $+\infty$

11. Answer true or false. The value of k that makes f continuous for $f(x) = \begin{cases} \dfrac{\cos x - 1}{x}, & x \leq 0 \\ \cos x + k, & x > 0 \end{cases}$ is 0.

12. Answer true or false. The fact that $\lim\limits_{x \to 0} \dfrac{1 - \cos x}{x} = 0$ and that $\lim\limits_{x \to 0} x = 0$ guarantees that $\lim\limits_{x \to 0} \dfrac{(1 - \cos x)^2}{x} = 0$ by the Squeeze Theorem.

13. Answer true or false. The Squeeze Theorem can be used to show $\lim\limits_{x \to 0} \dfrac{\sin(4x)}{6x} = 1$ utilizing $\lim\limits_{x \to 0} \dfrac{\sin(4x)}{4x} = 1$ and $\lim\limits_{x \to 0} \dfrac{\sin(6x)}{6x} = 1$.

14. Answer true or false. The Intermediate-Value Theorem can be used to show that the equation $y^3 = \sin^2 x$ has at least one solution on the interval $[-5\pi/6, 5\pi/6]$.

15. $\lim\limits_{x \to 0} \left(\dfrac{\sin x}{2x} + \dfrac{x}{2 \sin x} \right) =$

    A. 1   B. 2   C. $\dfrac{1}{2}$ D. 0

CHAPTER 2 TEST

1.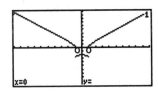

   The function f is graphed. $\lim\limits_{x \to -1} f(x) =$

   A. 2   B. -2 C. 0   D. undefined

2. Approximate $\lim\limits_{x \to -5} \dfrac{x^2 - 25}{x + 5}$ by evaluating $f(x) = \dfrac{x^2 - 25}{x + 5}$ at $x = -4, -4.5, -4.9, -4.99, -4.999, -6,$
   $-5.5, -5.1, -5.01,$ and -5.001.

   A. 5   B. -5 C. 10   D. -10

3. Use a graphing utility to approximate the y-coordinate of the horizontal asymptote of
   $$y = f(x) = \frac{9x + 3}{4x + 2}$$

   A. $\dfrac{9}{4}$ B. $\dfrac{4}{9}$ C. $\dfrac{3}{2}$ D. $\dfrac{2}{3}$

4. Answer true or false. A graphing utility can be used to show that $f(x) = \left(8 + \dfrac{2}{2x}\right)^{2x}$ has a horizontal asymptote.

5. Answer true or false. $\lim\limits_{x \to +\infty} \dfrac{5}{x^2}$ is equivalent to $\lim\limits_{x \to 0^+} 5x^2$.

6. Given that $\lim\limits_{x \to a} f(x) = 5$ and $\lim\limits_{x \to a} g(x) = -5$, find $\lim\limits_{x \to a}[2f(x) + 4g(x)]$.

   A. 0   B. -5 C. -10 D. 30

7. $\lim\limits_{x \to 6} 4 =$

   A. 6   B. -6 C. 4   D. does not exist

8. $\lim\limits_{x \to 1} \dfrac{x^8 - 1}{x - 1} =$

   A. 0   B. $+\infty$ C. 4   D. 8

9. $\lim\limits_{x \to 6} \dfrac{1}{x - 6} =$

   A. $\dfrac{1}{12}$ B. 0   C. $+\infty$ D. does not exist

10. Let $f(x) = \begin{cases} x^2, & x \le 1 \\ x, & x > 1 \end{cases}$. $\lim\limits_{x \to 1} f(x) =$

    A. 1   B. -1 C. 0   D. does not exist

11. Find a least number δ such that $|f(x) - L| < \epsilon$ if $0 < |x - a| < \delta$. $\lim\limits_{x \to 5} 4x = 20; \epsilon < 0.01$

    A. 0.01   B. 0.025   C. 0.05   D. 0.0025

12. Find a least number δ such that $|f(x) - L| < \epsilon$ if $0 < |x - a| < \delta$. $\displaystyle\lim_{x \to -6} \frac{x^2 - 36}{x + 6} = -12; \; \epsilon < 0.001$

    A. 0.001   B. 0.000001   C. 0.006   D. 0.03

13. Answer true or false. It is possible to prove that $\displaystyle\lim_{x \to -\infty} \frac{1}{x^7} = 0$.

14. To prove $\displaystyle\lim_{x \to 2}(3x + 1) = 7$, a reasonable relationship between δ and ϵ would be

    A. $\delta = \dfrac{\epsilon}{3}$ B. $\delta = 3\epsilon$ C. $\delta = \epsilon$ D. $\delta = \epsilon - 1$

15. Answer true or false. It is possible to show that $\displaystyle\lim_{x \to +\infty}(x - 3) = -3$.

16. On the interval $[-10, 10]$ where is f not continuous. f is the function graphed to the left.

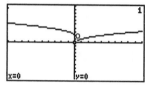

    A. 0   B. -2 C. 2   D. nowhere

17. Find the x-coordinate of each point of discontinuity of $f(x) = \dfrac{x + 2}{x^2 - 3x - 10}$.

    A. 5   B. $-2, 5$ C. $2, 5$ D. $-5, 2$

18. Find the value of k, if possible, that will make the function $f(x) = \begin{cases} kx + 3, & x \le 3 \\ x^2, & x > 3 \end{cases}$ continuous.

    A. 3   B. 0   C. 2   D. None exists.

19. Answer true or false. $f(x) = \dfrac{1}{x - 6}$ has a removable discontinuity at $x = 6$.

20. Answer true or false. $f(x) = x^5 + 6 = 0$ has at least one solution on the interval $[-2, -1]$.

21. Find $\displaystyle\lim_{x \to 0} \frac{\sin(-3x)}{\sin(2x)}$.

    A. 0   B. $\dfrac{-3}{2}$ C. $\dfrac{3}{2}$ D. not defined

22. Find $\displaystyle\lim_{x \to 0} \frac{\sin x}{\tan x}$.

    A. 0   B. -1 C. 1   D. undefined

23. Answer true or false. $\displaystyle\lim_{x \to 0} \frac{\sin x}{1 - \cos x} = 0$.

ANSWERS TO SAMPLE TESTS

SECTION 2.1:

1. A 2. F 3. D 4. T 5. D 6. C 7. A 8. A 9. A 10. A 11. B 12. T 13. F 14. T 15. F 16. F

SECTION 2.2:

1. B 2. A 3. T 4. B 5. D 6. A 7. A 8. A 9. B 10. C 11. A 12. A 13. D 14. F 15. F

SECTION 2.3:

1. D 2. A 3. T 4. A 5. C 6. C 7. T 8. T 9. F 10. F 11. B 12. T 13. T 14. A 15. F

SECTION 2.4:

1. A 2. C 3. T 4. F 5. A 6. D 7. A 8. B 9. T 10. F 11. F 12. T 13. T 14. F 15. C

SECTION 2.5:

1. T 2. B 3. B 4. A 5. C 6. C 7. B 8. B 9. D 10. D 11. F 12. T 13. F 14. F 15. A

CHAPTER 2 TEST:

1. D 2. D 3. A 4. F 5. T 6. C 7. C 8. D 9. D 10. A 11. D 12. A 13. T 14. A 15. F 16. A 17. B 18. C 19. F 20. T 21. B 22. C 23. F

CHAPTER 3
Sample Exams

SECTION 3.1

1. Find the average rate of change of y with respect to x over the interval $[1,5]$. $y = f(x) = \dfrac{1}{x^2}$.

   A. 0.24   B. -0.24 C. 0.48   D. -0.48

2. Find the average rate of change of y with respect to x over the interval $[1,4]$. $y = f(x) = x^3$.

   A. 21   B. -21 C. 31.5   D. -31.5

3. Find the instantaneous rate of change of $y = x^4$ with respect to x at $x_0 = 3$.

   A. 108   B. 27   C. 54   D. 13.5

4. Find the instantaneous rate of $y = \dfrac{1}{x}$ with respect to x at $x_0 = -2$.

   A. 0.25   B. 0.5   C. -0.25 D. -0.5

5. Find the instantaneous rate of $y = 2x^3$ with respect to x at a general point x_0.

   A. $6x_0^2$ B. $4x_0^2$ C. $\dfrac{2x_0^2}{3}$ D. x_0^4

6. Find the instantaneous rate of $y = \dfrac{2}{x}$ with respect to x at a general point x_0.

   A. $-\dfrac{3}{x_0}$ B. $-\dfrac{3x_0}{2}$ C. $-\dfrac{3}{x_0^2}$ D. $-\dfrac{2}{x_0^2}$

7. Find the slope of the tangent to the graph of $f(x) = x^2 - 2$ at a general point x_0.

   A. $2x_0 - 2$ B. $2x_0^2 - 2$ C. $2x_0^2$ D. $2x_0$

8. Answer true or false. The slope of the tangent line to the graph of $f(x) = x^2 - 4$ at $x_0 = 3$ is 2.

9. Answer true or false. Use a graphing utility to graph $y = x^3$ on $[0,5]$. If this graph represents a position versus time curve for a particle, the instantaneous velocity of the particle is increasing over the graphed domain.

10. Use a graphing utility to graph $y = x^2 - 6x + 4$ on $[0,10]$. If this graph represents a position versus time curve for a particle, the instantaneous velocity of the particle is zero at what time? Assume time is in seconds.

    A. 0 s   B. 3 s   C. 5 s   D. 10 s

11. A rock is dropped from a height of 64 feet and falls toward earth in a straight line. What is the instantaneous velocity downward when it hits the ground?

    A. 64 ft/s   B. 32 ft/s   C. 2 ft/s   D. 16 ft/s

12. Answer true or false. The magnitude of the instantaneous velocity is never less than the magnitude of the average velocity.

13. Answer true or false. If a rock is thrown straight upward from the ground, when it returns to earth its average velocity will be zero.

14. Answer true or false. If an object is thrown straight upward with a positive instantaneous velocity, its instantaneous velocity when it returns to the ground will be negative.

15. An object moves in a straight line so that after t s its distance in mm from its original position is given by $s = t^3 + t$. Its instantaneous velocity at $t = 5$ s is

A. 128 mm
B. 28 mm
C. 27 mm
D. 76 mm

SECTION 3.2

1. Find the equation of the tangent line to $y = f(x) = 4x^2$ at $x = 2$.

A. $y = 16x$
B. $y = 16x - 32$
C. $y = 16x - 16$
D. $y = 16x + 16$

2. Find the equation of the tangent line to $y = f(x) = \sqrt{x+2}$ at $x = 7$.

A. $y = \dfrac{x}{6} + \dfrac{11}{6}$
B. $y = \dfrac{x}{6} - 4$
C. $y = \dfrac{x}{6}$
D. $y = \dfrac{1}{3}$

3. $y = x^2$. $dy/dx =$

A. 2
B. $2x^2$
C. $2x$
D. $\dfrac{x}{2}$

4. $y = \sqrt{x}$. $dy/dx =$

A. $\dfrac{\sqrt{x}}{2x}$
B. $\dfrac{\sqrt{x}}{x}$
C. $\dfrac{\sqrt{x}}{2}$
D. $\dfrac{2\sqrt{x}}{x}$

5.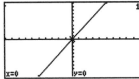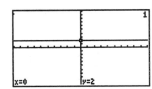

Answer true or false. The derivative of the function graphed on the left is graphed on the right.

6. Answer true or false. Use a graphing utility to help in obtaining the graph of $y = f(x) = |x|$. The derivative $f'(x)$ is not defined at $x = 0$.

7. Find $f'(t)$ if $f(t) = 4t^3 - 2$.

A. $12t^3 - 2$
B. $3t^2$
C. $4t^2$
D. $12t^2$

8. $\displaystyle\lim_{h \to 0} \dfrac{(4+h)^3 - 64}{h}$ represents the derivative of $f(x) = x^3$ at $x = a$. Find a.

A. 4
B. -4
C. 64
D. -64

9. $\displaystyle\lim_{h \to 0} \dfrac{\sqrt[3]{(27+h)} - 3}{h}$ represents the derivative of $f(x) = \sqrt[3]{x}$ at $x = a$. Find a.

A. 27
B. 3
C. -3
D. -27

10. Find an equation for the tangent line to the curve $y = x^3 - x^2 + x + 1$ at $(1, 2)$.

A. $y = -2$
B. $y = 2$
C. $y = x - 2$
D. $y = 2x$

11. Let $f(x) = \cos x$. Estimate $f'\left(\dfrac{\pi}{4}\right)$ by using a graphing utility.

A. $\dfrac{1}{4}$
B. $-\dfrac{\sqrt{2}}{2}$
C. $\dfrac{1}{2}$
D. $\dfrac{\pi}{4}$

12. An air source constantly increases the air supply rate of a balloon. The volume V in cubic feet is given by $V(t) = t^2$ $[0 \le t \le 5]$, where t is time in seconds. How fast is the balloon increasing at $t = 3$ s?

   A. 6 ft^3/s   B. 9 ft^3/s   C. 18 ft^3/s   D. 3 ft^3/s

13. Answer true or false. Using a graphing utility it can be shown that $f(x) = \sqrt[5]{x}$ is differentiable everywhere on $[-10, 10]$.

14. Answer true or false. A graphing utility can be used to determine that $f(x) = \begin{cases} x^3, & x \le 1 \\ x^2, & x > 1 \end{cases}$ is differentiable at $x = 1$.

15. Answer true or false. A graphing utility can be used to determine that $f(x) = \begin{cases} x^3, & x \le 0 \\ x^5, & x > 0 \end{cases}$ is differentiable at $x = 0$.

SECTION 3.3

1. Find dy/dx if $y = 7x^9$.

   A. $16x^9$ B. $63x^9$ C. $16x^8$ D. $63x^8$

2. Find dy/dx if $y = e^3$.

   A. $3e^2$ B. $2e^2$ C. $2e^3$ D. 0

3. Find dy/dx if $y = 3(x^2 - 2x + 4)$.

   A. $6x - 6$ B. $3x^2 - 6x + 4$
   C. $9x^3 - 12x^2 + 4x$ D. $2x - 2$

4. Answer true or false. If $f(x) = \sqrt{x} + x^2$, $f'(x) = \dfrac{\sqrt{x}}{2} + 2x$.

5. Answer true or false. If $y = \dfrac{1}{4x + 2}$, $y'(x) = \dfrac{1}{4}$.

6. If $y = \dfrac{2x}{x - 4}$, $dy/dx|_1 =$

   A. $-\dfrac{8}{3}$ B. $\dfrac{8}{3}$ C. $-\dfrac{8}{9}$ D. $\dfrac{8}{9}$

7. $y = \dfrac{4}{x + 5}$, $y'(0) =$

   A. 0   B. $\dfrac{4}{5}$ C. $-\dfrac{4}{25}$ D. $-\dfrac{4}{5}$

8. $g(x) = x^2 f(x)$. Find $g'(2)$, given that $f(2) = 4$ and $f'(2) = 8$.

   A. 48   B. -16 C. 16   D. 32

9. $y = 9x^2 + 4x + 6$. Find d^2y/dx^2.

   A. 19   B. $18x + 4$ C. 18   D. 9

10. $y = x^{-6} + x^3$. Find y'''.

   A. $-120x^{-4} + 6$ B. $-336x^{-9} + 6$ C. $120x^{-4} + 6$ D. $336x^{-9} + 6$

11. Answer true or false. $y = y''' + 12y' - 48x^3$ is satisfied by $y = x^4 + 4x^3 + 2$.

12. Use a graphing utility to locate all horizontal tangent lines to the curve $y = x^3 + 6x^2 + 2$.

   A. $x = 0, 4$ B. $x = -4, 0$ C. $x = 0$ D. $x = -4$

13. Find the x-coordinate of the point on the graph of $y = x^4$ where the tangent line is parallel to the secant line that cuts the curve at $x = 0$ and at $x = 1$.

   A. $\dfrac{1}{\sqrt[3]{4}}$ B. 4   C. 1   D. $\dfrac{1}{2}$

14. The position of a moving particle is given by $s(t) = 3t^2 + 2t + 1$ where t is time in seconds. The velocity in m/s is given by ds/dt. Find the velocity at $t = 2$.

   A. 6 m/s   B. 8 m/s   C. 16 m/s   D. 14 m/s

15. Answer true or false. If f, g, and h are differentiable functions, and $h \neq 0$ anywhere on its domain, then $\left(\dfrac{fg}{h}\right)' = \dfrac{hf'g' - fgh'}{h^2}$.

SECTION 3.4

1. Find $f'(x)$ if $f(x) = x^4 \sin x$.

   A. $4x^3 \cos x$ B. $-4x^3 \cos x$

   C. $4x^3 \sin x + x^4 \cos x$ D. $4x^3 \sin x - x^4 \cos x$

2. Find $f'(x)$ if $f(x) = \sin x \tan x$.

   A. $\cos x$ B. $(\sin x)(1 + \sec^2 x)$

   C. $(\sin x)(1 - \sec^2 x)$ D. $-\cos x$

3. Find $f'(x)$ if $f(x) = \sin^2 x + \cos x$.

   A. $\sin x$ B. $2 \sin x \cos x - \sin x$

   C. $2 \sin x - \cos x$ D. $3 \sin x$

4. Find d^2y/dx^2 if $y = x \sin x$.

   A. $-x \sin x + 2 \cos x$ B. 0

   C. $-\cos x$ D. $\cos x$

5. Answer true or false. If $y = \sec x$, $d^2y/dx^2 = \sec x$.

6. Find the equation of the line tangent to the graph of $y = \sin x$ at the point where $x = 0$.

   A. $y = -1$ B. $y = -x$ C. $y = x$ D. $y = 1$

7. Find the x-coordinates of all points in the interval $[-2\pi, 2\pi]$ at which the graph of $f(x) = \csc x$ has a horizontal tangent line.

   A. $-3\pi/2, -\pi/2, \pi/2, 3\pi/2$ B. $-\pi, \pi$

   C. $-\pi, 0, \pi$ D. $-3\pi/2, 0, 3\pi/2$

8. Find $d^{93} \cos x/dx^{93}$.

   A. $\cos x$ B. $y = -\cos x$ C. $\sin x$ D. $-\sin x$

9. Find all x-values on $(0, 2\pi)$ where $f(x)$ is not differentiable. $f(x) = \tan x \cos x$

   A. $\pi/2, 3\pi/2$ B. π C. $\pi/2, \pi, 3\pi/2$ D. None

10. Answer true or false. If x is given in radians, the derivative formula for $y = \tan x$ in degrees is
$y' = \dfrac{\pi}{180} \sec^2 x$.

11. A rock at an elevation angle of θ is falling in a straight line. If at a given instant it has an angle of elevation of $\theta = \pi/4$ and has a horizontal distance s from an observer, find the rate at which the rock is falling with respect to θ.

 A. $\cos\left(\dfrac{\pi}{4}\right)$
 B. $s\cos\left(\dfrac{\pi}{4}\right)$
 C. $\dfrac{\cos\left(\frac{\pi}{4}\right)}{s}$
 D. $\cos\left(\dfrac{s\pi}{4}\right)$

12. Answer true or false. If $f(x) = \tan x \cos x - \cot x \sin x$, $f'(x) = \cos x - \sin x$.

13. Answer true or false. If $f(x) = \dfrac{1}{\tan x}$, $f'(x) = -\csc^2 x$.

14. Answer true or false. $f(x) = \dfrac{\sin x}{1 - \cos x}$ is differentiable everywhere.

15. If $y = x^3 \sin x$, find d^2y/dx^2.
 A. $6x \sin x$
 B. $6x \sin x + 6x^2 \cos x + x^3 \sin x$
 C. $6x \sin x + 6x^2 \cos x - x^3 \sin x$
 D. $6x \sin x - x^3 \sin x$

SECTION 3.5

1. $f(x) = \sqrt{x^2 - 4x + 3}$. $f'(x) =$
 A. $\dfrac{x - 2}{\sqrt{x^2 - 4x + 3}}$
 B. $\dfrac{x - 4}{\sqrt{x^2 - 4x + 3}}$
 C. $\dfrac{1}{2\sqrt{x^2 - 4x + 3}}$
 D. $2x - 4$

2. $f(x) = (x^5 - 2)^{20}$. $f'(x) =$
 A. $20(x^5 - 2)^{19}$
 B. $100x^4(x - 2)^{19}$
 C. $100x^5(x - 2)^{20}$
 D. $100x^4$

3. $f(x) = \sin(3x)$. $f'(x) =$
 A. $\cos(3x)$
 B. $3\cos(3x)$
 C. $-\cos(3x)$
 D. $-3\cos(3x)$

4. Answer true or false. If $f(x) = \sqrt{\sin^2 x + 3}$, $f'(x) = \dfrac{\cos x}{\sqrt{\sin^2 x + 3}}$.

5. $f(x) = x^3\sqrt{x^2 - 2}$. $f'(x) =$
 A. $\dfrac{x^3}{2\sqrt{x^2 - 2}} + 3x^2\sqrt{x^2 - 2}$
 B. $3x^2\sqrt{x^2 - 2}$
 C. $6x^4$
 D. $\dfrac{x^4}{\sqrt{x^2 - 2}} + 3x^2\sqrt{x^2 - 2}$

6. $y = \sin(\cos x)$. Find dy/dx.
 A. $-\cos(\cos x)\sin x$
 B. $\cos(\cos x)\sin x$
 C. $\sin(\cos x)\cos x$
 D. $-\sin(\cos x)\cos x$

7. $y = x^4 \tan(6x)$. Find dy/dx.
 A. $24x^3 \sec^2(6x)$
 B. $4x^3 \tan(6x)$
 C. $6x^4 \sec^2(6x) + 4x^3 \tan(6x)$
 D. $6x^4 \sec^2 x + 4x^3 \tan x$

8. $y = \left(\dfrac{1 + \sin^2 x}{\cos x}\right)$. $dy/dx =$

A. $\dfrac{\sin x + 2 \sin x \cos^2 x + \sin^3 x}{\cos^2 x}$

B. $\dfrac{\sin x + 2 \sin x \cos^2 x - \sin^3 x}{\cos^2 x}$

C. $\dfrac{2 \cos x}{\sin x}$

D. $-\dfrac{2 \cos x}{\sin x}$

9. Answer true or false. If $y = \cos(5x^3)$, $d^2y/dx^2 = -\cos(5x^3)$.

10. Answer true or false. $y = \sin x^3 - \cos x^2$. $d^2y/dx^2 = 6x \cos x^3 - 9x^4 \sin x^3 + 2 \sin x^2 + 4x^2 \cos x^2$.

11. Find an equation for the tangent line to the graph of $y = x \tan x$ at $x = \pi/4$.

A. $y - \dfrac{\pi}{4} = \left(\dfrac{\pi}{2} + 1\right)\left(x - \dfrac{\pi}{4}\right)$

B. $y - 1 = x - \dfrac{\pi}{4}$

C. $y - \dfrac{\pi}{4} = x - 1$

D. $y - \dfrac{\pi}{4} = \dfrac{\sqrt{2}}{2}\left(x - \dfrac{\pi}{4}\right)$

12. $y = \sin^3(\pi - 2\theta)$. Find $dy/d\theta$.

A. $-6 \sin^2(\pi - 2\theta) \cos(\pi - 2\theta)$

B. $-6 \sin^2(\pi - 2\theta)$

C. $-6 \sin^3(\pi - 2\theta)$

D. $3 \sin^2(\pi - 2\theta) \cos(\pi - 2\theta)$

13. Use a graphing utility to obtain the graph of $f(x) = (x + 2)^3 \sqrt{x}$. Determine the slope of the tangent line to the graph at $x = 1$.

A. 1   B. 54   C. 27   D. 40.5

14. Find the value of the constant A so that $y = A \cos 3t$ satisfies $d^2y/dt^2 + 3y = \cos 3t$.

A. $-\dfrac{1}{12}$ B. $\dfrac{1}{6}$ C. $-\dfrac{1}{6}$ D. $-\dfrac{9}{2}$

15. Answer true or false. Given $f'(x) = \sqrt{x + 2}$ and $g(x) = x^3$, then $F'(x) = \sqrt{x^3 + 2}(3x^2)$ if $F(x) = f(g(x))$.

SECTION 3.6

1. If $y = \sqrt[3]{x}$, find the formula for Δy.

A. $\Delta y = \sqrt[3]{x + \Delta x} - \sqrt[3]{x}$

B. $\Delta y = \sqrt[3]{x + \Delta x}$

C. $\Delta y = \dfrac{1}{3\sqrt[3]{(x + \Delta x)^2}} - \dfrac{1}{3\sqrt[3]{x^2}}$

D. $\Delta y = \dfrac{1}{3\sqrt[3]{(x + \Delta x)^2}}$

2. If $y = x^4$, find the formula for Δy.

A. $\Delta y = (x + \Delta x)^4$

B. $\Delta y = 4x^3 \Delta x$

C. $\Delta y = 4(x - \Delta x)^3$

D. $\Delta y = (x + \Delta x)^4 - x^4$

3. If $y = \cos x$, find the formula for Δy.

A. $\Delta y = \cos(x + \Delta x) - \cos x$

B. $\Delta y = \cos(x + \Delta x)$

C. $\Delta y = -\sin x \Delta x$

D. $\Delta y = \Delta x + \cos x$

4. Answer true or false. The formula for dy is obtained from the formula for Δy by replacing Δx with dx.

5. $y = x^5$. Find the formula for dy.

A. $dy = (x + dx)^5$

B. $dy = (x + dx)^5 - x^5$

C. $dy = x^5 + (dx)^5$

D. $dy = 5x^4 dx$

6. $y = \tan x$. Find the formula for dy.

    A. $dy = \sec^2 x\, dx$ B. $dy = \tan x\, dx$
    C. $dy = \tan(x + dx) - \tan x$ D. $dy = \tan(x + dx)$

7. $y = x^3 \sin x$. Find the formula for dy.

    A. $dy = (3x^2 \sin x + x^3 \cos x)dx$

    B. $dy = 3(x + dx)^3 \sin(x + dx)$

    C. $dy = 3(x + dx)^3 \sin(x + dx) - 3x^3 \sin x$

    D. $dy = (x + dx)^3 \sin(x + dx) - x^3 \sin x$

8. Let $y = \dfrac{1}{x^2}$. Find dy at $x = 1$ if $dx = 0.01$.

    A. 0.02   B. -0.02 C. -0.001 D. 0.001

9. Let $y = x^5$. Find dy at $x = 1$ if $dx = -0.01$.

    A. 0.00000005   B. -0.00000005 C. 0.05   D. -0.05

10. Let $y = \sqrt{x}$. Find Δy at $x = 3$ if $\Delta x = 1$.

    A. -0.268 B. 0.268   C. 0.289   D. 0.250

11. Use dy to approximate $\sqrt{3.96}$ starting at $x = 4$.

    A. 2.01   B. 1.99   C. 4.01   D. 3.99

12. Answer true or false. A circular spill is spreading so that when its radius r is 2 m, $dr = 0.05$ m. The corresponding change in the area covered by the spill, A, is, to the nearest hundredth of a square meter, 0.63 m^2.

13. A small suspended droplet of radius 10 microns is evaporating. If $dr = -0.001$ micron find the change in the volume, dV, to the nearest thousandth of a cubic micron.

    A. -420.237 B. -1.257 C. -0.419 D. -4.189

14. Answer true or false. A cube is expanding as temperature increases. If the length of the cube is changing at a rate of $\Delta x = 2$ mm when x is 1 m, the volume is experiencing a corresponding change of 0.006 mm^3, correct to the nearest thousandth.

15. Answer true or false. The radius of the base of a cylinder is 2 mm with a possible error of ± 0.01 mm. The height of the cylinder is exactly 4m. Using differentials to estimate the maximum error of the volume, it is found to be 50.27 mm^3, correct to the nearest hundredth.

CHAPTER 3 TEST:

1. Find the average rate of change of y with respect to x over the interval $[1,2]$. $y = f(x) = 3x^2$.

   A. 9 B. -9 C. 11 D. -11

2. Find the instantaneous rate of change of $y = 2x^4$ with respect to x at $x_0 = 3$.

   A. 216 B. 54 C. 108 D. 27

3. An object moves in a straight line so that after t s its distance from its original position is given by $s = t^3 - 2t$. Its instantaneous velocity at $t = 4$ s is

   A. 56 B. 46 C. 14 D. 11.5

4. Find the equation of the tangent line to $y = f(x) = 3x^3$ at $x = 3$.

   A. $y = 27x - 60$ B. $y = 27x + 60$ C. $y = 81x + 162$ D. $y = 81x - 162$

5. If $y = x^8$, $dy/dx =$

   A. $8x^7$ B. $8x^8$ C. $7x^7$ D. $7x^8$

6.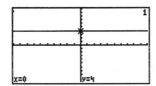

   Answer true or false. The derivative of the function graphed on the left is graphed on the right.

7. $\displaystyle\lim_{h \to 0} \frac{(6 - 2h)^2 - (2h)^2}{h}$ represents the derivative of $f(x) = (2x)^2$ at $x =$

   A. 6 B. 3 C. -6 D. -3

8. Let $f(x) = \tan x$. Estimate $f'(5\pi/4)$ by using a graphing utility.

   A. 1 B. -1 C. 0 D. 2

9. Find dy/dx if $y = \pi^5$.

   A. $5\pi^4$ B. π^5 C. 0 D. $4\pi^5$

10. Answer true of false. If $f(x) = \sqrt{x^3} + x^3$, $f'(x) = \dfrac{1}{2\sqrt{x^3}} + 3x^2$.

11. If $y = \dfrac{5x}{x - 2}$, $\dfrac{dy}{dx}\bigg|_1 =$

    A. 10 B. -10 C. 8 D. -8

12. $g(x) = \sqrt{x} f(x)$. Find $g'(4)$ given that $f(4) = 4$ and $f'(4) = 6$.

    A. 24 B. 1.5 C. 13 D. 14

13. Find $f'(x)$ if $f(x) = x^3 \tan x$.

    A. $3x^2 \sec^2 x$ B. $-3x^2 \sec^2 x$
    C. $3x^2 \tan x + x^3 \sec^2 x$ D. $3x^2 \tan x - x^3 \sec^2 x$

14. Find d^2y/dx^2 if $y = -2(\sin x)(\cos x)$

    A. $8(\cos x)(\sin x)$ B. $-8(\cos x)(\sin x)$ C. $2(\cos x)(\sin x)$ D. $-2(\cos x)(\sin x)$

15. Find the x-coordinates of all the points over the interval $(0, \pi)$ where the graph of $f(x) = \cot x$ has a horizontal tangent line.

    A. $\pi/4, \pi/2, 3\pi/4$ B. $\pi/4, 3\pi/4$ C. $\pi/2$ D. None exist.

16. Answer true or false. $\dfrac{d^{105}}{dx^{105}} \sin x = \cos x$.

17. Answer true or false. If $f(x) = \sqrt{x^3 - 2x^2}$, $f'(x) = \dfrac{3x^2 - 4x}{\sqrt{x^3 - 2x^2}}$.

18. If $f(x) = \sin(6x)$, $f'(x) =$

    A. $6\cos(6x)$ B. $-6\cos(6x)$ C. $\cos(6x)$ D. $-\cos(6x)$

19. If $y = \sqrt[9]{x}$, find the formula for Δy.

    A. $\Delta y = \sqrt[9]{x - \Delta x} + \sqrt[9]{x}$ B. $\Delta y = \sqrt[9]{x + \Delta x} - \sqrt[9]{x}$

    C. $\Delta y = \dfrac{\Delta x}{9\sqrt[9]{x^8}}$ D. $\Delta y = \sqrt[9]{x + \Delta x} + \sqrt[9]{x}$

20. If $y = x^2 \tan x$, find the formula for dy.

    A. $dy = 2x \tan x \, dx$ B. $dy = x^2 \sec^2 x \, dx$

    C. $dy = (2x \tan x + x^2 \sec^2 x) dx$ D. $dy = (2x \tan x - x^2 \sec^2 x) dx$

21. Answer true or false. If $y = \dfrac{1}{x^5}$, dy at $x = 2$ is $-\dfrac{5}{16} dx$.

22. Answer true or false. A spherical balloon is deflating. The rate the volume is changing at $r = 2$ m is given by $dV = -16\pi dr$.

ANSWERS TO SAMPLE TESTS

SECTION 3.1:

1. B 2. A 3. A 4. C 5. A 6. D 7. D 8. F 9. T 10. B 11. A 12. F 13. T 14. T 15. D

SECTION 3.2:

1. B 2. A 3. C 4. A 5. T 6. T 7. D 8. A 9. B 10. D 11. B 12. A 13. F 14. F 15. T

SECTION 3.3:

1. D 2. D 3. A 4. F 5. F 6. C 7. C 8. A 9. C 10. B 11. F 12. B 13. A 14. D 15. F

SECTION 3.4:

1. C 2. B 3. B 4. A 5. F 6. C 7. A 8. D 9. A 10. F 11. B 12. F 13. T 14. F 15. C

SECTION 3.5:

1. A 2. B 3. B 4. T 5. D 6. A 7. C 8. A 9. F 10. T 11. A 12. A 13. D 14. C 15. T

SECTION 3.6:

1. A. 2. D 3. A 4. F 5. D 6. A 7. A 8. B 9. D 10. B 11. D 12. T 13. B 14. F 15. T

CHAPTER 3 TEST:

1. A 2. A 3. B 4. D 5. A 6. T 7. B 8. D 9. C 10. F 11. B 12. C 13. C 14. A 15. C 16. T 17. T 18. A
19. B 20. C 21. F 22. T

CHAPTER 4
Sample Exams

SECTION 4.1

1. Answer true or false. The functions $f(x) = \sqrt[3]{x+3}$ and $g(x) = x^3 - 3$ are inverses of each other.

2. Answer true or false. The functions $f(x) = \sqrt[6]{x}$ and $g(x) = x^6$ are inverses of each other.

3. Answer true or false. $\sec x$ is a one-to-one function.

4. Find $f^{-1}(x)$ if $f(x) = x^7$.

   A. $\sqrt[7]{x}$
   B. $\dfrac{1}{x^7}$
   C. $-\sqrt[7]{x}$
   D. $-\dfrac{1}{x^7}$

5. Find $f^{-1}(x)$ if $f(x) = 3x - 4$.

   A. $\dfrac{1}{3x-4}$
   B. $\dfrac{x+4}{3}$
   C. $\dfrac{x}{3} + 4$
   D. $\dfrac{1}{3x} - 4$

6. Find $f^{-1}(x)$ if $f(x) = \sqrt[9]{x+3}$.

   A. $x^9 - 3$
   B. $(x+3)^9$
   C. $x^9 + 3$
   D. $\dfrac{1}{\sqrt[9]{x+3}}$

7. Find $f^{-1}(x)$, if it exists, for the function $f(x) = \begin{cases} -x^2, & x < 0 \\ x^2, & x \geq 0 \end{cases}$.

   A. $\begin{cases} -\sqrt{x}, & x < 0 \\ \sqrt{x}, & x \geq 0 \end{cases}$
   B. $\begin{cases} -\dfrac{1}{x}, & x < 0 \\ \dfrac{1}{x}, & x \geq 0 \end{cases}$
   C. $\sqrt{|x|}$
   D. It does not exist.

8. Answer true or false. If f has a domain of $0 \leq x \leq 10$, then f^{-1} has a domain of $0 \leq x \leq 10$.

9. The graphs of f and f^{-1} are reflections of each other about the

   A. x-axis
   B. y-axis
   C. line $x = y$
   D. origin

10. Answer true or false. A 200 foot fence is used as a perimeter about a rectangular plot. The formula for the length of the fence is the inverse of the formula for the width of the fence.

11. Find the domain of $f^{-1}(x)$ if $f(x) = (x+3)^2, x \geq -3$.

    A. $x \geq -3$
    B. $x \geq 3$
    C. $x \geq 0$
    D. $x \leq 0$

12. Find the domain of $f^{-1}(x)$ if $f(x) = -\sqrt{x-5}$.

    A. $x \leq 0$
    B. $x \geq 0$
    C. $x \leq 5$
    D. $x \geq 5$

13. Let $f(x) = x^2 + 6x + 9$. Find the smallest value of k such that $f(x)$ is a one-to-one function on the interval $[k, \infty)$.

    A. 0
    B. -3
    C. 3
    D. -9

14. Answer true or false. $f(x) = -x$ is its own inverse.

15. Answer true or false. To have an inverse a trigonometric function must have its domain restricted to $[0, 2\pi]$.

SECTION 4.2

1. $2^{-5} =$

   A. $\dfrac{1}{10}$　　　　　B. $-\dfrac{1}{10}$　　　　　C. $\dfrac{1}{32}$　　　　　D. $-\dfrac{1}{32}$

2. Use a calculating utility to approximate $\sqrt[6]{29}$. Round to four decimal places.

   A. 1.7528　　　　　B. 5.3852　　　　　C. 1.7530　　　　　D. 5.3854

3. Use a calculating utility to approximate $\log 28.4$. Round to four decimal places.

   A. 3.3464　　　　　B. 3.3462　　　　　C. 1.4533　　　　　D. 1.4535

4. Find the exact value of $\log_3 81$.

   A. 12　　　　　B. $\dfrac{3}{4}$　　　　　C. $\dfrac{1}{4}$　　　　　D. 4

5. Use a calculating utility to approximate $\ln 39.1$ to four decimal places.

   A. 1.5920　　　　　B. 3.6661　　　　　C. 1.5922　　　　　D. 3.6663

6. Answer true or false. $\ln \dfrac{a^3 b}{c^2} = 3 \ln a + \ln b - 2 \ln c$.

7. Answer true or false. $\log(5x\sqrt{x-2}) = (\log 5)(\log x)(\log^{1/2}(x-2))$.

8. Rewrite the expression as a single logarithm. $5 \log 2 - \log 12 + \log 24$

   A. $\log 64$　　　　　B. $\log 22$　　　　　C. $\dfrac{\log 24}{5}$　　　　　D. $\log 44$

9. Solve $\log_{10}(x + 5) = 1$ for x.

   A. 5　　　　　B. -5　　　　　C. 0　　　　　D. no solution

10. Solve for x. $\log_{10} x^{5/2} - \log_{10} x^{3/2} = 4$.

    A. 4　　　　　B. 40　　　　　C. 1,000　　　　　D. 10,000

11. Solve $4^{-2x} = 6$ for x to four decimal places.

    A. 0.6462　　　　　B. -0.6462　　　　　C. 1.2925　　　　　D. -1.2925

12. Solve for x. $3e^x - xe^x = 0$

    A. 3　　　　　B. -3　　　　　C. $\dfrac{1}{3}$　　　　　D. $-\dfrac{1}{3}$

13.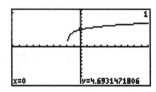

    This is the graph of

    A. $4 - \ln(2 + x)$　　　　　B. $4 + \ln(2 + x)$　　　　　C. $4 - \log(x - 2)$　　　　　D. $4 + \log(x - 2)$

14. Use a calculating utility and change of base formula to find $\log_3 4$.

    A. 0.2007　　　　　B. 0.7925　　　　　C. 1.2619　　　　　D. 0.4621

15. The equation $Q = 6e^{-0.052t}$ gives the mass Q in grams of a certain radioactive substance remaining after t hours. How much remains after 6 hours?

    A. 4.3919 g   B. 4.3920 g   C. 4.3921 g   D. 2.3922 g

SECTION 4.3

1. Answer true or false. If $y = \sqrt[5]{4x+2}$, $\dfrac{dy}{dx} = \dfrac{4}{5\sqrt{4x+2}}$.

2. Answer true or false. If $y^3 = x$, $\dfrac{dy}{dx} = \dfrac{1}{3y^2}$.

3. Find dy/dx if $\sqrt[3]{y} - \cos x = 2$.

    A. $dy/dx = -3y^{2/3}\sin x$ B. $dy/dx = 3y^{2/3}\sin x$

    C. $dy/dx = -6y^{2/3}\sin x$ D. $dy/dx = 6y^{2/3}\sin x$

4. Find dy/dx if $x^2 + y^2 = 25$.

    A. $\dfrac{25x}{y}$ B. $\dfrac{x}{y}$ C. $-\dfrac{x}{y}$ D. $-\dfrac{25x}{y}$

5. Answer true or false. If $y^2 + 2xy = 5x$, $\dfrac{dy}{dx} = \dfrac{5}{2y + 2x}$.

6. $2x^2 + 3y^2 = 9$. Find d^2y/dx^2.

    A. $\dfrac{d^2y}{dx^2} = \dfrac{16x^2 + 4y}{36y^3}$ B. $\dfrac{d^2y}{dx^2} = \dfrac{16x^2 + 4y}{6y^3}$

    C. $\dfrac{d^2y}{dx^2} = \dfrac{16x^2 - 4y}{36y^3}$ D. $\dfrac{d^2y}{dx^2} = \dfrac{18y^2 + x^2}{54y^3}$

7. Find the slope of the tangent line to $x^2 + y^2 = 5$ at (1,2).

    A. $\dfrac{1}{2}$ B. $-\dfrac{1}{2}$ C. $\dfrac{5}{2}$ D. $-\dfrac{5}{2}$

8. Find the slope of the tangent line to $xy^2 = 4$ at (1,2).

    A. 4   B. -4 C. 1   D. -1

9. Find dy/dx if $xy^4 = x^3$.

    A. $\dfrac{3x}{4y^4}$ B. $\dfrac{3x^2 - y^4}{4xy^3}$ C. $-\dfrac{3x^2}{4y^4}$ D. $\dfrac{3x^2 + y^4}{4xy^3}$

10. Find dy/dx if $x = \cos(xy)$.

    A. $-\dfrac{1}{\sin(xy)}$ B. $\dfrac{1}{\sin(xy)}$ C. $\dfrac{1 + y\sin(xy)}{x\sin(xy)}$ D. $-\dfrac{1 + y\sin(xy)}{x\sin(xy)}$

11. Answer true or false. If $\cos x = \sin y$, $dy/dx = \tan x$.

12. Answer true or false. If $\tan(xy) = 4$, $\dfrac{dy}{dx} = -\dfrac{y\sec^2(xy)}{x}$.

13. $xy^2 = x^3 - 2x$ has a tangent line parallel to the x-axis at

    A. (1,1)   B. (0,0)   C. (2,2)   D. (1,2)

14. $x^2 + y^2 = 16$ has tangent lines parallel to the y-axis at

    A. $(0, -16)$ and $(0,16)$ B. $(0, -4)$ and $(0,4)$
    C. $(-4, 0)$ and $(4,0)$ D. $(-16, 0)$ and $(16,0)$

15. Find dy/dx if $y^2 t + t^2 y = 2$ and $dt/dx = 3$.

    A. $\dfrac{-3y^2 - 6ty}{2yt + t^2 - 1}$ B. $-3y^2$ C. $\dfrac{-3y^2 - y}{2y + 1}$ D. $\dfrac{-6y^2 - 12ty}{2yt + t^2}$

SECTION 4.4

1. If $y = \ln 6x$ find dy/dx.

   A. $\dfrac{1}{6x}$ B. $\dfrac{6}{x}$ C. $\dfrac{1}{x}$ D. $\dfrac{6 \ln 6x}{x}$

2. If $y = \ln(\cos x)$ find dy/dx.

   A. $\tan x$ B. $-\tan x$ C. $\dfrac{1}{\cos x}$ D. $-\dfrac{1}{\cos x}$

3. If $y = \sqrt{3 + \ln^2 x^2}$, $dy/dx =$

   A. $\dfrac{2}{x\sqrt{3 + \ln^2 x^2}}$ B. $\dfrac{2}{\sqrt{3 + \ln^2 x^2}}$ C. $\dfrac{1}{\sqrt{3 + \ln^2 x^2}}$ D. $\dfrac{2 \ln x^2}{x\sqrt{3 + \ln^2 x^2}}$

4. Answer true or false. If $y = x^8 e^{7x}$, $dy/dx = 56x^7 e^{7x}$.

5. Answer true or false. If $y = \ln(x^3)$, $\dfrac{dy}{dx} = \dfrac{3}{x}$.

6. If $y = (\ln x)e^{2x}$, $dy/dx =$

   A. $2(\ln x)e^{2x} + \dfrac{e^{2x}}{x}$ B. $2(\ln x)e^{2x}$

   C. $2(\ln x)e^{2x}\dfrac{e^{2x-1}}{x}$ D. $\dfrac{e^{2x}}{x}$

7. Answer true or false. If $x + e^{xy} = 2$, $\dfrac{dy}{dx} = \dfrac{-ye^{xy} - 1}{xe^{xy}}$.

8. $y = \ln\left[\dfrac{1}{\sin x}\right]$. Find $\dfrac{dy}{dx}$.

   A. $\cos x \sin x$ B. $\cot x$
   C. $\tan x$ D. $-\cot x$

9. If $y = \sqrt[8]{\dfrac{x+2}{x+3}}$, find $\dfrac{dy}{dx}$ by logarithmic differentiation.

   A. $\dfrac{1}{8}\left(\dfrac{x+2}{x+3}\right)^{-7/8}$ B. $\dfrac{1}{8(x+3)^2}$

   C. $\dfrac{1}{8}\left(\dfrac{1}{x+2} - \dfrac{1}{x+3}\right)\sqrt[8]{\dfrac{x+2}{x+3}}$ D. $\sqrt[7]{\dfrac{x+2}{x+3}}$

10. $f(x) = 5^x$. Find $df(x)/dx$.

    A. $5^x \ln 5$ B. 5^{x-1} C. $x \ln 5^x$ D. $5^x \ln x$

11. Answer true or false. If $f(x) = \pi^{\sin x + \cos x}, dy/dx = (\sin x + \cos x)\pi^{\sin x + \cos x - 1}$.

12. $y = \ln(kx)$. $d^n y/dx^n =$

    A. $\dfrac{1}{k^n x^n}$ B. $\dfrac{(-1)^n}{k^n x^n}$ C. $\dfrac{(-1)^{n+1}}{x^n}$ D. $\dfrac{1}{x}$

13. Answer true or false. If $y = x^{\cos x}, \dfrac{dy}{dx} = \left(\dfrac{\cos x}{x} - \sin x \ln x\right) x^{\cos x}$.

14. $y'x = -yx$ Is satisfied by $y =$
    A. e^x B. $\cos x$ C. $\sin x$ D. e^{-x}

15. $\displaystyle \lim_{h \to 0} \dfrac{3^h - 1}{2h} =$

    A. 1   B. 0   C. $+\infty$ D. $\dfrac{\ln 3}{2}$

SECTION 4.5

1. Find the exact value of $\sin^{-1}(1)$.
    A. 0   B. $\pi/2$ C. π D. $3\pi/2$

2. Find the exact value of $\cos^{-1}(\cos(3\pi/4))$.
    A. $3\pi/4$ B. $\pi/4$ C. $-\pi/4$ D. $5\pi/4$

3. Use a calculating utility to approximate x if $\tan x = 3.1, -\pi/2 < x < \pi/2$.
    A. 1.2582   B. 1.2588   C. 1.2593   D. 1.2595

4. Use a calculating utility to approximate x if $\sin x = 0.15, \pi/2 < x < 3\pi/2$
    A. 0.1506   B. 2.9910
    C. 3.2932   D. There is no solution.

5. Answer true or false. $\cos^{-1} x = \dfrac{1}{\cos x}$ for all x.

6. $y = \sin^{-1}(2x)$. Find dy/dx.

    A. $\dfrac{2}{\sqrt{1 - 2x^2}}$ B. $\dfrac{2}{\sqrt{1 - x^2}}$ C. $\dfrac{1}{\sqrt{1 - 4x^2}}$ D. $\dfrac{2}{\sqrt{1 - 4x^2}}$

7. $y = \tan^{-1}\sqrt{x}$. Find dy/dx.

    A. $\dfrac{\sqrt{x}}{2x(1 + x)}$ B. $\dfrac{x}{1 + x}$ C. $\dfrac{x}{2(1 + x^2)}$ D. $\sqrt{\dfrac{1}{1 + x^2}}$

8. $y = e^{\sin^{-1} x}$. $dy/dx =$

    A. $\dfrac{e^{\sin^{-1} x}}{\sqrt{1 - x^2}}$ B. $-\sin^{-2} x e^{\sin^{-1} x}$ C. $\dfrac{1}{\cos x e^{\sin x}}$ D. $-\dfrac{\cos^{-1} x e^{\sin^{-1} x}}{\sqrt{1 - x^2}}$

9. $y = \ln(x \cos^{-1} x)$. Find dy/dx.

   A. $\dfrac{1}{x \cos^{-1} x}$

   B. $\dfrac{\sqrt{1-x^2}}{-x + \cos^{-1} x \sqrt{1-x^2}}$

   C. $\dfrac{\dfrac{-x}{\sqrt{1-x^2}} + \cos^{-1} x}{x \cos^{-1} x}$,

   D. $\dfrac{1}{x}$

10. $y = \sqrt{\sin^{-1} x}$. Find dy/dx.

    A. $y = \dfrac{1}{\sqrt[4]{1-x^2}}$

    B. $y = \dfrac{1}{2(\sqrt{\sin^{-1} x})(\sqrt{1-x^2})}$

    C. $y = \dfrac{1}{2\sqrt[4]{1-x^2}}$

    D. $y = -\dfrac{1}{2(\sqrt{\sin^{-1} x})(\sqrt[4]{1-x^2})}$

11. $x^2 - \sin^{-1} y = \ln x$. Find dy/dx.

    A. $\left(\dfrac{1}{x} - 2x\right)\sqrt{1-y^2}$

    B. $\left(-\dfrac{1}{x} + 2x\right)\sqrt{1-y^2}$

    C. $\dfrac{\sin^{-2} y - 2x^2}{x \sin^{-2} y}$

    D. $\dfrac{-\sin^{-2} y + 2x^2}{x \sin^{-2} y}$

12. Approximate $\sin(\sin^{-1} 3)$.

    A. 3.0000   B. 0.3096   C. 0.3000   D. 0

13. A ball is thrown at 5 m/s and travels 25 m before coming back to its original height. Given that the acceleration due to gravity is 9.8 m/s^2, and air resistance is negligible, the range formula is $R = \dfrac{v^2}{9.8}\sin 2\theta$, where θ is the angle above the horizontal at which the ball is thrown. Find all possible positive angles in radians above the horizontal at which the ball can be thrown.

    A. 1.5708

    B. 1.5708 and 3.1416

    C. 0.7854 and 1.5708

    D. 0.7854

14. Answer true or false. $\sin^{-1} x$ is an odd function.

15. Answer true or false. $\tan^{-1}(1) + \tan^{-1}(2) = \tan^{-1}(-3)$.

SECTION 4.6

1. The volume of a sphere is given by $V = \dfrac{4}{3}\pi r^3$. Find $\dfrac{dV}{dt}$ in terms of $\dfrac{dr}{dt}$.

   A. $\dfrac{dV}{dr} = 4\pi r^2 \dfrac{dr}{dt}$ B. $\dfrac{dV}{dr} = \dfrac{4}{3}\pi r^3 \dfrac{dr}{dt}$ C. $\dfrac{dV}{dr} = \dfrac{4}{3}\pi r^2 \dfrac{dr}{dt}$ D. $\dfrac{dV}{dr} = 3r^2 \dfrac{dr}{dt}$

2. A cylinder of length 2 m and radius 1 m is expanding such that $dl/dt = 0.01$ m and $dr/dt = 0.02$ m. Find dV/dt.

   A. 0.0013 m   B. 0.2827 m   C. 0.015 m   D. 0.03 m

3. A 10-ft ladder rests against a wall. If it were to slip so that when the bottom of the ladder is 6 feet from the wall it will be moving at 0.02 ft/s, how fast would the ladder be moving down the wall?

   A. 0.02 ft/s   B. 0.0025 ft/s   C. 0.015 ft/s   D. 0.12 ft/s

4. A plane is approaching an observer with a horizontal speed of 200 ft/s and is currently 10,000 ft from being directly overhead at an altitude of 20,000 ft. Find the rate at which the angle of elevation, θ, is changing with respect to time, $d\theta/dt$?

    A. 0.020 rad/s   B. 0.010 rad/s   C. 0.018 rad/s   D. 0.009 rad/s

5. Answer true or false. Suppose $z = y^5 x^3$. $dz/dt = (dy/dt)^5 + (dx/dt)^3$.

6. Suppose $z = \sqrt{x^2 + y^2}$. $dz/dt =$

    A. $2x\,dx/dt + 2y\,dy/dt$ B. $dx/dt + dy/dt$

    C. $\sqrt{(dx/dt)^2 + (dy/dt)^2}$ D. $\dfrac{2x\,dx/dt + 2y\,dy/dt}{2\sqrt{x^2 + y^2}}$

7. The power in watts for a circuit is given by $P = I^2 R$. How fast is the power changing if the resistance, R, of the circuit is 1,000 Ω, the current, I, is 2 A, and the current is decreasing with respect to time at a rate of 0.03 A/s.

    A. -0.09 w/s   B. -60 w/s   C. -120 w/s   D. -1.8 w/s

8. Gravitational force is inversely proportional to the distance between two objects squared. If $F = \dfrac{5}{d^2}$ N at a distance $d = 3$ m, how fast is the force diminishing if the objects are moving away from each other at 2 m/s?

    A. 2 N/s   B. -0.74 N/s   C. -6.7 N/s   D. -1.1 N/s

9. A point P is moving along a curve whose equation is $y = \sqrt{x^4 + 9}$. When $P = (2,5)$, y is increasing at a rate of 2 units/s. How fast is x changing?

    A. 2 units/s   B. $\dfrac{5}{8}$ units/s   C. 64 units/s   D. $\dfrac{5}{16}$ units/s

10. Water is running out of an inverted conical tank at a rate of 3 ft^3/s. How fast is the height of the water in the tank changing if the height is currently 5 ft and the radius is 5 ft.

    A. 3 ft/s   B. 0.377 ft/s   C. 1.131 ft/s   D. 9.425 ft/s

11. Answer true or false. If $z = x \ln y$, $\dfrac{dz}{dt} = \left(\dfrac{dx}{dt}\right)\left(\dfrac{dy}{dt}\right)$.

12. Answer true or false. If $z = e^x \ln y$, $\dfrac{dz}{dt} = \dfrac{e^x}{y}\dfrac{dy}{dt} + e^x \ln y \dfrac{dx}{dt}$.

13. Answer true or false. If $\sin \theta = 3xy$, $\dfrac{d\theta}{dt} = 3x\dfrac{dy}{dt} + 3y\dfrac{dx}{dt}$.

14. Answer true or false. If $V = 3x^2 y$, $\dfrac{dy}{dt} = \dfrac{dV}{dt} - 6x\dfrac{dx}{dt}$.

15. Answer true or false. If $V = 10x^3$, $\dfrac{dx}{dt} = \dfrac{1}{30x^2}\dfrac{dV}{dt}$.

SECTION 4.7

1. $\lim\limits_{x \to 0} \dfrac{\sin 7x}{\sin x} =$

    A. 7   B. $\dfrac{1}{7}$ C. -7 D. $-\dfrac{1}{7}$

2. $\lim\limits_{x\to 0}\dfrac{x^2-9}{x^2-3x}=$

  A. 1   B. $+\infty$ C. $-\infty$ D. 0

3. $\lim\limits_{x\to 0}\dfrac{\tan^2 x}{x}=$

  A. 1   B. $+\infty$ C. $-\infty$ D. 0

4. $\lim\limits_{x\to 0^+}\dfrac{\ln(x+1)}{e^x-1}=$

  A. 0   B. 1   C. $+\infty$ D. $-\infty$

5. $\lim\limits_{x\to +\infty}\dfrac{e^x}{x^4}=$

  A. 1   B. 0   C. $+\infty$ D. $-\infty$

6. $\lim\limits_{x\to +\infty}\ln x\, e^{-x}=$

  A. 0   B. 1   C. $+\infty$ D. $-\infty$

7. $\lim\limits_{x\to 0}(1+3x)^{1/x}=$

  A. 0   B. $+\infty$ C. $-\infty$ D. 3

8. $\lim\limits_{x\to 0^+}\dfrac{\sin x}{\ln(x+1)}=$

  A. 10   B. 1   C. $+\infty$ D. $-\infty$

9. Answer true or false. $\lim\limits_{x\to 0}\dfrac{\cos\left(\frac{1}{x}\right)}{\cos\left(\frac{2}{x}\right)}=\dfrac{1}{2}$.

10. $\lim\limits_{x\to\infty}\left(e^{-x}-\dfrac{1}{x}\right)=$

  A. $+\infty$ B. $-\infty$ C. 1   D. 0

11. $\lim\limits_{x\to 0^+}(1-\ln x)^x=$

  A. 0   B. 1   C. $+\infty$ D. $-\infty$

12. Answer true or false. $\lim\limits_{x\to 0}\dfrac{\sin 3x}{1-\cos x}=1$.

13. Answer true or false. $\lim\limits_{x\to +\infty}\dfrac{2x^3-2x^2+x-3}{x^3+2x^2-x+1}=2$.

14. Answer true or false. $\lim\limits_{x\to +\infty}\left(\sqrt{x^2-2x}-x\right)=0$.

15. $\lim\limits_{x\to 0^+}\left(\dfrac{\sin x}{x}-\dfrac{1}{x}\right)=$

  A. 0   B. 1   C. $+\infty$ D. $-\infty$

CHAPTER 4 TEST

1. Answer true or false. The functions $f(x) = \sqrt[3]{x-3}$ and $g(x) = x^3 + 3$ are inverses of each other.

2. If $f(x) = \dfrac{1}{x^3 + 2}$, find $f^{-1}(x)$.

    A. $\sqrt[3]{x-2}$ B. $\sqrt[3]{\dfrac{1-2x}{x}}$ C. $\sqrt[3]{1+2x}$ D. $\sqrt[3]{\dfrac{1+2x}{x}}$

3. Find the domain of $f^{-1}(x)$ if $f(x) = \sqrt{x-6}$.
    A. $x \geq 0$ B. $x \leq 0$ C. $x \geq 6$ D. $x \geq -6$

4. Use a calculating utility to approximate $\log 41.3$.
    A. 1.610   B. 1.613   C. 1.616   D. 1.618

5. Answer true or false. $\log \dfrac{ab^3}{\sqrt{c}} = \log a + 3\log b - \dfrac{1}{2}\log c$.

6. Solve for x. $5^{2x} = 8$.
    A. 1.292   B. 0.646   C. 0.204   D. 0.102

7. Answer true or false. If $y = \sqrt[7]{2x+9}$, $\dfrac{dy}{dx} = \dfrac{x^7 - 9}{2}$.

8. Find dy/dx, if $x^2 + 3y^2 = 9$.
    A. $\dfrac{9-2x}{6y}$ B. $-\dfrac{x}{3y}$ C. $\dfrac{x}{3y}$ D. $\dfrac{9+2x}{6y}$

9. Find dy/dx if $x^2 y^4 = x^7 + 1$.
    A. $\dfrac{7x^6 - 2xy^4}{4x^2 y^3}$ B. $\dfrac{7x^6 + 1 - 2xy^4}{4x^2 y^3}$

    C. $\dfrac{5x^4}{4y^3}$ D. $7x^6 - 2x$

10. If $y = \ln(5x^2)$ find dy/dx.
    A. $\dfrac{2}{x}$ B. $\dfrac{2}{x^2}$ C. $\dfrac{2}{5x^2}$ D. $\dfrac{1}{x^2}$

11. Answer true or false. If $y = 3\ln x \; e^{3x}$, $\dfrac{dy}{dx} = \dfrac{3e^{3x}}{x} + 9\ln x e^{3x}$

12. If $f(x) = 8^x$ find $df(x)/dx$.
    A. $8^x \ln x$ B. $x \ln 8^x$ C. 8^{x-1} D. $8^x \ln 8$

13. Use a calculating utility to approximate x if $\sin x = 0.42$, $3\pi/2 < x < 5\pi/2$.
    A. 6.715   B. 6.717   C. 6.719   D. 6.723

14. $y = \tan^{-1} \sqrt[4]{x}$. Find dy/dx.

    A. $\dfrac{\sqrt{x}}{2(1+\sqrt{x})}$ B. $\dfrac{\sqrt{x}}{1+\sqrt{x}}$ C. $\dfrac{\sqrt{x}}{2(1+x)}$ D. $\sqrt[4]{\dfrac{1}{1+x}}$

15. Answer true or false. If $y = \sqrt{\cos^{-1} x + 1}$, $\dfrac{dy}{dx} = \dfrac{-1}{2(\sqrt{\cos^{-1} x + 1})(\sqrt[4]{x^2 - 1})}$.

16. Answer true or false. If $z = x^7 y^8$, $\dfrac{dz}{dt} = 56x^6 y^7 \dfrac{dx}{dt}\dfrac{dy}{dx}$.

17. Find dV/dt for a spherical balloon of radius 3 m if $dr/dt = 0.2$ m/s when $r = 3$ m.

    A. 22.6 m^3/s   B. 2.7 m^3/s   C. 0.2 m^3/s   D. 7.5 m^3/s

18. $\displaystyle\lim_{x \to 0} \dfrac{\sin 8x}{\sin 9x} =$

    A. 1   B. $+\infty$ C. $-\infty$ D. $\dfrac{8}{9}$

19. $\displaystyle\lim_{x \to 0} \dfrac{\sin 2x}{2x} =$

    A. 0   B. 1   C. $\dfrac{1}{2}$ D. $+\infty$

20. Answer true or false. $\displaystyle\lim_{x \to 0}\left(8 + \dfrac{1}{x}\right)^x = e^8$.

ANSWERS TO SAMPLE TESTS

SECTION 4.1:

1. T 2. F 3. F 4. A 5. B 6. A 7. A 8. F 9. C 10. T 11. C 12. A 13. B 14. T 15. F

SECTION 4.2:

1. C 2. A 3. C 4. D 5. B 6. T 7. F 8. A 9. A 10. D 11. B 12. A 13. B 14. C 15. A

SECTION 4.3:

1. F 2. T 3. A 4. C 5. F 6. D 7. B 8. D 9. B 10. D 11. F 12. F 13. A 14. C 15. A

SECTION 4.4:

1. C 2. B 3. D 4. F 5. T 6. A 7. T 8. D 9. C 10. A 11. F 12. C 13. T 14. D 15. D

SECTION 4.5:

1. B 2. B 3. B 4. B 5. F 6. D 7. A 8. A 9. C 10. B 11. B 12. A 13. D 14. T 15. F

SECTION 4.6:

1. A 2. B 3. C 4. C 5. F 6. D 7. C 8. B 9. B 10. A 11. F 12. T 13. F 14. F 15. T

SECTION 4.7:

1. A 2. A 3. D 4. B 5. C 6. A 7. B 8. B 9. F 10. D 11. B 12. F 13. T 14. F 15. D

CHAPTER 4 TEST:

1. T 2. B 3. A 4. C 5. T 6. B 7. F 8. B 9. A 10. A 11. T 12. D 13. B 14. A 15. F 16. F 17. A 18. D 19. B 20. F

CHAPTER 5
Sample Exams

SECTION 5.1

1. Answer true or false. If $f'(x) > 0$ for all x on the interval I, then $f(x)$ is concave up on the interval I.

2. Answer true or false. A point of inflection always has an x-coordinate where $f''(x) = 0$.

3. The largest interval over which f is increasing for $f(x) = (x - 5)^4$ is
    A. $[5, \infty)$ B. $[-5, \infty)$ C. $(-\infty, 5]$ D. $(-\infty, -5]$

4. The largest interval over which f is decreasing for $f(x) = x^3 - 12x + 7$ is
    A. $(-\infty, -2]$ B. $[2, \infty)$ C. $[-2, 2]$ D. $[-2, \infty)$

5. The largest interval over which f is increasing for $f(x) = \sqrt[3]{x - 2}$ is
    A. $[2, \infty)$ B. $(-\infty, 2]$ C. $(-\infty, \infty)$ D. nowhere

6. The largest open interval over which f is concave up for $f(x) = \sqrt[3]{x - 5}$ is
    A. $(-\infty, 5)$ B. $(5, \infty)$ C. $(-\infty, \infty)$ D. nowhere

7. The largest open interval over which f is concave up for $f(x) = e^{x^4}$ is
    A. $(-\infty, 0)$ B. $(0, \infty)$ C. $(-\infty, \infty)$ D. nowhere

8. The function $f(x) = x^{4/5}$ has a point of inflection with an x-coordinate of
    A. 0   B. $\dfrac{4}{5}$ C. $-\dfrac{4}{5}$ D. None exist.

9. The function $f(x) = e^{x^6}$ has a point of inflection with an x-coordinate of
    A. $-e$ B. e C. 0   D. None exist.

10. Use a graphing utility to determine where $f(x) = \sin x$ is decreasing on $[0, 2\pi]$.
    A. $[0, \pi]$ B. $[\pi, 2\pi]$ C. $[\pi/2, 3\pi/2]$ D. $[0, 2\pi]$

11. Answer true or false. $\cot x$ has a point of inflection on $(0, \pi)$.

12. Answer true or false. All functions of the form $f(x) = ax^n$ have an inflection point.

13. $f(x) = x^4 - 16x^2 + 6$ is concave up on the interval $I =$
    A. $(-\infty, \infty)$ B. $[-2, \infty)$ C. $(-\infty, -2]$ D. $[-2, 2]$

14. Answer true or false. If $f''(-2) = -3$ and $f''(2) = 3$, then there must be a point of inflection on $(-2, 2)$.

15. The function $f(x) = \dfrac{x^2}{x^2 - 4}$ has

    A. points of inflection at $x = -4$ and $x = 4$.
    B. points of inflection at $x = -2$ and $x = 2$
    C. a point of inflection at $x = 0$
    D. no point of inflection

201

SECTION 5.2

1. Determine the x-coordinate of each stationary point of $f(x) = 2x^3 - 3x^2 - 72x + 6$.

   A. $x = -4$ and $x = 3$ B. $x = -3$ and $x = 4$

   C. $x = -6$ D. None exists.

2. Determine the x-coordinate of each critical point of $f(x) = \sqrt[5]{x - 3}$.

   A. 0   B. 3   C. -3 D. None exist.

3. Answer true or false. $f(x) = x^{2/7}$ has a critical point.

4. Answer true or false. A function has a relative extrema at every critical point.

5. $f(x) = x^2 + 6x + 8$ has a

   A. relative maximum at $x = -3$ B. relative minimum at $x = -3$

   C. relative maximum at $x = 3$ D. relative minimum at $x = 3$

6. $f(x) = \cos^2 x$ on $0 < x < 2\pi$ has

   A. a relative maximum at $x = \pi$; relative minima at $x = \pi/2$ and $x = 3\pi/2$

   B. relative maxima at $x = \pi/2$ and $x = 3\pi/2$; a relative minimum at $x = \pi$

   C. a relative maximum at $x = \pi$; no relative minimum

   D. no relative maximum; a relative minimum at $x = \pi$

7. $f(x) = x^4 - 4x^3$ has

   A. a relative maximum at $x = 0$; no relative minimum

   B. no relative maximum; a relative minimum at $x = 3$

   C. a relative maximum at $x = 0$; a relative minimum at $x = 3$

   D. a relative maximum at $x = 0$; relative minima at $x = -3$ and $x = 3$

8. Answer true or false. $f(x) = |\tan x|$ has no relative extrema on $(-\pi/2, \pi/2)$.

9. $f(x) = e^{2x}$ has

   A. a relative maximum at $x = 0$ B. a relative minimum at $x = 0$

   C. a relative minimum at $x = 2$ D. no relative extrema

10. $f(x) = |x^2 - 9|$ has

    A. no relative maximum; a relative minimum at $x = 3$

    B. a relative maximum at $x = 3$; no relative minimum

    C. relative minima at $x = -3$ and $x = 3$; a relative maximum at $x = 0$

    D. relative minima at $x = -9$ and $x = 9$; a relative maximum at $x = 0$

11. $f(x) = \ln(x^2 + 2)$ has

    A. a relative maximum only

    B. a relative minimum only

    C. both a relative maximum and a relative minimum

    D. no relative extrema

12. On the interval $(0, 2\pi)$, $f(x) = \sin x \cos(2x)$ has

    A. a relative maximum only

    B. a relative minimum only

    C. both a relative maximum and a relative minimum

    D. no relative extrema

13. Answer true or false. $f(x) = e^x \ln x$ has a relative minimum on $(0, \infty)$.

14. Answer true or false. A graphing utility can be used to show $f(x) = |x|$ has a relative minimum.

15. Answer true or false. A graphing utility can be used to show $f(x) = x^4 - 3x^2 + 3$ has two relative minima on $[-10, 10]$.

SECTION 5.3

1. Answer true or false. If $f''(-2) = -1$ and $f''(2) = 1$, then there must be an inflection point on $(-2, 2)$.

2. The polynomial function $x^2 - 6x + 8$ has

    A. one stationary point that is at $x = 3$

    B. two stationary points, one at $x = 0$ and one at $x = 3$

    C. one stationary point that is at $x = -3$

    D. one stationary point that is at $x = 0$

3. The rational function $\dfrac{3x + 6}{x^2 - 1}$ has

    A. a horizontal asymptote at $y = 0$

    B. a horizontal asymptote at $y = -2$

    C. horizontal asymptotes at $x = -1$ and $x = 1$

    D. no horizontal asymptote

4. The rational function $\dfrac{3x + 6}{x^2 - 1}$ has

    A. a stationary point at $x = -2$

    B. a stationary point at $x = 2$

    C. two stationary points, one at $x = -1$ and one at $x = 1$

    D. three stationary points, one at $x = -2$, one at $x = -1$, and one at $x = 1$

5. Answer true or false. The rational function $x^3 - \dfrac{1}{x^2}$ has no vertical asymptote.

6. On a $[-10, 10]$ by $[-10, 10]$ window on a graphing utility the rational function $f(x) = \dfrac{x^3 + 8}{x^3 - 8}$ can be determined to have

   A. one horizontal asymptote; no vertical asymptote

   B. no horizontal asymptote; one vertical asymptote

   C. one horizontal asymptote; one vertical asymptote

   D. one horizontal asymptote; three vertical asymptotes

7. Use a graphing utility to graph $f(x) = x^{1/7}$. How many points of inflection does the function have?

   A. 0   B. 1   C. 2   D. 3

8. Use a graphing utility to graph $f(x) = x^{-1/7}$. How many points of inflection are there?

   A. 0   B. 1   C. 2   D. 3

9. Determine which function is graphed.

   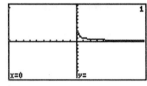

   A. $f(x) = x^{1/2}$ B. $f(x) = x^{-1/3}$ C. $f(x) = x^{-1/2}$ D. $f(x) = x^{1/3}$

10. Use a graphing utility to generate the graph of $f(x) = x^2 e^{3x}$, then determine the x-coordinate of all relative extrema on $(-10, 10)$ and identify them as a relative maximum or a relative minimum.

    A. There is a relative maximum at $x = 0$.

    B. There is a relative minimum at $x = 0$.

    C. There is a relative minimum at $x = 0$ and relative maxima at $x = -1$ and $x = 1$.

    D. There is no relative extremum.

11. Answer true or false. Using a graphing utility it can be shown that $f(x) = x^2 \tan^2 x$ has a maximum on $0 < x < 2\pi$.

12. Answer true or false. $\displaystyle\lim_{x \to 0^+} \sqrt{x} \ln x = 0$.

13. $\displaystyle\lim_{x \to +\infty} x^{3/2} \ln x =$

    A. 0   B. 1   C. $+\infty$ D. It does not exist.

14. Answer true or false. A fence is to be used to enclose a rectangular plot of land. If there are 160 feet of fencing, it can be shown that a 40 ft by 40 ft square is the rectangle that can be enclosed with the greatest area. (A square is considered a rectangle.)

15. Answer true or false. $f(x) = \dfrac{x^2 + 3x + 4}{x - 1}$ has an oblique asymptote.

CHAPTER 5 TEST

1. The largest interval on which $f(x) = x^2 - 4x + 7$ is increasing is

   A. $[0, \infty)$ B. $(-\infty, 0]$ C. $[2, \infty)$ D. $(-\infty, 2]$

2. Answer true or false. The function $f(x) = \sqrt{x - 2}$ is concave down on its entire domain.

3. The function $f(x) = x^3 - 8$ is concave down on

   A. $(-\infty, 2)$ B. $(2, \infty)$ C. $(-\infty, 0)$ D. $(0, \infty)$

4. Answer true or false. $f(x) = x^4 - 2x + 3$ has a point of inflection.

5. $f(x) = |x^2 - 4|$ is concave up on

   A. $(-\infty, -2) \cup (2, \infty)$ B. $(-\infty, -4) \cup (4, \infty)$ C. $(-2, 2)$ D. $(-4, 4)$

6. The largest open interval on which $f(x) = e^{2x^6}$ is concave up is

   A. $(-\infty, 0)$ B. $(0, \infty)$ C. $(-\infty, \infty)$ D. $(-\infty, e)$

7. Use a graphing utility to determine where $f(x) = \sin x$ is increasing on $[0, 2\pi]$.

   A. $[0, \pi]$ B. $[\pi, 2\pi]$
   C. $[\pi/2, 3\pi/2]$ D. $[0, \pi/2] \cup [3\pi/2, 2\pi]$

8. Answer true or false. $f(x) = x^4 - 2x^2 + 10$ has a point of inflection.

9. $f(x) = -x^4 - 6x^3 + 2x^2$ is concave down on

   A. $(-\infty, \infty)$ B. $(-\infty, -81)$ C. $(-\infty, -9)$ D. nowhere

10. Answer true or false. If $f''(-1) = 4$ and $f''(1) = 4$, and if f is continuous on $[-1, 1]$, then there is a point of inflection on $(-1, 1)$.

11. Determine the x-coordinate of each stationary point of $f(x) = 4x^4 - 16$.

    A. -1 B. 0 C. 16 D. 1

12. Answer true or false. $f(x) = x^{4/9}$ has a critical point at $x = 0$.

13. $f(x) = x^2 - 8x + 9$ has

    A. a relative maximum at $x = 4$ B. a relative minimum at $x = 4$
    C. a relative maximum at $x = -4$ D. a relative minimum at $x = -4$

14. $f(x) = -e^{7x}$ has

    A. a relative maximum at $x = 0$ B. a relative minimum at $x = 0$
    C. a relative maximum at $x = 7$ D. no relative extremum

15. $f(x) = |16x^2|$ has

    A. no relative maximum; a relative minimum at $x = 4$
    B. a relative maximum at $x = 4$; no relative minimum
    C. a relative maximum at $x = 0$; relative minima at $x = -4$ and $x = 4$
    D. no relative maximum; a relative minimum at $x - 0$

16. Answer true or false. $f(x) = -e^{2x} \ln(2x)$ has a relative minimum on $(0, \infty)$.

17. The rational function $\dfrac{4x+20}{x^2-25}$ has

    A. a horizontal asymptote at $y = 0$

    B. a horizontal asymptote at $y = 5$

    C. a horizontal asymptote at $y = 4$

    D. no horizontal asymptote

18. Answer true or false $f(x) = \dfrac{3}{x-5}$ has a vertical asymptote.

19.

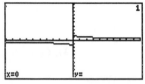

This is the graph that would appear on a graphing utility if the function that is graphed is

  A. $f(x) = x^{1/5}$ B. $f(x) = x^{1/6}$ C. $f(x) = x^{-1/5}$ D. $f(x) = x^{-1/6}$

20. Answer true or false. $\displaystyle\lim_{x \to 0^+} \sqrt[3]{x}\,\ln x = 0$

21. A weekly profit function for a company is $P(x) = -0.01x^2 + 3x - 2{,}000$, where x is the number of the company's only product that is made and sold. How many individual items of the product must the company make and sell weekly to maximize the profit?

  A. 300   B. 150   C. 600   D. 60

ANSWERS TO SAMPLE TESTS

SECTION 5.1:

1. F 2. F 3. A 4. C 5. C 6. A 7. C 8. D 9. D 10. C 11. T 12. F 13. A 14. F 15. D

SECTION 5.2:

1. B 2. B 3. T 4. F 5. B 6. A 7. B 8. F 9. D 10. C 11. B 12. C 13. F 14. T 15. T

SECTION 5.3:

1. F 2. A 3. A 4. A 5. F 6. C 7. B 8. A 9. C 10. B 11. F 12. T 13. A 14. T 15. T

CHAPTER 5 TEST:

1. C 2. T 3. C 4. F 5. A 6. C 7. D 8. F 9. A 10. T 11. B 12. T 13. B 14. D 15. D 16. F 17. A 18. T 19. C 20. T 21. B

CHAPTER 6
Sample Exams

SECTION 6.1

1. $f(x) = 3x^2 - x + 2$ has an absolute maximum on $[-2, 2]$ of

    A. 16   B. 2   C. 12   D. 4

2. $f(x) = |5 - 2x|$ has an absolute minimum of

    A. 0   B. 3   C. 1   D. 5

3. Answer true or false. $f(x) = x^3 - x^2 + 2$ has an absolute maximum and an absolute minimum.

4. Answer true or false. $f(x) = x^3 - 18x^2 + 20x + 2$ restricted to a domain of $[0, 20]$ has an absolute maximum at $x = 2$ of -22, and an absolute minimum at $x = 10$ of -598.

5. $f(x) = \sqrt{x - 2}$ has an absolute minimum of

    A. 0 at $x = 2$ B. 0 at $x = 0$ C. -2 at $x = 0$ D. 0 at $x = -2$

6. $f(x) = \sqrt{x^2 + 5}$ has an absolute maximum, if one exists, at

    A. $x = -5$ B. $x = 5$ C. $x = 0$ D. None exist

7. Find the location of the absolute maximum of $\tan x$ on $[0, \pi]$, if it exists.

    A. 0   B. π C. $\dfrac{\pi}{2}$ D. None exist

8. $f(x) = x^2 - 3x + 2$ on $(-\infty, \infty)$ has

    A. only an absolute maximum
    B. only an absolute minimum
    C. both an absolute maximum and an absolute minimum
    D. neither an absolute maximum nor an absolute minimum

9. $f(x) = \dfrac{1}{x^2}$ on $[1, 3]$ has

    A. an absolute maximum at $x = 1$ and an absolute minimum at $x = 3$
    B. an absolute minimum at $x = 1$ and an absolute maximum at $x = 3$
    C. no absolute extrema
    D. an absolute minimum at $x = 2$ and absolute maxima at $x = 1$ and $x = 3$

10. Answer true or false. $f(x) = \sin x \cos x$ on $[0, \pi]$ has an absolute maximum at $x = \dfrac{\pi}{2}$.

11. Use a graphing utility to assist in determining the location of the absolute maximum of $f(x) = -(x^2 - 3)^2$ on $(-\infty, \infty)$, if it exists.

    A. $x = \sqrt{3}$ And $x = -\sqrt{3}$ B. $x = \sqrt{3}$ only
    C. $x = 0$ D. None exist

12. Answer true or false. If $f(x)$ has an absolute minimum at $x = 2$, $-f(x)$ also has an absolute minimum at $x = 2$.

13. Answer true or false. Every function has an absolute maximum and an absolute minimum if its domain is restricted to where f is defined on an interval $[-a, a]$, where a is finite.

14. Use a graphing utility to locate the value of x where $f(x) = x^4 - 3x + 2$ has an absolute minimum, if it exists.

    A. 1   B. $\sqrt[3]{\dfrac{3}{4}}$ C. 0   D. None exist

15. Use a graphing utility to estimate the absolute maximum of $f(x) = (x - 5)^2$ on [0,6], if it exists.

    A. 25   B. 0   C. 1   D. None exist

SECTION 6.2

1. Express the number 20 as the sum of two nonnegative numbers whose product is as large as possible.

    A. 5, 15   B. 1, 19   C. 10, 10   D. 0, 20

2. A right triangle has a perimeter of 16. What are the lengths of each side if the area contained within the triangle is to be maximized?

    A. $\dfrac{16}{3}, \dfrac{16}{3}, \dfrac{16}{3}$ B. 5, 5, 6

    C. $16 - 8\sqrt{2}, 16 - 8\sqrt{2}, -16 + 16\sqrt{2}$ D. 4, 5, 7

3. A rectangular sheet of cardboard 2 m by 1 m is used to make an open box by cutting squares of equal size from the four corners and folding up the sides. What size squares should be cut to obtain the largest possible volume?

    A. $\dfrac{3 + \sqrt{3}}{4}$ B. $\dfrac{3 - \sqrt{3}}{4}$ C. $\dfrac{1}{2}$ D. $\dfrac{1}{4}$

4. Suppose that the number of bacteria present in a culture bacteria at time t is given by $N = 10,000e^{-t/10}$. Find the smallest number of bacteria in the culture during the time interval $0 \le t \le 50$.

    A. 67   B. 10,000   C. 3,679   D. 73,891

5. An object moves a distance s away from the origin according to the equation $s(t) = 4t^4 - 2t + 1$, where $0 \le t \le 10$. At what time is the object farthest from the origin?

    A. 0   B. 2   C. 10   D. $\dfrac{1}{8}$

6. An electrical generator produces a current in amperes starting at $t = 0$ s and running until $t = 6\pi$ s that is given by $\sin(2t)$. Find the maximum current produced.

    A. 1 A   B. 0 A   C. 2 A   D. $\dfrac{1}{2}$ A

7. A storm is passing with the wind speed in mph changing over time according to $v(t) = -x^2 + 10x + 55$, for $0 \le t \le 10$. Find the highest wind speed that occurs.

    A. 55 mph   B. 80 mph   C. 110 mph   D. 30 mph

8. A company has a cost of operation function given by $C(t) = 0.01t^2 - 6t + 1,000$ for $0 \le t \le 500$. Find the minimum cost of operation.

    A. 1,000   B. 100   C. 500   D. 0

9. Find the point on the curve $x^2 + y^2 = 4$ closest to (0,3).

    A. (0,4)   B. (0,2)   C. (2,0)   D. (4,0)

10. Answer true or false. The point on the parabola $y = x^2$ closest to (0,0.9) is (0,0).

11. For a triangle with sides 3 m, 4 m, and 5 m, the smallest circle that contains the triangle has a diameter of

   A. 3 m   B. 4 m   C. 5 m   D. 10 m

12. Answer true or false. If $f(t) = 3e^{4t}$ represents a growth function over the time interval $[a, b]$, the absolute maximum must occur at $t = b$.

13. Answer true or false. The rectangle with the largest area that can be inscribed inside a circle is a square.

14. Answer true or false. The rectangle with the largest area that can be inscribed in a semi-circle is a square.

15. Answer true or false. An object that is thrown upward and reaches a height of $s(t) = 50 + 120t - 32t^2$ for $0 \leq t \leq 2$. The object is highest at $t = 2$.

   A. 3   B. 0   C. 1   D. 0

SECTION 6.3

1.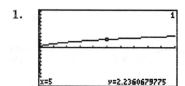

   The graph represents a position function. Determine what is happening to the velocity.

   A. It is speeding up.   B. It is slowing down.
   C. It is constant.   D. There is insufficient information to tell.

2.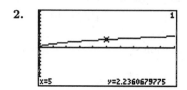

   The graph represents a position function. Determine what is happening to the acceleration.

   A. It is positive.   B. It is negative.
   C. It is zero.   D. There is insufficient information to tell.

3.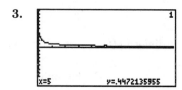

   The graph represents a velocity function. The acceleration is

   A. positive   B. negative
   C. zero   D. There is insufficient information to tell.

4.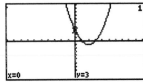

Answer true or false. This is the graph of a particle that is moving to the right at $t = 0$.

5.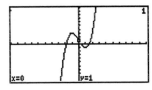

Answer true or false. For the position function graphed, the acceleration at $t = 1$ is positive.

6.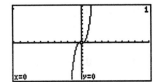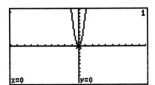

Answer true or false. If the graph on the left is a position function, the graph on the right represents the corresponding velocity function.

7. Let $s(t) = \cos t$ be a position function of a particle. At $t = \dfrac{\pi}{2}$ the particle's velocity is

A. positive   B. negative   C. zero

8. Let $s(t) = t^3 - t$ be a position function of a particle. At $t = \dfrac{\pi}{2}$ the particle's acceleration is

A. positive   B. negative   C. zero

9. $s(t) = t^4 - 2t, t \geq 0$. The velocity function is

A. $t^3 - 2$ B. $4t^3 - 2$ C. $12t^2$ D. $12t^2 - 2$

10. $s(t) = t^4 - 2t, t \geq 0$. The acceleration function is

A. $t^3 - 2$ B. $4t^3 - 2$ C. $12t^2$ D. $12t^2 - 2$

11. A projectile is thrown upward at 100 m/s. How long does it take the projectile to reach its highest point?

A. 1,020 s   B. 510 s   C. 5 s   D. 10 s

12. Answer true or false. If a particle is dropped a distance of 100 m. It has a speed of 44.27 m/s (rounded to the nearest hundredth of a m/s) when it hits the ground.

13. $s(t) = t^4 - 4t^2$. Find t when $a = 0$.

A. 12   B. -12 C. $\sqrt{\dfrac{2}{3}}$ D. $-\dfrac{2}{3}$

14. $s(t) = t^3 - 3t, t \geq 0$. Find s when $a = 0$.

A. 1   B. 2   C. $-2, 2$ D. -1

15. Let $s(t) = \sqrt{3t^2 - 2}$ be a position function. Find v when $t = 1$.

A. 3   B. 6   C. 1   D. 0

SECTION 6.4

1. Approximate$\sqrt{3}$ by applying Newton's Method to the equation $x^2 - 3 = 0$.
   A. 1.73205080757   B. 1.73205079216
   C. 1.73205084126   D. 1.73205094712

2. Approximate $\sqrt[3]{9}$ by applying Newton's Method to the equation $x^3 - 9 = 0$.
   A. 2.08008381347   B. 2.08008382305
   C. 2.08008397111   D. 2.08008382176

3. Use Newton's Method to approximate the solutions of $x^3 + 2x^2 - 5x - 10 = 0$.
   A. $-2.236, 2.236$ B. $-5, 0, 5$
   C. $-3.1623, 0, 3.1623$ D. $-3.1623, 3.1623$

4. Use Newton's Method to find the largest positive solution of $x^3 + x^2 + 2x + 4 = 0$.
   A. 1.414   B. 1.000   C. 2.828   D. 3.721

5. Use Newton's Method to find the largest positive solution of $x^3 - x^2 + 3x - 3 = 0$.
   A. 1.7325   B. 1.7321   C. 1.7319   D. 1.7316

6. Use Newton's Method to find the largest positive solution of $x^4 + 6x^3 - x^2 - 6 = 0$.
   A. 6.000   B. 2.449   C. 1.732   D. 1.412

7. Use Newton's Method to find the largest positive solution of $x^4 + x^3 - 4x - 4 = 0$.
   A. 4.000   B. 1.000   C. 0.500   D. 1.587

8. Use Newton's Method to find the largest positive solution of $x^5 - 2x^3 - 14x^2 + 28 = 0$.
   A. 3.742   B. 2.410   C. 1.414   D. 1.260

9. Use Newton's Method to find the largest positive solution of $x^5 + 2x^3 - 2x^2 - 4 = 0$.
   A. 1.260   B. 1.414   C. 1.587   D. 2.000

10. Use Newton's Method to find the largest positive solution of $x^4 - 13x^2 + 30 = 0$.
    A. 3.162   B. 2.340   C. 5.477   D. 1.732

11. Use Newton's Method to find the largest positive solution of $x^5 + x^4 + x^3 - 5x^2 - 5x - 5 = 0$.
    A. 2.236   B. 1.380   C. 1.710   D. 1.621

12. Use Newton's Method to find the x-coordinate of the intersection of $y = 2x^3 - 2x^2$ and $y = -x^5 + 4$.
    A. 3.742   B. 2.410   C. 1.414   D. 1.260

13. Use Newton's Method to approximate the greatest x-coordinate of the intersection of $y = 2x^3 - 2x^2$ and $y = -x^5 + 4$.
    A. 3.742   B. 1.414   C. 2.410   D. 1.260

14. Use Newton's Method to approximate the x-coordinate intersection of $y = x^5 + x^3 - 5$ and $y = -x^4 + 5x^2 + 5x$.
    A. 2.236   B. 1.380   C. 1.710   D. 1.627

15. Use Newton's Method to find the greatest x-coordinate of the intersection of $y = x^4 - 7x^2$ and $y = 6x^2 - 30$.
    A. 3.162   B. 2.340   C. 5.477   D. 1.732

SECTION 6.5

1. Answer true or false. $f(x) = \dfrac{1}{x}$ on $[-1, 1]$ satisfies the hypotheses of Rolle's Theorem.

2. Find the value c such that the conclusion of Rolle's Theorem are satisfied for $f(x) = x^2 - 4$ on $[-2, 2]$.
    A. 0   B. -1 C. 1   D. 0.5

3. Answer true or false. The Mean-Value Theorem is used to find the average of a function.

4. Answer true or false. The Mean-Value Theorem can be used on $f(x) = |x|$ on $[-2, 1]$.

5. Answer true or false. The Mean-Value Theorem guarantees there is at least one c on $[0,1]$ such that $f'(x) = 1$ when $f(x) = \sqrt{x}$.

6. If $f(x) = \sqrt[3]{x}$ on $[0,1]$, find the value c that satisfies the Mean-Value Theorem.

    A. 1   B. $\dfrac{1}{3}$ C. $\left(\dfrac{1}{3}\right)^{3/2}$ D. $\dfrac{1}{9}$

7. Answer true or false. The hypotheses of the Mean-Value Theorem are satisfied for $f(x) = \sqrt[3]{|x|}$ on $[-1, 1]$.

8. Answer true or false. The hypotheses of the Mean-Value Theorem are satisfied for $f(x) = \sin x$ on $[0, 4\pi]$.

9. Answer true or false. The hypotheses of the Mean-Value Theorem are satisfied for $f(x) = \dfrac{1}{\sin x}$ on $[0, 4\pi]$.

10. Find the value for which $f(x) = x^2 + 3$ on $[1,3]$ satisfies the Mean-Value Theorem.

    A. 2   B. $\dfrac{9}{4}$ C. $\dfrac{7}{3}$ D. $\dfrac{11}{4}$

11. Find the value for which $f(x) = x^3$ on $[2,3]$ satisfies the Mean-Value Theorem.
    A. 2.5166   B. 2.5000   C. 2.2500   D. 2.1250

12. Answer true or false. A graphing utility can be used to show that Rolle's Theorem can be applied to show that $f(x) = (x - 2)^2$ has a point where $f'(x) = 0$.

13. Answer true or false. According to Rolle's Theorem if a function does not cross the x-axis its derivative cannot be zero anywhere.

14. Find the value c that satisfies Rolle's Theorem for $f(x) = \sin x$ on $[0, \pi]$.

    A. $\dfrac{\pi}{4}$ B. $\dfrac{\pi}{2}$ C. $\dfrac{3\pi}{4}$ D. $\dfrac{\pi}{3}$

15. Find the value c that satisfies the Mean-Value Theorem for $f(x) = x^3 + 3x$ on $[0,1]$.

    A. $\dfrac{\sqrt{3}}{3}$ B. $\dfrac{\sqrt{3}}{2}$ C. $\dfrac{\sqrt{2}}{2}$ D. $\dfrac{\sqrt{2}}{3}$

CHAPTER 6 TEST

1. $f(x) = 6x^2 - 2$ has an absolute minimum on $[-3, 3]$ of

   A. 2   B. -2 C. 52   D. -52

2. $f(x) = x^3 + 3$ has an absolute maximum on $[-2, 2]$ of

   A. 0   B. 6   C. 11   D. 8

3. $f(x) = 3\sin(x + 2)$ has an absolute minimum of

   A. -5 B. -3 C. $-\dfrac{1}{3}$ D. $-\dfrac{2}{3}$

4. $f(x) = \dfrac{1}{x^5}$ has an absolute maximum on $[1, 3]$ of

   A. 1   B. $\dfrac{1}{243}$ C. 243   D. None exist.

5. Answer true or false. $f(x) = \dfrac{1}{x^7}$ has an absolute maximum of 1 on $[-1, 1]$.

6. Express the number 40 as the sum of two nonnegative numbers whose product is as large as possible.

   A. 5, 35   B. 10, 30   C. 20, 20   D. 1, 39

7. An object moves a distance s away from the origin as given by $s(t) = t^4 - 2, 0 \le t \le 10$. At what time is the object farthest from the origin?

   A. 0   B. 2   C. 8   D. 10

8. Find the point on the curve $x^2 + y^2 = 16$ closest to $(0, 5)$.

   A. $(0, 4)$ B. $(4, 0)$ C. $(-4, 0)$ D. $(0, -4)$

9. Answer true or false. A growth function $f(x) = 4e^{0.02t}$, $0 \le t \le 10$ has an absolute maximum at $t = 10$.

10.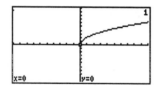

    The graph represents a position function. Determine what is happening to the velocity.

    A. It is increasing.   B. It is decreasing.

    C. It is constant.   D. More information is needed.

11.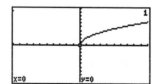

    The graph represents a position function. Determine what is happening to the acceleration.

    A. It is positive.   B. It is negative.

    C. It is zero.   D. More information is needed.

12. Let $s(t) = t^4 - 2$ be a position function particle. The particle's acceleration for $t > 0$ is

    A. positive   B. negative

    C. zero   D. More information is needed.

13. Let $s(t) = 4 - t^2$ be a position function. The particle's velocity for $t > 0$ is

    A. positive   B. negative

    C. zero   D. More information is needed.

14. $s(t) = 4t^2 - 8$. $a = 0$ when $t =$

    A. 0   B. 8   C. 2   D. nowhere

15. Approximate $\sqrt{11}$ using Newton's Method.

    A. 3.31662479036   B. 3.31662478727

    C. 3.31662479002   D. 3.31662478841

16. Use Newton's Method to approximate the great solution of $x^3 + 4x^2 - 5x - 20 = 0$.

    A. 4.000   B. 2.646   C. 5.292   D. 3.037

17. Use Newton's Method to approximate the greatest x-coordinate where the graphs of $y = x^3 + 2x^2$ and $y = -2x^2 + 5x + 20$ cross.

    A. 4.000   B. 2.646   C. 5.292   D. 3.037

18. Answer true or false. The hypotheses of Rolle's Theorem are satisfied for $f(x) = \dfrac{1}{x^6} - 1$ on $[-1, 1]$.

19. Answer true or false. Given $f(x) = x^2 - 16$ on $[-4, 4]$, the value c that satisfies Rolle's Theorem is 0.

20. Answer true or false. $f(x) = x^5$ on $[-1, 1]$. The value c that satisfies the Mean-Value Theorem is 0.

ANSWERS TO SAMPLE TESTS

SECTION 6.1:

1. A 2. A 3. F 4. F 5. A 6. D 7. D 8. B 9. A 10. F 11. A 12. F 13. F 14. B 15. A

SECTION 6.2:

1. C 2. C 3. B 4. A 5. C 6. A 7. B 8. B 9. B 10. F 11. C 12. T 13. T 14. F 15. F

SECTION 6.3:

1. B 2. B 3. B 4. F 5. T 6. T 7. C 8. C 9. B 10. C 11. D 12. T 13. A 14. C 15. A

SECTION 6.4:

1. A 2. B 3. A 4. A 5. B 6. B 7. D 8. B 9. A 10. A 11. C 12. D 13. B 14. C 15. A

SECTION 6.5:

1. F 2. A 3. F 4. F 5. T 6. C 7. F 8. T 9. F 10. A 11. A 12. F 13. F 14. B 15. A

CHAPTER 6 TEST:

1. B 2. C 3. B 4. A 5. F 6. C 7. D 8. A 9. T 10. A 11. B 12. A 13. B 14. D 15. A 16. B 17. B 18. F 19. T 20. F

CHAPTER 7
Sample Exams

SECTION 7.1

1. $f(x) = 2x$; $[0,1]$ Use the rectangle method to approximate the area using 4 rectangles.
   A. 1
   B. 0.5
   C. 0.75
   D. 0.875

2. $f(x) = 5 + x$; $[0,2]$ Use the rectangle method to approximate the area using 4 rectangles.
   A. 5.625
   B. 5.375
   C. 6.000
   D. 5.750

3. $f(x) = \sqrt{1 + x}$; $[0,1]$ Use the rectangle method to approximate the area using 4 rectangles.
   A. 1.166
   B. 1.250
   C. 1.500
   D. 1.141

4. Use the antiderivative method to find the area under $x^3/3$ on $[0,1]$
   A. 0.0805
   B. 0.0735
   C. 0.0850
   D. 0.0833

5. Use the antiderivative method to find the area under x^4 on $[2,3]$
   A. 42.2
   B. 40.5
   C. 45.1
   D. 44.3

6. Use the antiderivative method to find the area under $x - 3$ on $[5,6]$.
   A. 3.5
   B. 2.5
   C. 4.5
   D. 3.0

7. Use the antiderivative method to find the area under $x^2 + 2$ on $[0,1]$.
   A. 2.00
   B. 2.50
   C. 2.33
   D. 3.00

8. Use the antiderivative method to find the area under x^3 on $[3,4]$.
   A. 43.75
   B. 44.25
   C. 44.50
   D. 45.00

9. Use the antiderivative method to find the area under $\frac{x}{2}\sqrt{x^2 + 5}$ on $[1,2]$.
   A. 2.15
   B. 2.10
   C. 2.05
   D. 2.01

10. Use the antiderivative method to find the area under $\frac{1}{2}\cos^{-1} x$ on $[0,1]$.
    A. 0.50
    B. 0.52
    C. 0.35
    D. 0.48

11. Use the antiderivative method to find the area under $x^4 + 2x$ on $[0,2]$.
    A. 9.2
    B. 9.8
    C. 10.4
    D. 10.8

12. Use the antiderivative method to find the area between the curve $y = e^x$ and the interval $[0,2]$.
    A. 6.39
    B. 6.51
    C. 6.62
    D. 6.84

13. Use the antiderivative method to find the area between $y = 3x^6$ and the interval $[2,4]$.
    A. 6,967
    B. 6,872
    C. 6,901
    D. 6,885

14. Use the antiderivative method to find the area under $x + x^2$ on $[1,3]$.
    A. 2.75
    B. 12.81
    C. 12.61
    D. 12.67

15. Use the antiderivative method to find the area under $5x + 20$ on $[2,5]$.
    A. 110.5
    B. 112.5
    C. 114.5
    D. 116.5

SECTION 7.2

1. $\int x^6 dx =$

  A. $\dfrac{x^5}{5} + C$
  B. $\dfrac{x^7}{7} + C$
  C. $\dfrac{x^7}{6} + C$
  D. $\dfrac{x^6}{7} + C$

2. $\int x^{2/5} dx =$

  A. $\dfrac{5}{2x^{3/5}} + C$
  B. $\dfrac{5}{7}x^{7/5} + C$
  C. $-\dfrac{5}{7}x^{7/5} + C$
  D. $-\dfrac{5}{2x^{3/5}} + C$

3. $\int \sqrt[3]{x}\,dx =$

  A. $\dfrac{3}{2x^{2/3}} + C$
  B. $\dfrac{3}{4}x^{4/3} + C$
  C. $-\dfrac{3}{4}x^{4/3} + C$
  D. $-\dfrac{3}{x^{2/3}} + C$

4. $\int x^{-2} dx =$

  A. $-\dfrac{3}{x^3} + C$
  B. $-\dfrac{1}{x} + C$
  C. $\dfrac{1}{x^3} + C$
  D. $\dfrac{3}{x^3} + C$

5. $\int \sin x\,dx =$

  A. $\sin^2 x + C$
  B. $\cos x + C$
  C. $-\cos x + C$
  D. $-\sin^2 x + C$

6. $\int 3e^x dx =$

  A. $3e^x + C$
  B. $\dfrac{e^x}{3} + C$
  C. $-3e^x + C$
  D. $-\dfrac{e^x}{3} + C$

7. $\int \dfrac{\cos x}{\sin^2 x}\,dx =$

  A. $-\dfrac{1}{\sin^3 x} + C$
  B. $-\dfrac{1}{\sin x} + C$
  C. $\dfrac{1}{\sin x} + C$
  D. $\dfrac{1}{\sin^3 x} + C$

8. $\int \dfrac{5}{x}\,dx =$

  A. $\dfrac{5}{2x^2} + C$
  B. $-\dfrac{5}{2x^2} + C$
  C. $-5\ln x + C$
  D. $5\ln x + C$

9. Answer true or false. $\int \dfrac{1}{x} + 3e^x dx = \ln x + 3e^x + C$

10. Answer true or false. $\int \sin x \cos x\,dx = \sin x \cos x + C$

11. Answer true or false. $\int x + \dfrac{1}{\sin x}\,dx = \dfrac{x^2}{2} + \ln|\sin x| + C$

12. Answer true or false. $\int \sqrt{x} + \sqrt[3]{x} + \sqrt[4]{x}\,dx = x^{3/2} + x^{4/3} + x^{5/4} + C$

13. Answer true or false. $\int \sin x + \cos x\,dx = -\cos x + \sin x + C$

14. Find $y(x)$. $\dfrac{dy}{dx} = x^2, y(0) = 1$.

    A. $\dfrac{x^3}{3} + 1$ B. $\dfrac{x^3}{3}$ C. $\dfrac{x^3}{3} - 1$ D. $\dfrac{x^3 - 1}{3}$

15. Find $y(x)$. $\dfrac{dy}{dx} + e^x, y(0) = 2$.

    A. $e^x + 1$ B. $e^x + 2$ C. e^x D. $e^x - 2$

SECTION 7.3:

1. $\displaystyle\int 2x(x^2 - 5)^{30} dx =$

    A. $\dfrac{(x^2 - 5)^{31}}{31} + C$ B. $\dfrac{(x^2 - 5)^{29}}{29} + C$

    C. $31(x^2 - 5)^{31} + C$ D. $29(x^2 - 5)^{29} + C$

2. $\displaystyle\int \sin^2 x \cos x \, dx =$

    A. $\sin^3 \dfrac{x}{3} + C$ B. $\cos^3 \dfrac{x}{3} + C$

    C. $\cos^3 x \sin^2 x + C$ D. $3 \sin x + C$

3. $\displaystyle\int 2x e^{x^2} dx =$

    A. $\dfrac{e^{x^2}}{2x} + C$ B. $2e^{x^2} + C$ C. $x^2 + e^{x^2} + C$ D. $e^{x^2} + C$

4. $\displaystyle\int \dfrac{\ln x}{x} dx =$

    A. $\ln x + C$ B. $(\ln x)^2 + C$ C. $\dfrac{(\ln x)^2}{2} + C$ D. $2(\ln x)^2 + C$

5. $\displaystyle\int e^{-8} dx =$

    A. $-8e^{-8x} + C$ B. $-\dfrac{e^{-8x}}{8} + C$ C. $8e^{-8x} + C$ D. $\dfrac{e^{-8x}}{8} + C$

6. $\displaystyle\int (x + 9)^5 dx =$

    A. $5(x + 9) + C$ B. $\left(\dfrac{x^2}{2} + 9\right)^5 + C$

    C. $\dfrac{(x + 9)^6}{6} + C$ D. $\dfrac{(x + 9)^4}{4} + C$

7. $\displaystyle\int \dfrac{1}{5x} dx =$

    A. $\ln 5x + C$ B. $\dfrac{\ln x}{5} + C$ C. $5 \ln x + C$ D. $\ln x + C$

8. Answer true or false. $\displaystyle\int x\sqrt{x + 2} \, dx = \dfrac{2}{5}(x + 2)^{5/2} - 4/3(x + 2)^{3/2} + C$

9. Answer true or false. For $\int x \sin x^2 dx$ a good choice for u is x^2.

10. Answer true or false. For $\int \frac{e^x}{e^x - 2} dx$ a good choice for u is $e^x - 2$.

11. Answer true or false. $\int x\sqrt{3x^3 - 2}dx$ can be easily solved by letting $u = x^3$.

12. Answer true or false. $\int x^2(x^3 - 4)^{2/5} dx$ can be easily solved by letting $u = x^3 - 4$.

13. Answer true or false. $\int e^{x^2} dx$ can be easily solved by letting $u = x^2$.

14. Answer true or false. $\int \sin^3 x dx$ can be easily solved by letting $u = \sin x$.

15. Answer true or false. $\int e^{9x} dx$ can be easily solved by letting $u = 9x$.

SECTION 7.4:

1. $\displaystyle\sum_{k=1}^{5} k^2 =$

    A. 15   B. 55   C. 26   D. 6

2. $\displaystyle\sum_{j=2}^{4} 3^j =$

    A. 90   B. 18   C. 120   D. 117

3. $\displaystyle\sum_{k=1}^{4} \sin(k\pi) =$

    A. 4   B. 0   C. 2   D. 3

4. Answer true or false. $\displaystyle\sum_{i=1}^{4}(i + 1) = 14$.

5. Express in sigma notation, but do not evaluate. $1 + 2 + 3 + 4$

    A. $\displaystyle\sum_{i=0}^{3} i$ B. $\displaystyle\sum_{i=1}^{4} i$ C. $\displaystyle\sum_{i=1}^{4} i^2$ D. $\displaystyle\sum_{i=0}^{4} i + 1$

6. Express in sigma notation, but do not evaluate. $1 + 4 + 9 + 16 + 25$

    A. $\displaystyle\sum_{i=1}^{5} i$ B. $\displaystyle\sum_{i=0}^{5} i + 1$

    C. $\displaystyle\sum_{i=1}^{5} i^2$ D. $\displaystyle\sum_{i=2}^{5} i^2$

7. Express in sigma notation, but do not evaluate. $2 + 8 + 18 + 50$

    A. $\displaystyle\sum_{i=1}^{4} i^2$ B. $\displaystyle\sum_{i=1}^{4} 2i^2$

    C. $\displaystyle\sum_{i=1}^{4} 2i + 6$ D. $\displaystyle\sum_{i=1}^{4} 2(i + 6)$

8. Answer true or false. $4 + 9 + 16 + 25 + 36$ can be expressed in sigma notation as $\displaystyle\sum_{i=2}^{6} i^2$.

9. Answer true or false. $8 + 27 + 64$ can be expressed in sigma notation as $\displaystyle\sum_{i=1}^{3} i^3$.

10. $\displaystyle\sum_{i=5}^{100} i =$

    A. 5,040   B. 5,050   C. 5,035   D. 5,000

11. $\displaystyle\lim_{n \to +\infty} \sum_{k=1}^{n} \left(\frac{1}{5^k} \right) =$

    A. 0   B. $\dfrac{4}{5}$ C. $\dfrac{1}{5}$ D. $\dfrac{1}{4}$

12. $\displaystyle\lim_{n \to +\infty} \sum_{k=1}^{n} \left(\frac{4}{5} \right)^k =$

    A. $\dfrac{4}{5}$ B. 4   C. 20   D. $\dfrac{5}{4}$

13. Answer true or false. $\displaystyle\sum_{i=1}^{n} x_i^3 = \left(\sum_{i=1}^{n} x_i \right)^3$

14. Answer true or false. $\displaystyle\sum_{i=1}^{n} (a_i + b_i) = \sum_{i=1}^{n} a_i + \sum_{i=1}^{n} b_i$

15. Answer true or false. $\displaystyle\sum_{i=1}^{n} 2a_i = 2 \sum_{i=1}^{n} a_i$

SECTION 7.5:

1. $\displaystyle\int_{1}^{5} x\,dx =$

    A. 12   B. 6   C. 24   D. 4

2. $\displaystyle\int_{0}^{4} 3\,dx =$

    A. 3   B. 12   C. 6   D. 24

3. $\int_{-5}^{5} |x - 10| dx =$

    A. 100   B. -100 C. 0   D. 10

4. $\int_{-2}^{2} x\sqrt{4 - x^2} dx =$

    A. $\dfrac{8}{3}$ B. $\dfrac{16}{3}$ C. $-\dfrac{16}{3}$ D. 0

5. $\int_{0}^{1} \dfrac{x}{2 + x} dx =$

    A. 0.095   B. 0.189   C. 0   D. 1

6. $\int_{-\pi/4}^{\pi/4} \sin x\, dx =$

    A. 0   B. 0.134   C. 0.268   D. 0.293

7. Answer true or false. $\int_{1}^{3} [f(x) + 3g(x)] dx = 5$ if $\int_{1}^{3} f(x) dx = -1$ and $\int_{1}^{3} g(x) dx = 2$.

8. $\int_{1}^{4} x + x^3 dx =$

    A. 71.25   B. 162.75   C. 3   D. 4.5

9. Answer true or false. $\int_{0}^{5} \dfrac{x^2}{1 + x} dx$ is positive.

10. Answer true or false. $\int_{-2}^{0} |x + 2| dx$ is negative.

11. Answer true or false. $\int_{-2}^{-1} \dfrac{1}{x^2} dx$ is negative.

12. Answer true or false. $\int 3x\, dx = \lim_{\max \Delta x \to 0} \sum_{i=1}^{k} 3i \Delta x_i$

13. $\int_{-1}^{1} x^3 dx =$

    A. 0   B 3   C. 13.5   D. 9

14. $\int_{0}^{1} x - 1 dx =$

    A. 0.5   B. -0.5 C. 1   D. -1

15. $\int_{-2}^{2} x\sqrt{x^2 + 5} dx =$

    A. 0   B. 5.27   C. 10.55   D. 4

SECTION 7.6:

1. Answer true or false. $\int_2^4 x\,dx = \frac{x^2}{2}\Big]_2^4$

2. Answer true or false. $\int_0^\pi \sin x\,dx = \cos x\Big]_0^\pi$

3. $\int_{-2}^2 x^4\,dx =$

   A. 0   B. 12.8   C. 6.4   D. 4

4. $\int_1^e \frac{1}{x}\,dx =$

   A. 1   B. e C. $\frac{1}{e}$ D. 0

5. Find the area under the curve $y = x^2 - 2$ on [2,3].

   A. 1   B. 2.17   C. 4.33   D. 8.66

6. Find the area under the curve $y = -(x - 3)(x + 2)$ and above the x-axis.

   A. 20.83   B. 41.67   C. 5   D. 0

7. Find the area under the curve $y = e^x$ and above the x-axis on [0,1].

   A. 0   B. 0.63   C. 1.72   D. 2.7

8. Use the Fundamental Theorem of Calculus. $\int_1^2 x^{-3/4}\,dx =$

   A. 0.76   B. -0.76 C. 1   D. 0

9. $\int_{-\pi/4}^{\pi/4} \tan x\,dx =$

   A. 0   B. $\frac{\pi}{2}$ C. 0.70   D. 0.35

10. Answer true or false. $\int_{-5}^5 x^5\,dx = 0$

11. Answer true or false. $\int_{-1}^1 |x|\,dx = \int_{-1}^0 -x\,dx + \int_0^1 x\,dx$

12. Answer true or false. $\int_1^2 x^2\,dx = \int_3^4 x^2\,dx$

13. Answer true or false. $\int_{-8}^8 x^2\,dx = (x*)^2(8 - (-8))$ is satisfied when $x* = 0$.

14. Answer true or false. $\frac{d}{dx}\int_0^x x^3\,dx = x^3$

15. Answer true or false. $\frac{d}{dx}\int_0^x \sin x\,dx = \cos x$

SECTION 7.7:

1. Find the displacement of a particle if $v(t) = \cos t$; $[0, 2\pi]$.
   A. 0   B. 1   C. 2   D. 2π

2. Find the displacement of a particle if $v(t) = \sin t$; $[0, \pi/2]$.
   A. 1   B. 0   C. 2   D. 2π

3. Find the displacement of a particle if $v(t) = t^5$; $[0, 1]$.
   A. 0   B. -0.17 C. 0.17   D. 1

4. Find the displacement of a particle if $v(t) = t^2 - 2$; $[0, 3]$.
   A. 3   B. 9   C. 1.5   D. 6

5. Find the displacement of a particle if $v(t) = e^t + 2$; $[0, 2]$.
   A. 1.72   B. 16.39   C. 4.81   D. 3.15

6. Find the area between the curve and the x-axis on the given interval. $y = x^2 - 4$; $[0, 4]$
   A. 5.33   B. 10.67   C. 16   D. 8

7. Answer true or false. The area between the curve $y = x^3 - 2$ and the x-axis on $[0,2]$ is given by $\int_0^2 x^3 - 2dx$.

8. Answer true or false. If a velocity $v(t) = t^5$ on $[-2,2]$, the displacement is given by $\int_{-2}^0 -t^5 dt + \int_0^2 t^5 dt$.

9. Find the total area between $y = e^x$ and the x-axis on $[0,2]$.
   A. 6.39   B. 7.39   C. 6.45   D. 8.39

10. Find the total area between $y = \dfrac{1}{x}$ and the x-axis on $[0.5,1]$.
    A. 0   B. 1   C. 0.41   D. 0.69

11. Answer true or false. The area between $y = \dfrac{1}{x}$ and the x-axis on $[2,3]$ is $- \int_2^3 \dfrac{1}{x} dx$.

12. Answer true or false. The area between $y = x^4 + \sin x$ and the x-axis on $[0,7]$ is $\int_0^7 x^{-4} + \sin x dx$.

13. Answer true or false. The area between $y = \dfrac{1}{x^3}$ and the x-axis on $[-2,-1]$ is $- \int_{-2}^{-1} \dfrac{1}{x^3} dx$.

14. Answer true or false. The area between $y = x^4 - x^3$ and the x-axis on $[1,2]$ is $\int_1^2 x^4 dx + \int_1^2 x^3 dx$.

15. If the velocity of a particle is given by $v(t) = 4$; $[0, 2]$ the displacement is
    A. 0   B. 4   C. 8   D. 2

SECTION 7.8:

1. $\displaystyle\int_0^2 (x+5)^8 dx =$

   A. 4,268,720   B. 8   C. 3,842,780   D. 57

2. $\displaystyle\int_0^1 \frac{1}{5x+3} dx =$

   A. 0.197   B. 0.039   C. 0.981   D. 0.392

3. Answer true or false. $\displaystyle\int \tan^3 x \sec^2 x\, dx = \int u^3 du$ if $u = \tan x$.

4. Answer true or false. $\displaystyle\int_0^1 (x+4)(x-2)^{15} dx = \int_{-2}^{-1} u^{15} du$ if $u = x - 2$.

5. $\displaystyle\int_0^1 (5x+2)^3 dx =$

   A. 0.33   B. 119.25   C. 1.67   D. 3.67

6. Answer true or false. For $\displaystyle\int_0^1 e^x (1 + 5e^x)^2 dx$ a good choice for u is e^x.

7. Answer true or false. For $\displaystyle\int_0^1 e^x (7 + 8e^x) dx$ a good choice for u is $7 + 8e^x$.

8. Answer true or false. For $\displaystyle\int \frac{1}{\sqrt{x}(2 + \sqrt{x})} dx$ a good choice for u is $2 + \sqrt{x}$.

9. Answer true or false. For $\displaystyle\int_0^2 e^{5x} dx$ a good choice for u is $5x$.

10. $\displaystyle\int_0^1 e^{-3x} dx =$

    A. 0.216   B. 0.148   C. 0.317   D. 0.519

11. Answer true or false. $\displaystyle\int_{-2}^2 \sin^2 x\, dx = 2\int_0^2 \sin^2 x\, dx$

12. Answer true or false. $\displaystyle\int_{-4}^4 x^4 dx = 2\int_0^4 x^4 dx$

13. $\displaystyle\int_0^{\pi/2} 2\sin 4x\, dx =$

    A. 2.359   B. −2.359   C. 0   D. 1

14. $\displaystyle\int_1^2 x\sqrt{x+4}\, dx =$

    A. 3.53   B. 1.08   C. 0   D. 7.06

15. $\dfrac{d}{dx}\displaystyle\int_0^{x^2} t^3\,dt =$

   A. x^3 B. x^6 C. $2x^7$ D. $\dfrac{8x^7}{3}$

SECTION 7.9:

1. Simplify. $e^{3\ln x} =$
   A. x^3 B. $3x$ C. $\dfrac{x}{3}$ D. e^3

2. Simplify. $\ln(e^{-6x}) =$
   A. x^6 B. x^{-6} C. -6 D. 6

3. Simplify. $\ln(xe^{4x}) =$
   A. 4 B. $4 + \ln x$ C. $4x + \ln x$ D. $4\ln x$

4. Approximate $\ln 7/2$ to 3 decimal places.
   A. 1.250   B. 1.253   C. 1.256   D. 1.259

5. Approximate $\ln 7$ to 3 decimal places.
   A. 1.946   B. 1.948   C. 1.950   D. 1.952

6. Approximate $\ln 6.1$ to 3 decimal places.
   A. 1.800   B. 1.803   C. 1.805   D. 1.808

7. Let $f(x) = e^{-3x}$, the simplest exact value of $f(\ln 2) =$
   A. 6^{-6} B. $\dfrac{1}{8}$ C. -8 D. $-\dfrac{1}{8}$

8. Answer true or false. If $F(x) = \displaystyle\int_1^{x^2} \dfrac{2}{t}\,dt, F'(x) = \dfrac{2}{x}$.

9. Answer true or false. If $F(x) = \displaystyle\int_1^{x^3} \dfrac{2}{t}\,dt, F'(x) = \dfrac{6}{x}$.

10. Answer true or false. $\displaystyle\lim_{x\to\infty} \left(1 + \dfrac{1}{x}\right)^{3x} = 0$.

11. Answer true or false. $\displaystyle\lim_{x\to 0}(1 + 5x)^{1/(5x)} = e$

12. Answer true or false. $\displaystyle\lim_{x\to 0}(1 + 2x)^{1/(2x)} = 0$

13. Approximate $\ln 9.1$ to 3 decimal places.
   A. 2.011   B. 2.104   C. 2.208   D. 2.211

14. Approximate $\ln 4.1$ to 3 decimal places.
   A. 1.411   B. 2.014   C. 2.116   D. 2.120

15. Approximate $\ln 5.2$ to 3 decimal places.
   A. 1.641   B. 1.649   C. 1.654   D. 1.695

CHAPTER 7 TEST:

1. $f(x) = x; [0,4]$. Use the rectangle method to approximate the area using 4 rectangles. Use the left side of the rectangles.

   A. 1.5   B. 2.0   C. 1.25   D. 4.0

2. Use the antiderivative method to find the area under $y = x^2$ on $[0,1]$.

   A. 0.40   B. 0.33   C. 0.50   D. 0.67

3. Answer true or false. $\int x^9 dx = 9x^8 + C$

4. $\int 3\cos x + C =$

   A. $3\sin x + C$ B. $-3\sin x + C$
   C. $3\cos x + C$ D. $-3\cos x + C$

5. $\int 5e^x dx =$

   A. $5e^x + C$ B. $\dfrac{e^x}{5} + C$

   C. $-5e^x + C$ D. $-\dfrac{e^x}{5} + C$

6. Answer true or false. $\int x^2 + e^x dx = x^3 + e^x + C$

7. $\displaystyle\sum_{i=3}^{6} i^2 =$

   A. 50   B. 4   C. 86   D. 100

8. Answer true or false. $3 + 6 + 9 + 12 + 15 = \displaystyle\sum_{i=1}^{4} 3i$.

9. Answer true or false. $\int 2x(x^2 + 2)^5 dx = \dfrac{(x^2 + 2)^6}{6} + C.$

10. Answer true or false. For $\int e^{3x} dx$, a good choice for u is $3x$.

11. Answer true or false. For $\int x\sqrt{x+2}\,dx$, a good choice for u is $x + 2$.

12. Answer true or false. $\displaystyle\sum_{i=1}^{4} 3i = 3\sum_{i=1}^{4} i$

13. $\displaystyle\lim_{n \to +\infty} \sum_{k=1}^{n} \left(\frac{2}{3}\right)^k =$

   A. $\dfrac{2}{3}$ B. $\dfrac{1}{2}$ C. 2   D. $\dfrac{3}{2}$

14. $\displaystyle\int_6^{10} |x + 5|dx =$

    A. 60   B. 52   C. 5   D. 20

15. Answer true or false. $\displaystyle\int_5^6 \frac{x}{2+x}dx$ is positive.

16. $\displaystyle\int_{-3}^3 x^5 - x^3 + 3xdx =$

    A. 0   B. 114.75   C. −114.75   D. 229.5

17. $\displaystyle\int_1^e \frac{3}{x}dx =$

    A. 3.00   B. 6.48   C. 5.14   D. 3.30

18. Find the displacement of a particle if $v(t) = t^5; [0, 2]$.

    A. 4   B. 8.33   C. 10.67   D. 2

19. Answer true or false. $\displaystyle\int_1^2 \frac{1}{3x+1}dx = \frac{\ln 7 - \ln 1}{3}$

20. Approximate $\ln 12.4$ to 3 decimal places.

    A. 2.487   B. 2.501   C. 2.518   D. 2.531

21. Answer true or false. $\displaystyle\lim_{x \to +\infty} \left(1 + \frac{1}{5x}\right)^{5x} = e$.

ANSWERS TO SAMPLE TESTS

SECTION 7.1:

1. C 2. D 3. A 4. D 5. A 6. B 7. C 8. A 9. C 10. A 11. C 12. A 13. A 14. D 15. B

SECTION 7.2:

1. B 2. B 3. B 4. B 5. C 6. A 7. B 8. D 9. T 10. F 11. F 12. F 13. T 14. A 15. A

SECTION 7.3:

1. A 2. A 3. D 4. C 5. B 6. C 7. B 8. T 9. T 10. T 11. F 12. T 13. F 14. F 15. T

SECTION 7.4:

1. B 2. D 3. B 4. T 5. B 6. C 7. B 8. T 9. F 10. A 11. D 12. B 13. F 14. T 15. T

SECTION 7.5:

1. A 2. B 3. A 4. D 5. B 6. A 7. T 8. A 9. T 10. F 11. F 12. T 13. A 14. B 15. A

SECTION 7.6:

1. T 2. F 3. B 4. A 5. C 6. A 7. C 8. A 9. A 10. T 11. T 12. F 13. T 14. T 15. F

SECTION 7.7:

1. A 2. A 3. C 4. A 5. B 6. C 7. F 8. F 9. A 10. D 11. F 12. F 13. T 14. F 15. C

SECTION 7.8:

1. A 2. A 3. T 4. F 5. B 6. F 7. T 8. 8 9. T 10. C 11. T 12. T 13. B 14. A 15. C

SECTION 7.9:

1. A 2. C 3. B 4. B 5. A 6. D 7. B 8. F 9. T 10. F 11. T 12. F 13. C 14. A 15. B

CHAPTER 7 TEST:

1. A 2. B 3. F 4. A 5. A 6. F 7. C 8. T 9. T 10. T 11. T 12. T 13. C 14. B 15. T 16. A 17. D 18. C 19. T 20. C 21. T